INTRODUCTION
TO THE
STATISTICAL
METHOD

KNOPF CORE SERIES

KENNETH·R·HAMMOND

Professor of Psychology

UNIVERSITY OF COLORADO

JAMES·E·HOUSEHOLDER

Assistant Professor of Mathematics

HUMBOLDT STATE COLLEGE

Alfred·A·Knopf NEW YORK

INTRODUCTION
TO THE
STATISTICAL
METHOD

Foundations and Use
in the
Behavioral Sciences

1963

L. C. catalog card number: 61–17923

THIS IS A BORZOI BOOK,
PUBLISHED BY ALFRED A. KNOPF, INC.

Published 1962
Reprinted 1963

WHEN COLERIDGE *tried to define beauty, he returned always to one deep thought: beauty, he said, is "unity in variety." Science is nothing else than the search to discover unity in the wild variety of nature —or more exactly, in the variety of our experience. Poetry, painting, the arts are the same search, in Coleridge's phrase, for unity in variety. Each in its own way looks for likenesses under the variety of human experience. What is a poetic image but the seizing and the exploration of a hidden likeness, in holding together two parts of a comparison which are to give depth each to the other?*

J. BRONOWSKI
Science and Human Values *

ACKNOWLEDGMENTS

STRICTLY SPEAKING, an author's indebtedness knows no beginning, and possibly no end, and so an arbitrary point of departure must be taken. We begin, therefore, with our teachers—too many to be listed—to whom we acknowledge our obligations, and hope that they will be pleased with what they find here.

Our heaviest obligation, however, is to our editors, David Krech and Richard Crutchfield, who in reality became full partners in our enterprise because of their remarkable ability to immerse themselves with vigor and enthusiasm in our efforts to realize our plans, hopes and aspirations. It was a privilege, in the full sense of the word, to share the excitement of our venture with them and to find their encouragement unfailing.

We also express our thanks to Frederick J. Todd, Carolyn J. Fink, David Card, Nancy Anderson, and David Hawkins, who read all or parts of the manuscript. We owe a special debt, however, to Rheem Jarrett, who read an early draft with a degree of care and thoughtfulness far beyond the call of duty. And we wish to express our thanks to Howard E. Gruber for his valuable suggestions. We are indebted to Sir Ronald A. Fisher, F.R.S., Cambridge and to Dr. Frank Yates, F.R.S., Rothamsted, also to Messrs. Oliver & Boyd Ltd., Edinburgh, for permission to reprint Table No. VII from their book "Statistical Tables for Biological, Agricultural and Medical Research," and Table No. III from Sir Ronald Fisher's book, "Statistical Methods for Research Workers."

Our wives typed the manuscript, and they have our thanks for that. But our true gratitude extends to their forebearance—a point which requires no elaboration.

FOREWORD

IT IS SELDOM apparent to a student of the behavioral sciences why he must study statistics. Ordinarily he notes that "Statistics" is listed as a prerequisite for a course in which he wishes to enroll and dutifully registers for the course in statistics, although perhaps not without misgivings as well as a few evasive maneuvers. Should the student happen to ask why a course in statistics is necessary, he will find that answers are readily forthcoming. The student will learn that he should—indeed, *must*—take the course in statistics in order to take more advanced courses in his major (among these advanced courses he will find at least one advanced course in statistics); that he will be unable to understand research in his field without a knowledge of statistics; and that, in any event, he could not possibly carry out a Master's thesis or a Doctoral dissertation without a course in statistics. Moreover, he will be told that statistics enables us to become quantitative and exact. Finally, it will be pointed out that a knowledge of statistics, or at least a record of a course in statistics, is essential to his professional training. Statistics, it seems, is always "for" something else—no more than a means to an end.

But this is all wrong. For the statistical method is one of man's great intellectual accomplishments—a marvelous illustration of his ingenuity and resourcefulness in coping with a difficult and challenging problem basic to all scientific work. And as a solution to the problem, the statistical method not only is neat; it is elegant and powerful. Every student of man and his works—particularly the student interested in man's attempts to cope with scientific, logical, and mathematical problems—owes it to himself to understand the logic of the statistical method. To "learn statistics" only because someone urges that it is a "good tool" or that it is a "prerequisite" is to miss something very important. Indeed, we believe that most students miss the importance of the statistical method and fail to perceive its power and elegance precisely because too often the statistical method is presented merely as a "tool."

This brings us to the reason why we wrote this book. It was our aim to write a book which addresses itself to the logic of the statistical method for its own sake, and it was our purpose to show and explain to the student one of man's greater rational accomplishments irrespective of whether the student might expect to find immediate application of his knowledge. Thus, we do not limit ourselves to the preparation of a book of formulas by which answers may be ground out with little or no understanding of the processes involved. We explain and discuss, for example, not seven or eight different methods of correlation, but only two methods. However, we discuss these two in detail, because we believe that when the student understands the principles underlying these, he will understand the special varieties of correlation when and if he has occasion to make use of them.

In short, we address ourselves not only to the student who may have an occasion to calculate a mean or a correlation coefficient, who may take the advanced course for which statistics is a prerequisite, and who may carry out a graduate thesis, but also (and primarily) we address ourselves to the student who wishes to undertake an adventure of the mind and to the instructor who wishes to conduct the expedition.

A NOTE TO THE STUDENT ABOUT
THE ORGANIZATION OF THIS BOOK

EACH CHAPTER of this book is divided into two parts. The *first* part of each chapter considers the need for certain methods, and the requirements those methods must meet if they are to be good ones; that is, methods appropriate to the problems with which the behavioral scientist deals. Descriptions of current methods are presented as well as evaluations of how effectively they meet the needs and requirements of the behavioral scientist. The *second* part of each chapter shows the mathematical reasoning which lies behind the various procedures described in the first part.

The book is organized in this way because it seems to us that the student must have a clear perception of *why* he is studying a given method if he is to be expected to master, in a mature way, the reasoning behind the method. All too often, we believe, the student of the statistical method fails to grasp the fundamental nature of the problem he is coping with because he has become entangled in arithmetic or algebra. Failing to understand why he is attempting to solve a problem, and failing to master the abstract, mathematical development of it, the student is apt to resort to the worst possible solution—learning by rote. In an effort to prevent this unhappy outcome, we have attempted to set forth the needs and requirements of the behavioral scientist for various methods prior to presenting the mathematics implicit in the method.

This does not mean that we believe that mathematics is unimportant. On the contrary, we firmly believe that a knowledge of the statistical method which is to be more than untidily superficial *must* encompass the mathematical reasoning which is the cornerstone of the statistical method. We simply wish to make certain that the student understands the nature of the problem to which the mathematics are to be applied before he is introduced to the mathematical foundations. Therefore, we have reserved the mathematical reasoning for the second part of the chapter.

One will find that this type of presentation leads to a moderate amount of repetition. Indeed, the mathematical section of each chapter considers the same topics as the 'non-mathematical' section. Thus, repetition is inevitable. It is important to note, however, that although the same topic is discussed twice, it is discussed in a different way or from a different point of view. We believe that this kind of repetition is all to the good because it represents a convergence of different means toward a single goal—that being, understanding the logic of the statistical method.

CONTENTS

PART
I

The Description
of Data

CHAPTER

I

GENERALIZATIONS, INDUCTION, AND VARIABILITY

FOR MOST PEOPLE the statistical method is simply a complicated way of keeping records. When one speaks of "vital statistics" (records of births and deaths), "business statistics" (the record of the rise and fall of stock-market averages), or "baseball statistics" (a pitcher's record of wins and losses), he refers always to a record of past events. The word "statistics" merely seems to imply a way of keeping track of things in the form of tables or charts.

There is a good historical reason for this. When "statistics" was first introduced in the eighteenth century, it was really a political term applied to the records of governments or states. Indeed, this is the origin of the very form of the word: stat-istics was a way of studying political science through the examination of state records. Of course, the meaning of the term gradually expanded to include any type of data-recording. And, in the main, this is what the man in the street pictures when he thinks of statistics —long lists of data recorded for some possible future use.

But there is a much more significant sense in which "statistics" is used. Unfortunately, however, there is no single word which we can apply to the more significant implications of the term. We shall have to employ the phrase "statistical method" in order to make the distinction between statistics as record-keeping and statistics as a powerful problem-solving technique. It is the statistical *method* that scientists employ to cope with the problem of *induction* in order to establish *scientific generalizations* despite the *variability* in social, biological, and physical events. This is the prime function of the statistical method.

In this chapter we will see how the need for the statistical method arises out of the search for scientific generalizations, the discovery of which is the main business of the scientist. The statistical method is highly important and useful in this search, because the establishment of a general inference requires a method of reasoning from a specific experiment to all cases. This is known as "induction"—making a generalization from the specific event to the general rule. Inference from a specific experiment to the general rule would not be a prime difficulty for the scientist if it were not for the fact that there is a great deal of variability among the events. This is particularly true for the behavioral and biological scientist. People differ widely in both structural and behavioral characteristics—and, of course, so do animals. It is this wide variability among the objects which these scientists study that provides the stumbling block to easy generalizations. Were it not for such wide variation, there would be less difficulty in making the inductive inference that assumes that what holds true for one subject holds true for all others. And if the problem of inductive inference were not so pervasive and formidable—that is, if it were easy to generalize the results of a single experiment—it would be easier to establish scientific generalizations about behavior. Because the statistical method copes with variability and provides a useful approach to the problem of inductive inference, thereby making it possible to establish scientific generalizations, it meets a most important methodological need of all scientists.

It is essential that one understand why the scientist employs the statistical method. Because this is not perfectly obvious at first glance, and because it is so fundamental, we shall here examine in somewhat greater detail each of three aspects of the scientific task—generalization, induction, and variability.

GENERALIZATION

As part of man's effort to understand and cope with the world around him, he seeks to describe his environment. But he does this in several ways. The artist, the poet, the writer, or the scientist, each in his own manner, describes the environment as he sees it. Each gives his own version, makes his own interpretation, and describes what he sees from the stance of humanist or scientist. Although we need not be concerned here with the various similarities and differences between humanists and scientists, it is important to point out the central feature of the scientist's descriptions—*generalization.* The scientist's work entails increasingly accurate generalizations about the facts and processes of nature.

At the risk of oversimplification, we shall make a distinction between two types of generalization. One type concerns the establishment of *facts,* and the second concerns the establishment of regular relations among the facts, which we call *laws.*

Generalizations about facts

The investigator may be concerned about establishing a fact which is widely if not universally held to be true. The natural historian best illustrates this type of investigator. He wants to know, for example, how the various flora are distributed, what the breeding habits of certain animals are, and the like. For the psychologist who wishes to know how much variation there is in intelligence, the sociologist who wishes to compare birth rates in various societies, the anthropologist who seeks to discover the form of puberty rites or kinship systems in various parts of the world— for all of these, investigations are carried out in the form of "natural history." And in each case the search is for dependable facts.

Of course, dependable facts are important because they form an intrinsic part of the scientist's search for *laws*—regular, dependable relations among regular, dependable facts. This is by no means the only approach to the establishment of scientific laws, but the search for dependable facts is frequently a prerequisite for law-finding. Sooner or later, generalizations about facts require the employment of the statistical method. Generalization implies inductive inference, and it is inductive inference which requires the statistical method.

Scientific laws

What are scientific laws? For our purposes, it is enough to say that relationships among facts, when sufficiently established, become laws.

One of the reasons the scientist wants to describe the universe and all of its processes in terms of laws is because such laws, once discovered, afford him brief and succinct descriptions of natural processes. Thus, the laws of physical mechanics provide a concise description of the ways in which physical bodies interact; the laws of thermodynamics economically describe the relation between motion and heat; and the laws of behavior, once they are discovered, will describe in a few words how animals and people behave under various conditions. Of course, it is the task of the behavioral scientists—the psychologists, sociologists, anthropologists, educators, and others who study the behavior of men and animals—to discover the laws of behavior. They hope thereby to increase our understanding of ourselves, and of animals as well.

Once a scientific law has been firmly established, has been accepted as true, a very important change takes place. Prior to the establishment of the law, the scientific investigator simply reports what has happened under certain conditions; that is, he reports on events which he has observed in his experiment—events which have already taken place. He reports, for example, that he found a relation between A and B, such that increasing A (say, temperature) led to an increase in B (say, pressure). However once the relation repeatedly is confirmed and established as lawful, his thinking about it changes. The investigator now anticipates that what *has* happened *will* happen. For lawfulness implies that the same relation will occur again and again in the future—in fact, whenever it is investigated. Thus, the description applied to events which have taken place in the past can be extended now to events in the future. In short, lawfulness implies that the behavior of the events can be predicted prior to their occurrence. *The law describes events not yet studied, as well as those already studied.*

Thus, two aspects of scientific laws are most important: not only do such laws provide succinct descriptions, but, once established, they allow us to *predict*. (See Box 1.)

INDUCTION

It is well known to the reader that we are able to predict and to describe in advance many relations among physical events with admirable precision; yet there remains a highly interesting and significant question about the process of prediction with which, in all likelihood, the reader is not at all familiar. The point is this: How is it possible to generalize from the results obtained in a specific experiment, or in a series of experiments, to similar events not yet studied? Put otherwise, what is the logic by which we argue that what *has* happened *will* happen? Granted that an experimenter may observe 100, or even 1,000, times that A is related to B, why does he anticipate that A will be related to B in the next test? And how can he be sure that it will? By what reasoning can the scientist assert that the law of gravitation will hold in the future because it has been observed to hold in the past? This problem is at the very root of the need for the statistical method. It is known as the problem of *induction*. Because of its importance, we shall examine this problem more closely.

B O X   1

Scientific Laws—Representativeness—Chance

Philosophers of science have frequently addressed themselves to the question—What is a scientific law? Therefore, it may be well to pause here and observe how C. S. Peirce, one of the most respected philosophers of science of the early part of the twentieth century, looked at scientific laws. According to Peirce, ". . . there are two common characters of all the truths called laws of nature. The first of these characters is that every such law is a generalization from a collection of results of observations, *gathered* upon the principle that the observing was done so well to conform to outward conditions, but not *selected* with any regard to what the results themselves were found to be—a harvest or a gleaning of the fruit of known seed, not culled or select, but fairly representative.

"The second character is that a law of nature is neither a mere chance coincidence among the observations on which it has been based, . . . but is of such a nature that from it can be drawn an endless series of proph-

ecies, or predictions, respecting other observations . . . ; and experiment shall verify these prophecies, though perhaps not absolutely (which would be the ideal of a law of nature), yet in the main. Nor is a proposition termed a 'law of nature' until its predictive power has been tried and proved so thoroughly that no real doubt of it remains."

Note that Peirce refers to laws as generalizations from observations of facts *representative* of "outward conditions." Also observe that a law must not be based on a *"chance coincidence."* It was because Peirce's description of a law of nature included both these points that we chose to include it here. For, as we shall see, both points are essential elements in the logic of the statistical method.

Peirce, C. S.: "Values in a universe of chance" from *Selected writings of Charles S. Peirce,* edited by Philip Wiener. Copyright © 1958 by Philip Wiener. Reprinted by permission of Doubleday & Company, Inc.

Consider a simple example: "All crows so far observed are black. Therefore, all the crows in the world (all the crows we might ever observe) are black." This is an inductive inference, the conclusion of which extends a property of observed crows to those not yet observed. It is *inferred* that what is true of the objects observed will be true of those not yet observed. Of course, we constantly make such inductive inferences in our daily lives and as scientists. Inductive inferences are inescapable; to do without them in everyday living would mean withholding a conclusion until all cases—past, present, and future—were examined. As a result, it would be difficult to the point of impossibility to take any action of any consequence with respect to the future. In our daily comings and goings, therefore, we are quite ready to make the "inductive leap." The same holds true for scientific work—but with a major exception.

As scientists, we must be very explicit as to the rules by which we make inductive inferences. Without carefully thought out, explicit rules, each investigator would be leaping to conclusions, making inductive inferences, extending the results of studies of people or objects observed to those not yet observed according to whim or according to his own rules, or most likely, remaining puzzled as to whether he should examine more cases or not. But this would result in the very dispute which we encounter in everyday life: Jones makes inferences based on his experience, Smith makes inferences based on his, and the inferences reached may be as different as Jones's and Smith's experiences. Very little knowledge of a dependable or consensual sort is gained in this way. Therefore, the scientist needs a good, commonly agreed upon, workable procedure for knowing under what conditions it is reasonable to make inductive inferences as well as how much confidence he can place in them. The statistical method, as we shall see, fills this need.

Repetition and induction

No matter how satisfied we are with our inductive inferences made under everyday conditions, we know that they may always be challenged by those whose inferences differ. And the challenge, "Prove it!" is ordinarily turned back by evidence which enumerates cases illustrating our point. The rarity of examples counter to our inference is also stressed. Although the cases we cite to bolster the evidence on which we base our inductive inference may be of doubtful validity, and although counterexamples may exist outside our knowledge, it is important to note that our procedure for justifying our everyday inductive inference—enumeration—

is also the procedure the scientist uses to justify his inductive inferences. Somehow, man accepts repetition as confirmation. But repetition as the criterion of confirmation presents two difficulties—the first *logical* and the second *procedural*.

No matter how accustomed the student is to accepting repetition as confirmation, the plain fact is that his acceptance is a psychological matter. One might say that it is a mere "habit." But such acceptance does not follow from an invulnerable rule of logic. The fact that A has followed B a thousand times is not proof that A will always follow B (or that A causes B). There is no rule of logic that permits us to argue that what has happened a large number of times in the past must happen in the future. It was the Scottish philosopher David Hume, writing in the eighteenth century, whose careful analysis of the concept of causality made it clear that our inference of "cause" was dependent upon repetition—or, as he put it, "constant conjunction"—and that such an inference was psychological, a mere "habit of mind" and not a result of rigorous proof. (See Box 2.)

Whatever credence one assigns to Hume's argument, one fact will be perfectly apparent: no matter how cogent the logic of Hume's argument might be, it seems to have made very little if any difference to the scientist's work. As far as most scientists and engineers are concerned, Hume's logic is at best a curiosity, an abstraction, and certainly nothing to worry about when actually doing research.

Logic aside, however, the rule of repetition as proof raises a very difficult procedural question: How much repetition is enough? For example, suppose we have examined five instances and have found a regular relation between A and B. Should we examine a sixth instance? Or should we try to examine all instances? The latter suggestion has a great deal of force, for it must be admitted that only by examining all instances of the point in question could we be absolutely certain that the relation between A and B held without exception. But it is procedurally impossible to examine *all* instances, particularly in the case of the behavioral scientist. How, then, can the behavioral scientist answer the question, Will the next subject behave in the same way as the last? If the question cannot be answered without actually studying the next subject, the scientist is obviously restricted merely to recording what has happened; he can never infer what *will* happen, and scientific laws cannot be established.

No matter how easily the physical scientist may be able to brush aside Hume's argument, the biological or behavioral scientist comes face to face with the problem of induction because his living subjects are so much more variable in their behavior than the physical scientist's inanimate subjects. The behavioral scientist can ignore the logical problem if he chooses to do so, but, as we shall see, he cannot ignore the practical procedural problem because of the variability of his subjects.

B O X   2

"It may surely be allowed a philosopher . . ."

David Hume, a Scottish philosopher of the eighteenth century, will be forever remembered as the man who brought the problem of induction to the attention of the academic world in such a clear and forceful manner that it could never be ignored or forgotten. In the words of Alfred North Whitehead, "The theory of induction is the despair of philosophy—and yet all our activities are based upon it." The following quotation should provide the student with the sense of Hume's attack on the question of the logic which is involved in reasoning from experience—in making the inference that what has happened will happen.

"In reality, all arguments from experience are founded on the similarity which we discover among natural objects, and by which we are induced to expect effects similar to those which we have found to follow from such objects. And though none but a fool or madman will ever pretend to dispute the authority of experience, or to reject that great guide of human life, it may surely be allowed a philosopher to have so much curiosity at least as to examine the principle of human nature, which gives this mighty authority to experience, and makes us draw advantage from that similarity which nature has placed among different objects. From causes which appear similar we expect similar effects. This is the sum of all our experimental conclusions. . . .

". . . For all inferences from experience suppose, as their foundation, that the future

---

VARIABILITY

Once a person has become alerted to the fact of variability in biological organisms, he cannot fail to notice it. Nor can he fail to notice its pervasiveness, for all features of living things vary widely. But it is important to note the striking difference between *inorganic* objects and *organic*, living creatures. When the physical scientist studying mechanics wishes to explore centrifugal force, for example, he can order a dozen metal rods, all cast from the same mold. He can, if he likes, specify the exact limits within which the bars can be permitted to vary with respect to their dimensions. And he can get what he orders. But the behavioral scientist knows in advance not only that he cannot order what he wants, but that what he wants

will resemble the past, and that similar powers will be conjoined with similar sensible qualities. If there be any suspicion that the course of nature may change, and that the past may be no rule for the future, all experience becomes useless, and can give rise to no inference or conclusion. It is impossible, therefore, that any arguments from experience can prove this resemblance of the past to the future; since all these arguments are founded on the supposition of that resemblance. Let the course of things be allowed hitherto ever so regular; that alone, without some new argument or inference, proves not that, for the future, it will continue so. In vain do you pretend to have learned the nature of bodies from your past experience. Their secret nature, and consequently all their effects and influence, may change, without any change in their sensible qualities. This happens sometimes, and with regard to some objects: Why may it not happen always, and with regard to all objects? What logic, what process of argument secures you against this supposition? My practice, you say, refutes my doubts. But you mistake the purport of my question. As an agent, I am quite satisfied in the point; but as a philosopher, who has some share of curiosity, I will not say scepticism, I want to learn the foundation of this inference. No reading, no enquiry has yet been able to remove my difficulty, or give me satisfaction in a matter of such importance. Can I do better than propose the difficulty to the public, even though, perhaps, I have small hopes of obtaining a solution? We shall, at least, by this means, be sensible of our ignorance, if we do not augment our knowledge."

Hume, D. 1777. *An enquiry concerning human understanding,* in *The English philosophers from Bacon to Mill,* ed. by E. A. Burtt. New York: Modern Library, 1939.

will never be made. In a sense, the "mold is broken" after each individual is created. No two people are alike—with the minor exception, perhaps, of very young identical twins.

Individual differences in anatomy and physiology are guaranteed not only by hereditary mechanisms, but by environmental conditions as well. There is no need to elaborate here on the role of environmental factors in the production of individual differences. It is enough to say that the environment adds both to individual variability and to uniformity, as does heredity. (See Box 3.)

When we turn to individual differences in behavior, we find that

---

BOX 3

Individual Variation—Past, Present, and Future

PAST: Darwin's perception of the significance of the enormous amount of variation among plants and animals played a large role in bringing him to his conclusions concerning evolution. His first topic in his first chapter in *The Origin of Species* is entitled "Causes of Variability." And he noted that ". . . the number and diversity of inheritable deviations of structure, both those of slight and considerable physiological importance, are endless." Furthermore, he saw the great significance of individual variations for adaptation and survival. Thus, ". . . as many more individuals of each species are born than can possibly survive; and as, consequently, there is a frequently recurring struggle for existence, it follows that any being, if it vary however slightly in any manner profitable to itself, under the complex and sometimes varying conditions of life, will have a better chance of surviving, and thus be *naturally selected*." In short, not only did Darwin perceive the wide varia-

tion among individuals; he saw the fundamental role it has played in our past and in the determination of the present.

PRESENT: R. J. Williams is a biochemist who, impressed with the striking variations in the anatomy and physiology of animals and man, has urged his colleagues, particularly in medicine, to give greater heed to individual differences among normal, healthy people. In one study of normal young men, Williams reports that "Among the distinctive differences observed in the mineral analysis study were (1) nearly a 6-fold difference between two individuals (no overlapping in values) in urinary calcium excretion, (2) nearly a 3-fold variation in plasma magnesium, (3) over a 30 percent difference (no overlapping of values) in the sodium content of blood cells, (4) a 4-fold variation (with no overlapping of values in 21 to 25 samples, respectively) in salivary sodium, (5) a 5-fold variation in salivary magnesium with no overlapping in 7 to 15 samples, (6) taste

---

variability is as prevalent, if not more so, than variability in anatomy and physiology. Figure 1 shows the variability in intelligence level of nearly 3,000 children tested by the Stanford-Binet Intelligence Test, and Figure 2 shows the scores of more than nine million men on a different intelligence test.

Although the wide variation in human intellectual abilities is generally

---

threshold values that often differed consistently from individual to individual over a 20-fold range." And Williams argues that it is better science to recognize individuality than to ignore it. Thus, "Admittedly applied biology would be simpler if individuality did not exist; but, since it does exist and is a potent factor, its recognition facilitates rather than stands in the way of successful application."

FUTURE: The evidence from modern genetics makes it clear that such variation as Williams has found is to be expected. For not only does heredity account for similarities among individuals, as we all recognize, but differences in structure and function are also an inevitable outcome of the mechanics of inheritance. As Krech and Crutchfield point out, for example, ". . . a single human male can produce 8,388,608 genetically different sperm, and similarly, a single human female 8,388,608 genetically different ova. In a single mating, any one of these 8 million chromosome combinations in the sperm might join any one of the 8 million chromosome combinations in the ovum to form a single zygote.

"The probabilities are even more bewildering than that. . . . chromosomes can exchange genes. This means that the number of different kinds of gene combinations is vastly greater than 8,388,608. This increases tremendously the already astronomically large number of genetically different zygotes which can eventuate from matings between the same parents. The number of possible combinations of chromosomes in the zygote is practically infinite and our reproductive system practically guarantees that, except in the case of identical twins . . . , no two brothers or sisters can ever be genetically the same. *Heredity means individual differences.*"

Undoubtedly, variety is the spice of life—but it is also Nature's first challenge to those who would discover her secrets.

Darwin, C. 1859. *The origin of species.* London: Murray.
Krech, D. and Crutchfield, R. 1958. *Elements of psychology.* New York: Knopf.
Williams, R. J. *Biochemical individuality.* New York: John Wiley & Sons, Inc. Copyright 1956. Reprinted by permission of the publishers.

---

known and accepted, it is not common knowledge that variability is found as well in all other studies of various behavioral phenomena (from over-all studies of personality to studies which intensively analyze even very small segments of behavior). The following quotation will serve to illustrate how human individuality stands in the way of easy generalization:

The impression generally left by a series of intensive case studies is one of almost boundless individual variation. If the studies are faithful to their subject matter they show us living people who are as distinctive as the ones we meet in everyday life. Such descriptive abun-

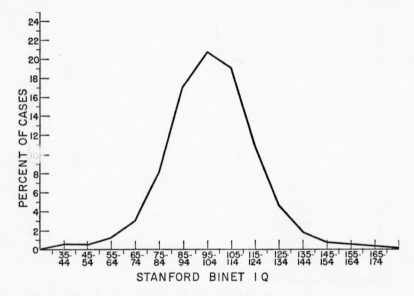

FIG. 1. Stanford-Binet I.Q.'s of 2,904 unselected children between the ages of two and eighteen. From *Measuring intelligence* by Lewis M. Terman and Maud A. Merrill. Copyright 1937 by Houghton Mifflin Company and reprinted with their permission.

dance is requisite in order to show the lawfulness within each personality. It is thus an essential step on the way to more general propositions about fundamental processes. The very wealth of individuality, however, looms as an obstacle to generalization. The comparative study of cases—the comparison of individual lives that differ in so many particulars—can be successfully carried out only when variables have been selected which draw attention to significant generalities beneath the crowding multitude of surface features. Generalities of this kind we have sought. . . . (Reprinted with permission from Smith, M. B., Bruner, J. S., and White, R. W., *Opinions and Personality*, copyright © 1957, John Wiley & Sons, Inc.)

In short, behavioral scientists continue to search for those regularities which govern behavior despite the wide variations of living things in both structure and function. Clearly the task would be insurmountable were it not for the fact that the statistical method provides the techniques for reducing the chaos of individual variation to sufficient order so that the data may be understood. The statistical method provides a rigorous set of rules

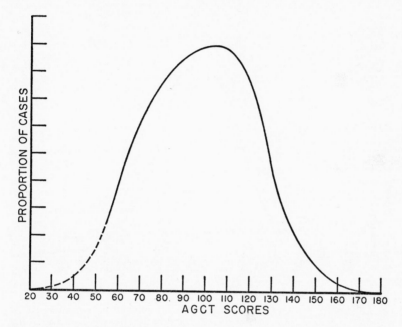

FIG. 2. Scores of 9⅓ million men on the Army General Classification Test. The dotted line indicates an assumption about the distribution of scores at the lower end of the curve. From *Differential psychology*, Third Edition, by Anne Anastasi. Copyright 1949 by The Macmillan Company and used with their permission.

and procedures for making inductive inferences despite the variability that is an integral part of life.

BY WAY OF SUMMARY

The scientist aims to establish generalizations concerning the facts and processes of nature. Scientific laws not only provide concise descriptions of natural processes but allow us to predict what will happen under various conditions. Of course, this is the aim of the behavioral as well as the physical scientist. However, the establishment of a generalization about facts, or a law concerning relations between facts, implies an inductive inference based on repetition; what has happened repeatedly in the past will happen in the future. But such inference has no basis in logic; no proof exists that repetition guarantees the future. Although every scientist pursues his work without consideration of this logical problem, behavioral scientists are particularly aware of its practical consequences. For they are constantly brought to face the fact that it is difficult to extend the results obtained with one subject, or even a group of subjects, to other subjects. The reason for this difficulty lies in the enormous variability among men and animals.

The need for the statistical method arises out of the fact that the variability among living creatures prevents easy inductive inferences; therefore, the establishment of scientific generalizations is made difficult. To cope with variability, the statistical method is used to permit inductive inferences to be made with logically defensible procedures, thus bringing the establishment of scientific generalizations within the realm of possibility. In a sense, the statistical method is a device for "extending man's reach beyond his grasp." The remaining chapters of this book explain how this comes about.

⟨[Mathematically . . .

The statistical method relies heavily upon its mathematical content for its usefulness in coping with the problems of variability and inductive inference. In order to make precise statements about variability and about the degree of confidence to be placed in an inductive inference, some means or technique is needed for quantifying or measuring variability and degree of confidence. Mathematics provides the means for constructing such techniques, besides interpreting and comparing them with respect to their advantages and limitations.

The mathematics used in this book are drawn wholly from elementary algebra or are fully explained in terms appropriate to that level. In order to facilitate later discussion, some of the basic terms of arithmetic and algebra will be defined here, and some of the most basic rules of algebraic manipulation will be reviewed.

BASIC TERMS AND RULES

The absolute value of a number

The phrase "numerical value of a number" indicates the magnitude of the number in question. The numerical value of both -7 and $+7$ is $+7$. The numerical value of a number is frequently called its "absolute value." The absolute value of a number may be thought of as its distance from zero, distance being considered in all cases to be positive.

The fundamental operations

With each of the four fundamental operations (addition, subtraction, multiplication, and division) are associated certain technical terms by means of which the basic rules are made more succinct and understandable. A number that is to be added is called an "addend." A number that is to be subtracted from another is called a "subtrahend." The number from which a subtrahend is to be subtracted is called a "minuend." Numbers used to form products are called "factors." The three elements of a division are the "divisor," the "dividend," and the "quotient." The quotient is the result of dividing the dividend by the divisor.

The algebraic rule for addition is as follows: To add two numbers of like sign, affix their common sign to the sum of their numerical values; to add two numerically unequal numbers of unlike sign, affix the sign of the numerically greater addend to the difference of their numerical values; the sum of two numerically equal numbers of unlike sign is zero.

For subtraction the rule is: To subtract one number from another, change the sign of the subtrahend and proceed as in addition.

The product or quotient of two numbers of like sign is a positive number. The product or quotient of two numbers of unlike sign is a negative number.

Examples are given here to cover every case which may arise under these rules.

$$(+8) + (+4) = +12$$
$$(-8) + (-4) = -12$$
$$(+8) + (-4) = +4$$
$$(-8) + (+4) = -4$$
$$(+8) - (+4) = (+8) + (-4) = +4$$
$$(-8) - (+4) = (-8) + (-4) = -12$$
$$(+8) - (-4) = (+8) + (+4) = +12$$

$$(-8) - (-4) = (-8) + (+4) = -4$$
$$(+8) + (-8) = 0$$
$$(+8)(+4) = +32$$
$$(+8)(-4) = -32$$
$$(-8)(-4) = +32$$
$$(+8) \div (+4) = +2$$
$$(+8) \div (-4) = -2$$
$$(-8) \div (-4) = +2$$

The division symbol is used very little in algebra, division being indicated by a fraction line. Thus $\frac{1}{n}(a + b)$ means that the sum $a + b$ is to be divided by n.

Signs of grouping

Signs of grouping—such as parentheses ( ), braces { }, and brackets [ ] — are used to enclose expressions which are to be considered as a single number with respect to some algebraic operation. The dot · is used to denote multiplication. Thus,

$$\tfrac{1}{4}(8 + 12) = 5, \text{ whereas}$$
$$\tfrac{1}{4} \cdot 8 + 12 = 14.$$

Note that in $\tfrac{1}{4} \cdot 8 + 12$ there appears to be a choice as to whether first to multiply $\tfrac{1}{4}$ and 8 and then to add 12, or whether first to add 8 and 12 and then to multiply by $\tfrac{1}{4}$. A universal algebraic convention requires, however, that whenever a choice exists, multiplication and division must precede addition and subtraction unless signs of grouping specifically indicate otherwise. In the expression $\tfrac{1}{4}(8 + 12)$ the parentheses constitute such a specific indication; accordingly, the addition is performed first in this case. If a minus sign is placed in front of such a sign of grouping, it has the effect of multiplying every enclosed term by -1; that is, such a minus sign changes the sign of every enclosed term. For example,

$$5 - \{3 - 4(2 + 6) + (3 - 5)\} = 5 - \{3 - 8 - 24 + 3 - 5\}$$
$$= 5 - 3 + 8 + 24 - 3 + 5$$
$$= 36.$$

The example here has two sets of grouping symbols enclosed within another set. The evaluation follows a method found by long experience to produce maximum accuracy: The innermost grouping signs should be eliminated first.

Exponents and radicals

Exponents and radical signs must be used in strict accordance with their definitions in order to avoid serious errors. If $a \cdot a = b$, then a is said to be the "square root" of b. The fact that every number except 0 has two distinctly different square roots makes it necessary to specify which is intended in any particular case. To illustrate this, notice that since $3 \cdot 3 = 9$ and $(-3)(-3) = 9$, both $+3$ and -3 are the square roots of 9. To avoid ambiguity, the symbol $\sqrt{}$ is so defined as to indicate only one of the two possible square roots of a number, $\sqrt{b}$ meaning the positive square root of b. The symbol leaves no choice as to which root is intended by its use; if it is to refer to the negative square root of b, the proper notation is $-\sqrt{b}$. It frequently happens that both square roots of a number, b, are acceptable in some context. In this case the proper notation is $\pm\sqrt{b}$, meaning that either the positive or the negative root may be used. The positive square root is called the "principal square root"; the symbol $\sqrt{}$ is called a "radical sign."

The number appearing under a radical sign is called the "radicand." While it is true that every number has two square roots, those of negative radicands are imaginary numbers. Imaginary numbers play a large role in the advanced theory of statistics, but no use will be made of them in this book.

The checking of errors

It is difficult, even for persons who are experienced computers, to avoid errors in long additions and multiplications. A desk calculator should be used because of its accuracy as well as its speed. If a calculator is not available, calculations should be checked. Various methods exist for checking additions and multiplications, such as repeating the computation in a different order, casting out nines (see Box 4), and comparing the answers with estimates. The first of these is the most accurate check on one's work, the second is usually adequate, and the third will reveal only gross errors.

The comparison of an answer with an estimate is an excellent method for avoiding a misplacement of the decimal point. For example, since 63.75^2 must lie between 60^2 and 70^2 or between 3,600 and 4,900, clearly there must be exactly four digits before the decimal point in 63.75^2. The sum of twenty numbers, none of which is much less or much greater than 60, will be in the neighborhood of 1,200. The value of $\sqrt{208.86}$ must lie

B O X 4

Casting Out Nines

Addition and multiplication problems can be checked for errors by the device called "casting out nines." To cast the nines out of a number, add its digits. If this sum exceeds 9, add the digits of this number. Continue this process until the result is a single digit. For example, in casting the nines out of 348926,

the first sum is 32; adding 3 and 2 gives 5, which is your "check" number. To check an addition or a multiplication, perform the same problem of addition or multiplication after casting the nines out of each addend or factor. The answers should agree when nines are cast out of the two results.

EXAMPLES

$$348 \qquad 3 + 4 + 8 = 15 \qquad 1 + 5 = 6$$
$$275 \qquad 2 + 7 + 5 = 14 \qquad 1 + 4 = 5$$
$$352 \qquad 3 + 5 + 2 = 10 \qquad 1 + 0 = 1$$
$$\overline{975} \qquad 9 + 7 + 5 = 21 \qquad \overline{12}$$
$$2 + 1 = 3 \qquad 1 + 2 = 3$$

$$28476 \qquad 2 + 8 + 4 + 7 + 6 = 27 \qquad 2 + 7 = 9$$
$$381 \qquad 3 + 8 + 1 = 12 \qquad 1 + 2 = 3$$
$$\overline{28476} \qquad\qquad\qquad\qquad\qquad \overline{27}$$
$$227808 \qquad\qquad\qquad\qquad\qquad 2 + 7 = 9$$
$$85428$$
$$\overline{10849356} \qquad 1 + 0 + 8 + 4 + 9 + 3 + 5 + 6 = 36$$
$$3 + 6 = 9$$

The method works for any number of addends and for any number of factors. If the final results do not agree, then an error exists. It is, of course, possible to make compensatory errors which will give the appearance of correctness. Thus the method is not a perfect check on accuracy, but it is still highly useful for detecting errors. Although a rigorous demonstration of the validity of this method is too complex to give

here, it may be pointed out that the mathematical basis for the method lies in the fact that every power of 10, the base of our number system, is 1 more than a multiple of 9. If our number base were 12, then elevens would be cast out.

The origin of this method is lost in antiquity. Mathematics, it must be remembered, is one of man's oldest intellectual activities.

between 14 and 15 because $14^2 = 196$ and $15^2 = 225$. Such rough checks will serve to eliminate many computational errors.

The methods mentioned above are not appropriate where letters are used to represent numbers in algebraic manipulations. There are, however, numerical methods for finding errors in such work. One of the easiest and best is to substitute numbers for the letters in the starting expression and then reduce it to a single number. When the algebraic result is treated similarly with the same numbers, an error has been made if the two numerical results are different. For example, suppose that the product $(2a - 3b)(a + 4b)(a - 3b)$ is to be found. The answer is $2a^3 - a^2b - 27ab^2 + 36b^3$. To check this, let $a = 4$ and $b = 2$. Then $(8 - 6)(4 + 8)(4 - 6) = -48$. Substituting the same numbers into the answer gives $128 - 32 - 432 + 288 = -48$. Had the two results differed, the same procedure could be applied to each step of the problem to determine exactly where the error occurred.

Statistics makes much use of the squares of numbers. It is worthwhile to note certain properties common to all squares. No square can end in 2, 3, 7, or 8. If all but the last two digits of a square are struck out, then the remaining two digit number must be divisible by 4 or have a remainder of 1 when divided by 4. If the number being squared is even, there is no remainder; if it is odd, the remainder of 1 will occur. These are easy checks to apply mentally and will often uncover errors of computation.

Subscripts and the generalized summation symbol

A variety of mathematical symbols and notational methods are used widely in statistics. Their use is brought about by the need for precision, simplification, and easy passage from hypothesis to conclusion. Moreover, the notations, operations, and conventions of mathematics constitute a common language throughout the scientific world.

One of the most helpful and widely used of mathematical devices is the *subscript*. Subscripts are simply labels used to distinguish one quantity from another. Of course, if only a few quantities are to be considered, a different letter of the alphabet can be used to represent each one. If the number of quantities to be dealt with is at all numerous, however, the alphabet becomes inadequate. In such a case a single letter, such as a, C, x, or Y, is selected to represent the whole set of quantities. To specify a particular one of several quantities represented by a single letter, such as X, an identifying subscript is attached to X. Thus X_1 stands for the first number of the set, X_7 stands for the seventh such number, and, in general, X_i stands for i^{th} number of the set. To illustrate further, suppose a list of thirty-seven numbers is to be discussed. It is inconvenient to write all these numbers or to describe them each time reference is made to them. They may be denoted by $X_1, X_2, X_3, \ldots, X_{37}$, or by X_i ($i = 1, 2, \ldots, 37$). This last method of notation makes it unnecessary to repeat the letter X for each datum, since the notation instructs the reader to consider the X to be repeated for every value of the subscript i indicated in the parentheses.

The use of the subscripts permits an important economy of expression when used in conjunction with the generalized summation symbol $\sum$. This symbol, the upper-case Greek Sigma, is used in lieu of a repetitive series of plus signs. The notation $\sum X_i$, ($i = 1, 2, \ldots, n$) means $X_1 + X_2 + \cdots + X_n$. The notation becomes more succinct in the form $\sum\limits_{i=1}^{n} X_i$, where the instruction "let the variable subscript i run over the numbers $1, 2, \ldots, n$" is recorded in the notation appearing below and above the $\sum$ symbol rather than in following parentheses; thus $\sum\limits_{i=5}^{10} X_i = X_5 + X_6 + X_7 + X_8 + X_9 + X_{10}$. The expression $\sum\limits_{i=1}^{n} X_i$ is read "the summation of the first to the nth values of X_i inclusive"; it is also often read "Sigma X sub i, i running from 1 to n." Of course, i is not the only letter used to indicate a variable subscript; The letters j, k, n, m, and others are often used for this purpose. However, brevity is not the only virtue of this notation. Its use makes possible a much simpler algebraic treatment of statistical measures than would otherwise be available.

The use of the $\sum$ symbol is not restricted to indicating a simple sum, as in the example above. It may be used to indicate the sum of a set of numbers obtained by manipulating each of the X's according to some rule or formula. For example, $\sum\limits_{i=1}^{n} X_i^2$ means the sum, not of all the X's, but of the squares of the X's. Similarly, $\sum\limits_{i=1}^{n} (X_i - m)^2$ means that each of the n

numbers X is to have the number m subtracted from it, the differences are to be squared, and the sum is to be taken over all these squares; that is,

$$(1) \quad \sum_{i=1}^{n} (X_i - m)^2 = (X_1 - m)^2 + (X_2 - m)^2 + \cdots + (X_n - m)^2$$

The expression $(X_i - m)^2$ in (1) is called the *general term* of the sum.

By writing the general term in (1) in a different way, some useful algebraic properties of sums can be illustrated. Since

$$(X_i - m)^2 = X_i^2 - 2mX_i + m^2$$

equation (1) may also be written as

$$(2) \quad \sum_{i=1}^{n} (X_i^2 - 2mX_i + m^2) = (X_1^2 - 2mX_1 + m^2) + \cdots + (X_n^2 - 2mX_n + m^2)$$

The right side of (2) has n terms each of which is enclosed in parentheses. Each of these n terms is itself composed of three simpler terms, making altogether $3n$ numbers to be added. These $3n$ addends may be rearranged without changing their sum, and it is advantageous to do so. The rearrangement desired here is obtained by placing all the X^2 terms first, then the $2mX$ terms, and finally all the m^2 terms. The result is

$$(3) \quad \sum_{i=1}^{n} (X^2 - 2mX_i + m^2) = (X_1^2 + X_2^2 + \cdots + X_n^2)$$
$$- (2mX_1 + 2mX_2 + \cdots + 2mX_n) + (m^2 + m^2 + \cdots + m^2)$$

Now the first parentheses on the right in (3) clearly enclose $\sum_{i=1}^{n} X_i^2$, and the second parentheses enclose $\sum_{i=1}^{n} 2mX_i$. The last parentheses enclose n terms, all of which are m^2, which may be denoted by $\sum_{i=1}^{n} m^2$, since an m^2 is to be added for each value of i from 1 to n inclusive. Use of these briefer forms for the three parts on the right in (3) gives

$$(4) \qquad \sum_{i=1}^{n} (X_i^2 - 2mX_i + m^2) = \sum_{i=1}^{n} X_i^2 - \sum_{i=1}^{n} 2mX_i + \sum_{i=1}^{n} m^2$$

Note that the general terms for the sums on the right are exactly the simple terms which compose the general term in the sum on the left. The general term $(X_i^2 - 2mX_i + m^2)$ has been used here to illustrate this important algebraic property of sums, but any other general term consisting of two or more simple terms could have been used. For example,

$$\sum_{k=1}^{100} (3X_k^2 + 2X_k) = \sum_{k=1}^{100} 3X_k^2 + \sum_{k=1}^{100} 2X_k$$

This property will be frequently used and will be referred to as *distributing the summation symbol over the general term*.

Equation (1) can now be expressed in a form which greatly facilitates the computation. By expanding the general term and distributing the summation symbol over it, the result

$$(5) \qquad \sum_{i=1}^{n} (X_i - m)^2 = \sum_{i=1}^{n} (X_i^2 - 2mX_i + m^2)$$

$$= \sum_{i=1}^{n} X_i^2 - \sum_{i=1}^{n} 2mX_i + \sum_{i=1}^{n} m^2$$

is obtained. Note that all the subtractions are combined into a single subtraction after the simple terms have all been added.

The second sum on the right in (5) can be used to illustrate another important property. The sum is

$$\sum_{i=1}^{n} 2mX_i = 2mX_1 + 2mX_2 + \cdots + 2mX_n$$

$$= 2m(X_1 + X_2 + \cdots + X_n)$$

$$(6) \qquad = 2m \sum_{i=1}^{n} X_i$$

This shows that, if the general term—$2mX_i$ in this case—contains a constant factor, then this factor may be removed from the general term; the original sum is then expressed as the constant factor times the sum having the new and simpler general term, as in (6). Another example of this property of sums is

$$\sum_{i=1}^{100} 4(X_i + X_i^2) = 4 \sum_{i=1}^{100} (X_i + X_i^2).$$

This property will be referred to hereafter as *removing a constant factor* from the general term.

The third and last property of sums to be illustrated here concerns sums all of whose addends are equal to a constant. Such a sum is

(7) $$\sum_{i=1}^{n} m^2 = m^2 + m^2 + \cdots + m^2$$

where there is an m^2 for each value of i from 1 to n inclusive. It will be recalled that this sum occurred in (5) when the summation symbol was distributed over the general term $(X_i^2 - 2mX_i + m^2)$. The value of the sum in (7) is nm^2, since there are n terms all equal to m^2. Another example of this property is

$$\sum_{k=1}^{50} 4 = 4 + 4 + \cdots + 4$$

$$= 200.$$

When used in the future, this property of sums will be referred to as *summing over the constant term*.

Returning now to (1) and using all three of the properties of sums discussed above, the sum $\sum_{i=1}^{n} (X_i - m)^2$ may be expressed as

$$\sum_{i=1}^{n} (X_i - m)^2 = \sum_{i=1}^{n} (X_i^2 - 2mX_i + m^2)$$

$$= \sum_{i=1}^{n} X_i^2 - 2m \sum_{i=1}^{n} X_i + nm^2.$$

The amount of computation has been greatly decreased, since it is no longer necessary to combine each X with m before squaring.

In every instance so far care has been taken to specify exactly the numbers over which the "summation variable" i was to run. It is obvious in many cases what these numbers are from the context of the work. The subscripts and their range may be omitted whenever such is the case; that is, $\sum_{i=1}^{n} X_i$ may be written simply as $\sum X$ if the context of one's work makes it clear what the value of n is. Whenever a $\sum$ symbol occurs without an accompanying specification as to the range of the subscript, an assumption is made that the reader will be able to supply this information as he reads. Accordingly, the abbreviated form should be used only where the context leaves no possibility of ambiguity.

In the following examples the sums are worked out in detail in two ways. The first evaluation is made without using the three properties developed above, while the second evaluation makes full use of them. The data used in all the examples are as follows:

$$X_1 = 2, X_2 = 4, X_3 = 5, X_4 = 8, X_5 = 9.$$

EXAMPLE 1.

$$\sum_{i=1}^{5} (X_i + 3) = (2+3) + (4+3) + (5+3) + (8+3) + (9+3)$$

$$= 5 + 7 + 8 + 11 + 12$$
$$= 43$$

$$\sum_{i=1}^{5} (X_i + 3) = \sum_{i=1}^{5} X_i + \sum_{i=1}^{5} 3$$

$$= (2 + 4 + 5 + 8 + 9) + 15$$
$$= 28 + 15$$
$$= 43$$

Here the summation symbol has been distributed over the general term, and a summation over the constant 3 has been made.

EXAMPLE 2.

$$\sum_{i=1}^{5} (3X_i^2 - 2X + 5) = (3 \cdot 2^2 - 2 \cdot 2 + 5) + (3 \cdot 4^2 - 2 \cdot 4 + 5)$$

$$+ (3 \cdot 5^2 - 2 \cdot 5 + 5) + (3 \cdot 8^2 - 2 \cdot 8 + 5) + (3 \cdot 9^2 - 2 \cdot 9 + 5)$$
$$= 13 + 45 + 70 + 181 + 230$$
$$= 539$$

$$\sum_{i=1}^{5} (3X_i^2 - 2X + 5) = 3 \sum_{i=1}^{5} X_i^2 - 2 \sum_{i=1}^{5} X_i + \sum_{i=1}^{5} 5$$

$$= 3(2^2 + 4^2 + 5^2 + 8^2 + 9^2) - 2(2 + 4 + 5 + 8 + 9) + 25$$
$$= 3(190) - 2(28) + 25$$
$$= 539$$

All three properties have been used to break up the general term $3X_i^2 - 2X + 5$ into the simpler general terms X_i^2, X_i, and 5, which may then be treated separately.

EXAMPLE 3.

$$\sum_{i=1}^{5} (X_i - 3)^2 = (2 - 3)^2 + (4 - 3)^2 + (5 - 3)^2 + (8 - 3)^2 + (9 - 3)^2$$

$$= 1 + 1 + 4 + 25 + 36$$
$$= 67$$
$$\sum (X - 3)^2 = \sum (X^2 - 6X + 9) = \sum X^2 - 6 \sum X + \sum 9$$
$$= (2^2 + 4^2 + 5^2 + 8^2 + 9^2) - 6(2 + 4 + 5 + 8 + 9) + 45$$
$$= 190 - 6(28) + 45$$
$$= 67$$

Percentages and proportions

Percentages and proportions represent two ways of conveying the same information. If one out of every four trials of an event succeeds, the proportion of successes is said to be $\frac{1}{4}$; that is, one fourth of all efforts will succeed. If this proportion is represented as a decimal fraction, .25, and if this decimal representation of the proportion is multiplied by 100, the result is a percentage; the percentage of successes for the above example is then 25 per cent. To find what proportion n is of d, n is divided by d, and the proportion is n/d. To find what per cent n is of d, the arithmetic is the same except that the fraction n/d is multiplied by 100 to obtain the percentage. To increase a given number, n, by a specified percentage, n is multiplied by 1 plus the proportion corresponding to the required percentage. For example, let us say that 8 is to be increased by 25 per cent: since the proportion corresponding to 25 per cent is .25, the number 8 must be multiplied by $1 + .25 = 1.25$, and the result is $8(1.25) = 10$. The 1 used in this process has the effect of carrying the original 8 into the answer, and the .25 has the effect of carrying an additional $\frac{1}{4}$ of 8 into the answer.

Though it has been shown that increasing 8 by 25 per cent produces 10, it does not follow that decreasing 10 by 25 per cent will produce 8. In fact, 10 decreased by 25 per cent is

$$10(1 - .25) = 10 - 2.5 = 7.5$$

Many measurements are made in terms of percentages or proportions. In order for such measurements to be meaningful, there must be a known fixed maximum for the variable involved, and its minimum must be at least theoretically 0. It would be meaningless, for instance, to say that the average age of a group of people is 93 per cent, since there is no maximum age against which the figure may be interpreted. A proportion or a percentage is always used to separate a range of variation into two parts, one reaching from zero up to the division point and the other reaching from the division point up to a well-defined and understood maximum. Both a zero minimum and a fixed maximum are necessary to give meaning to a proportion or a percentage.

The computation of proportions follows a simple rule: All the possible outcomes of an event are divided into two or more categories, and the proportion of outcomes in any category is the number of outcomes in that category divided by the total number of possibilities. The proportion of outcomes not in a given category is the number of such outcomes divided by the number of outcomes in all the categories combined. There are, for instance, thirty-six ways for a pair of dice to fall, six of which produce a seven; the proportion of sevens rolled with a pair of dice is $\frac{6}{36}$ or $\frac{1}{6}$.

Suggestions for Further Reading

CHURCHMAN, C. 1948. *Theory of experimental inference*. New York: Macmillan.

A good discussion of the problem of inference and the statistical method. The student will want to refer to this book in connection with Chapter 9 as well.

COHEN, M., and NAGEL, E. 1934. *An introduction to logic and scientific method.* New York: Harcourt, Brace.

Covers fundamental problems of logic as applied to scientific method. One chapter deals with statistical methods and there are three on inference and induction.

TOULMIN, S. 1953. *The philosophy of science.* London: Hutchinson.

A readable and interesting introduction to the general problems of discovery and scientific law.

WALKER, H. 1951. *Mathematics essential for elementary statistics.* New York: Holt.

Provides a handy reference for those who want to review arithmetic and elementary algebra.

PROBLEMS

(Answers, hints and references to aid in the solution of these problems will be found on pages 397 ff.)

1. The central feature of a scientist's descriptions is generalization. Give two examples of generalizations about facts and two examples of generalizations about relations between facts. To find these, it will be necessary to apply the principles in the text to your knowledge of the sciences.

2. What is the limited definition of a scientific law being used in this book?

3. Relations between facts will be regarded differently by a scientist according to whether the relations in question are considered as laws or as conjectures. In a short paragraph describe this difference.

4. What is the problem of induction?

5. A naturalist seeking to test the conjecture that all crows are black records the color of every crow he sees. He also records every non-black thing he sees which is not a crow. Do these latter observations support or oppose his conjecture? Or are they irrelevant to the conjecture?

6. It has been said above that "the problem of induction needs solution." Do you anticipate the finding of any complete solution which will always yield the right answer? Why?

7. Apply the technique of inductive inference to the following statements:

   (a) $(n-1)(n-2)(n-3)(n-4)(n-5)+1 = 1$ for all values of n.

   (b) The number $n^2 - 79n + 1601$ is a prime for all values of n. (A "prime" is an integer which has exactly two distinct divisors.)

8. What is the nature of the main obstacle in the process of generalization by means of induction?

9. What is the role of the statistical method in the establishment of scientific generalizations?

10. Find the absolute value of (a) 23, (b) -11, (c) 0.

11. The value of $a \cdot (b+c)$ is usually different from that of $a \cdot b + c$. Find values of a, b, and c for which

    (a) $a(b+c)$ is less than $a \cdot b + c$

    (b) $a(b+c) = a \cdot b + c$

    (c) $a \cdot (b+c)$ is greater than $a \cdot b + c$

12. Evaluate

    (a) $6 - \{4 - 5(3+7) + (4-6)\}$

    (b) $6 - \{4 - [5(3+7)+4] - 6\}$

13. The absolute or numerical value of a number n is denoted by $|n|$, but this notation gives no hint of the implied calculation. Another notation for $|n|$ is $\sqrt{n^2}$. Use this latter form to compute $|-6|$, $|-10|$, $|6|$, and $|3.5|$.

14. There is an error in the multiplication problem below. By substituting numbers (choose any you like), find the step in which the error occurred.

$$(2a-3b)(a+4b)(a-3b) = (2a^2 + 8ab - 3ab - 12b^2)(a-3b)$$
$$= (2a^2 + 5ab - 12b^2)(a-3b)$$
$$= 2a^3 - 6a^2b + 5a^2b - 15ab^2 - 9ab^2 + 36b^3$$
$$= 2a^3 - a^2b - 24ab^2 + 36b^3$$

15. Which of the following numbers can be excluded from the set of squares by means of a brief visual inspection? 5438, 5426, 5476, 5572, 5575. Suggest lower and upper limits between which the square roots of the given numbers must lie.

16. A certain amount of familiarity with numbers is necessary to give accuracy to one's estimates. To show the danger of poorly founded estimates in unfamiliar contexts, consider whether you would rather

have a semiannual salary increase of \$50 each six months or an annual salary increase of \$200 each year.

The following data are referred to in problems 17–30 inclusive.

$X_1 = 5$	$X_6 = 9$	$Y_1 = 15$	$Y_6 = 12$	$Y_{11} = 7$
$X_2 = 3$	$X_7 = 5$	$Y_2 = 13$	$Y_7 = 6$	$Y_{12} = 14$
$X_3 = 8$	$X_8 = 8$	$Y_3 = 4$	$Y_8 = 3$	$Y_{13} = 8$
$X_4 = 2$	$X_9 = 7$	$Y_4 = 9$	$Y_9 = 1$	$Y_{14} = 11$
$X_5 = 1$	$X_{10} = 5$	$Y_5 = 5$	$Y_{10} = 10$	$Y_{15} = 2$

17. If $U_i = Y_i - X_i$ for $i = 1, 2, \ldots, 10$, find (a) $U_4 + U_7$, (b) $U_3 U_5$, (c) $X_1 + U_2 + Y_3$, (d) $\frac{1}{5}(Y_1 + Y_2 + Y_3 + Y_4 + Y_5)$, (e) U_{X_6}.

18. Compute (a) $\sum_{i=1}^{10} X_i$, (b) $\sum_{j=6}^{15} Y_j$, (c) $\sum_{k=1}^{5} X_k Y_k$.

19. If 3 is subtracted from each of the X's, the results squared, and all such answers added, the final sum is $\sum_{i=1}^{10} (X_i - 3)^2$. Evaluate this sum.

20. Evaluate the sum $\sum_{i=1}^{10} (X_i^2 - 6X_i + 9)$.

21. Evaluate $\sum_{i=1}^{10} X_i^2 - 6 \sum_{i=1}^{10} X_i + 90$.

22. Explain the similarity of results in the last three problems.

23. Write, as in problem 19, a description of the operations to be performed on the X's individually and collectively in problem 20.

24. Evaluate $\sum_{m=1}^{6} X_m Y_m$.

25. Evaluate $\sum_{m=1}^{6} X^2{}_m$.

26. Evaluate

(a) $\sum_{k=1}^{4} \frac{Y_k}{X_k}$

(b) $\dfrac{\sum_{k=1}^{4} Y_k}{\sum_{k=1}^{4} X_k}$

27. Evaluate $\sum_{i=1}^{15} (X_i + Y_i)$, using $X_i = 0$ when $i > 10$.

28. Evaluate $\sum_{i=4}^{7} (2Y_i - 3X_i)$.

29. Evaluate $\sum_{k=1}^{6} (Y_k - 2X_k)^2$ by first expanding the general addend, distributing the summation sign over the resulting terms, and making use of the results in problems 24 and 25.

30. Evaluate (a) $\sum_{i=1}^{5} X_i Y_{3i}$, (b) $\sum_{i=1}^{3} X_i^i$, (c) $\sum_{i=1}^{4} X_{2i-1} Y_{2i+1}$.

31. Check the equality $\left(\sum_{i=1}^{n} i \right)^2 = \sum_{i=1}^{n} i^3$ for three different values of n chosen by yourself. Compare your results with the expression $\dfrac{n^2(n+1)^2}{4}$.

32. If n is 80 per cent of 400, what is the value of n? What proportion is n of 400?

33. What is the result of increasing 320 by 25 per cent?

34. If 400 is given a 20 per cent increase followed by a 20 per cent decrease, the result will be less than 400. What change in this result will occur if the 20 per cent decrease precedes the 20 per cent increase?

35. What generalization is suggested by the results of problem 34?

36. What will an item cost if its price of $5 is first marked up 50 per cent and then down $33\frac{1}{3}$ per cent?

37. An increase from 5 to 30 is often referred to as an increase of 600 per cent. This is a misuse of the term "percentage." How can the relation referred to be properly stated in terms of percentages?

38. In a deck of fifty-two playing cards, what is the proportion of (a) spades? (b) aces? (c) face cards? (d) cards with an even number of red pips? and (e) black odd cards?

39. What is the proportion of face cards in a deck of ordinary playing cards from which seven cards have already been drawn in unsuccessful attempts to draw a face card?

CHAPTER

2

MEASUREMENT AND MATHEMATICS

IT IS A CURIOUS FACT that, although physical scientists are far more skilled than behavioral scientists in making measurements, behavioral scientists must be much more aware of the nature of measurement itself. Therefore, to some extent we shall have to consider the nature of measurement. When the reader finishes this chapter, he should have a much broader grasp of the concept of measurement, and of the relation between measurement and mathematics as well.

When most people think of measurement, the first thing they are apt to picture is the ordinary foot rule. And when most people think of measurement in science, they are likely to have a mental picture of very precise, exact measurements of length, weight, time, velocity, and so forth (see Box 5). All of these measurements (including those made with the foot rule), however, make up only one kind of measurement; there are at least three other kinds of measurements. Furthermore, the one kind of measurement found most frequently in the physical sciences is almost never found in the behavioral sciences, while the other three kinds are.

BOX 5

On Being Exact

Although this chapter is concerned with the problem of measurement, we do not include a discussion of the problem of the *precision,* or exactness of measurements, despite the fact that consideration of this problem is quite appropriate in a book on statistics. Our only apology is that books, like animals, need to be the right size. However, we include the following quotation because it presents the concept of exactness in a nutshell.

"The word 'exact' has a practical and theoretical meaning. When a grocer weighs you out a certain quantity of sugar very carefully, and says it is exactly a pound, he means that the difference between the mass of the sugar and that of the pound weight he employs is too small to be detected by his scales. If a chemist had made a special investigation, wishing to be as accurate as he could, and told you this was exactly a pound of sugar, he would mean that the mass of the sugar differed from that of a certain standard piece of platinum by a quantity too small to be detected by *his* means of weighing, which are a thousand-fold more accurate than the grocer's. But what would a mathematician mean, if he made the same statement? He would mean this. Suppose the mass of the standard pound to be represented by a length, say a foot, measured on a certain line; so that half a pound would be represented by six inches, and so on. And let the difference between the mass of the sugar and that of the standard pound be drawn upon the same line to the same scale. Then, if that difference were magnified an infinite number of times, it would still be invisible. This is the theoretical meaning of exactness; the practical meaning is only very close approximation; how close depends upon the circumstances."

Clifford, W. K. "The exactness of mathematical laws" in Newman, J. R. 1956. *The world of mathematics.* Vol. I. New York: Simon and Schuster.

In the very broadest definition, measurement is a process whereby objects or events are classified and symbols attached to the classification. More specifically, in the process of measurement, symbols (for example, 4, 5, x, p) are used to represent real objects or events according to the rules of logic and mathematics. In a sense, mathematics is similar to language, for both involve the representation of objects and events by symbols according to rules. Thus scientists often talk of the value of describing the phenomena they observe in the language of mathematics. In this very general meaning, then, mathematics is a language. But there is a crucial difference between the language of mathematics and ordinary language.

The difference lies in the phrase "according to rules." The rules which govern the relation of symbol to event and the relation of symbol to symbol in mathematics are exact and orderly, and these rules must meet strict logical criteria. The rules of language, however, are relatively inexact and are not called upon to meet strict logical criteria. It is because of this very difference—the strict, logical character of the language of mathematics, as against the relatively inexact character of ordinary language—that it is of great advantage to make measurements and then to introduce the measurements into mathematics. Before elaborating on this point further, we turn to a consideration of four different ways of measuring—of representing events and objects by symbols.

TYPES OF MEASUREMENT

Not all writers on the topic of measurement agree as yet on the proper definition of measurement, nor do they agree on the number of types of measurement. The discussion of this topic here follows the more conventional views, which suggest that there are four types of *scales* used for measuring.

A scale may be thought of as a device for measuring; a foot rule is a scale, a speedometer is a scale, and of course, a weighing machine is a scale. We shall describe here the nominal scale, the ordinal scale, the interval scale, and the ratio scale.

Nominal scales

When a behavioral scientist engages in what we have called the "natural history" phase of his work, his task is generally that of categorizing the objects and events he observes. And when he assigns symbols (whether words, letters, or numerals) to the phenomena he has placed in these categories, he is employing a *nominal scale*. This is the simplest form of measurement; indeed, it is so simple that some theorists feel that this crude procedure hardly deserves to be dignified by the term "measurement." Nevertheless, the application of the term to categorizing in the form of nominal scales serves as a useful point of departure, for by starting with the simplest operation possible, we shall perceive more clearly the importance of the characteristics of the more refined measuring scales.

Examples of measurement on the nominal scale may be found in the work of the public-opinion analyst who finds that a certain percentage of people can be classed as favoring or opposing certain ideas, propositions, or candidates: he categorizes people as atheistic or religious, conservative or liberal, and so forth. The clinical psychologist who classifies an individual as schizophrenic as opposed to nonschizophrenic or as alcoholic instead of nonalcoholic also employs a nominal scale. Again, the sociologist who indicates that a person's residence should be considered rural rather than urban, or that this person is "other-directed" and that one "inner-directed," is using a nominal scale. The educational psychologist, similarly, uses a nominal scale when he describes one classroom situation as "student-oriented" and another as "teacher-oriented." As long as the categories (such as "student-oriented") into which the objects are placed *are not ordered*—as from, let us say, "small" to "large," or "weak" to "strong," or "bad" to "good"—the scale is a nominal one.

Thus, measurement with the use of a nominal scale involves only the separation of objects or events into mutually exclusive categories. It hardly needs to be pointed out that the objects or events in each category must be equivalent to one another with respect to the category. If, for example, people are being classified as either for or against high tariffs, all those in the "for" category must indeed be for high tariffs. Those who are neutral, or who cannot make up their minds, must be excluded from both the "for" and "against" categories; they cannot be included unless the labels are changed or a third category is provided.

It will be obvious that very little can be done with measurement by means of a nominal scale—but often this "very little" is enough for the purpose at hand. The number of cases in each category can be counted, and the comparison of these numbers may well be all that is necessary. If the number of people who are in one category (such as, "for") exceeds the number of people in the other category ("against"), this information may provide the answer the behavioral scientist was seeking. Butter need not be cut with a razor, and the refinement of the measuring scale to be employed depends on the nature of the problem to be solved.

Ordinal scales

As the behavioral scientist refines his ideas about the objects of his inquiry, he is apt to refine his methods of measurement. Once classification has been achieved, the scientist may perceive an orderly relation among the categories into which objects or events were placed. If so, he will attempt to employ a more refined method of measurement called the *ordinal scale*.

When biologists relate various species to one another in order—as higher or lower on the phylogenetic scale—they employ an ordinal scale. Similarly, when clinical psychologists, after observing patients in a mental hospital for six months, order them along a continuum by labeling them as "unimproved," "slightly improved," or "much improved," an ordinal scale is being used. The sociologist who orders individuals as being in "the lower socioeconomic group," "middle socioeconomic group," or "upper socioeconomic group," and the educational psychologist who uses a rating scale for "dull," "average," and "bright" students are also employing ordinal scales, because the categories are arranged in order. In each case, the categories are said to be in *rank order*.

Measuring with an ordinal scale rather than a nominal scale is usually preferable, because ordinal-scale measurement provides data in a numerical form, which permits more and better analyses of the data. As we shall see in the following chapters, measurement by an ordinal scale makes it possible to compute certain kinds of averages and certain correlations which could not be computed if a nominal scale were used. As a result, ordinal-scale measurement can enrich our understanding of the phenomena under study (see Box 6).

Direction and distance

It should be noted, however, that rank order implies *direction* ("greater than," or "less than") but not *distance*. Ordinal scales do not indicate *how much* A is "greater than" B, nor *how much* D is "less than" C. In short, the direction between objects is specified but not the amount of distance between them.

Rating scales provide a good illustration of an ordinal scale. Suppose we have the not untypical rating scale presented below. If this rating scale is to be used by teachers to evaluate essays written by students, arranging the evaluative words along a line eliminates the confusion as to whether "poor" is better or worse than "inferior," but we are still in the dark as to whether "average" is as much better than "poor" as "excellent" is better than "average." The order among the words is specified but not distance between them. The arrangement of the evaluative words under a line with marks equally spaced (as below) produces the illusion that the valuations themselves are equally spaced. This illusion must be avoided if the in-

BOX 6

A Case of Olives

The psychologists Mandler and Kessen describe lucidly the function of "ordinal numerals" and provide a clear example of how the use of ordinal numerals increases accuracy in communication, in contrast to mere labeling with words.

"A step of great importance to empirical science is taken when numerals are used to indicate sequence, succession, or order. Not only do numerals name class membership; they also carry an implication that one class has more of something than another, or is larger than another, or differs in an orderly way from another on some discriminable basis. Numerals in ordinary use share . . . the premise that 1 is somehow more than 0, that 2 is somehow more than 1; stated generally that $n + 1$ is greater than n. Unlike the case of . . . numerals, ordinary words rarely fulfill the purpose of ordering . . . , as the case of the olives will demonstrate.

"Ripe olives . . . are sold under the labels 'large,' 'extra large,' 'mammoth,' 'colossal,' and 'supercolossal.' Besides the wonderland quality of the smallest commercial olive having the name 'large,' there may be some confusion for the unwary housewife in deciding whether 'mammoth' is bigger than 'colossal' or the other way round. There might be poetic loss but there would be certain communication gain if the grading system were numerical. In that case we would know from a can labelled '#4 olives' that there are smaller sizes available and that '#5 olives' are larger than these. The improvement in unambiguous communication which follows the use of numerals to structure an ordered series is impressive, but it is only part of the value to empirical research of working with ordinal numerals. When a group of events or observations is laid out in an ordered way, so that the number series '1, 2, 3, 4, . . . , n' can be properly applied, . . . then the numerals are fit for mathematical manipulation of a fairly high order."

Mandler, G. and Kessen, W. 1959. *The language of psychology*. New York: John Wiley & Sons, Inc. Copyright, 1959. Reprinted by permission of the publishers.

vestigator is to think clearly about the relation between events and the data which represent them.

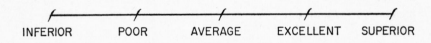

INFERIOR   POOR   AVERAGE   EXCELLENT   SUPERIOR

The fact that ordinal scales do imply direction is, of course, an advantage, as suggested above. The fact that ordinal scales do not indicate amount of distance is a disadvantage, however, for, unless distance is specified, the scale does not permit some of the common operations of arithmetic. This will be true even though the scale used assigns numerals, such as "first," "second," "third," and so on, instead of "poor," "fair," "good," and the like. The reason lies in the fact that most of the techniques of arithmetic are applicable only to numerals which represent quantity and not to numerals which merely represent sequential order. Thus it is possible to add 3 to 4 and obtain 7, but it is not possible to add "third" and "fourth." Therefore, although measurement by ordinal scale does make possible certain important types of analyses (to be elaborated upon in later chapters), it does not make possible many of those analyses which require that the operations of arithmetic be applied to the measurements. Where such analyses are required or desirable, the behavioral scientist will attempt to employ an *interval scale*.

Interval scales

An interval scale is one for which it is possible to quantify the intervals, the distances, which lie between the numbers constituting the data. "Quantifying the intervals" means expressing their length or extent in terms of some fixed, well-understood unit of measurement. It is the lack of this fixed unit of measurement that prevents the application of arithmetic to ordinal scales. If persons A, B, and C are, respectively, first, second, and third in amount of annual income, then the data are in ordinal scale form. The difference between first and second may be anything from a few dollars to a few million. There is no way to compare the difference between second and third with the difference between first and second, since no fixed unit is given for measuring these gaps or intervals between the data. If, on the other hand, we learn that A, B, and C, respectively, have incomes of $10,000, $6,000, and $5,000, it is easy to quantify the intervals between the data. It is now possible to compare the $4,000 difference between A and B with the $1,000 difference between B and C. It is still clear that A, B, and C rank first, second, and third in that order, but much more information is available. All of this additional information arises from the fact that the interval from 6,000 to 10,000 can be expressed as a quantity of fixed units—dollars in this case. Any scale which permits the quantification in fixed units of the intervals between the data is called an "interval scale."

True interval scales expressed in psychological units are rare. The sociologist finds income to be an interval scale because income is usually considered in terms of money. The interval between $8.00 and $12.00 is usually considered to be equal to the interval between $12.00 and $16.00. The educational psychologist is wary of treating grade averages in terms of an interval scale, however, because it is certainly doubtful whether the interval between a grade of C and a grade of B can be taken to be equal to the interval between grades B and A. Even intelligence test scores do not demonstrate beyond doubt that they are interval scales, for it is not clear that the distance between individual A's I.Q. of 112 and individual B's I.Q. of 116 is the same as between C's I.Q. of 116 and D's I.Q. of 120. Behavioral science has not yet reached that point of refinement when many of its measuring techniques consist of interval scales.

When available and appropriate, interval scales are of enormous advantage, however, because most of the ordinary procedures of arithmetic can be applied to the numerals which represent points on the scales. Interval-scale numbers may be added, subtracted, multiplied, and divided, for example. Naturally, this fact allows greater freedom in the application of statistical and mathematical ideas to interval-scale numerals, and, therefore, more thorough and powerful analyses of the data can be made. These statistical and mathematical ideas are described in detail in the following chapters.

Ratio scales

An interval scale can be converted into a *ratio scale* if it can be shown that it has an absolute zero or origin from which measurements are made. This zero must be absolute or real in the sense that there is only one possible point on the scale which may represent it. The Fahrenheit and Centigrade temperature scales are not ratio scales, because the zero is in each case placed merely for convenience. The zero in the Kelvin scale for temperatures, on the other hand, is an absolute zero, because no lower temperatures are *possible;* the Kelvin scale is thus a ratio scale.

The use of ratio scales makes possible the comparison of ratios constructed from the data. It is thus possible to say that increases from 100° to 200° and 250° to 500° are both cases of doubling the temperature when the Kelvin scale is used. If the Centigrade scale is used, such a statement is not possible: 100° Centigrade is not twice the temperature of 50° Centigrade.

Consider the following example. A student may take a language test in which he gets no items correct. If we are merely counting "items correct," or test scores, this is indeed an absolute zero. But a score of "zero items correct" does not mean zero *ability in language*. And, because the scale of ability does not contain an absolute zero, it cannot be said that a score of 100 items correct indicates twice as much ability in language as a score of 50 items correct. Hence, taken as measures of ability in language, the scores should be considered as taken from an interval scale. Since we are seldom, if ever, interested merely in "items correct," or test scores in themselves, but are almost always interested in what the scores tell us about the individual's position on the psychological dimension measured (as, for example, ability in language), it is the zero point of the psychological dimension that is important.

Demonstration of an absolute zero quantity is no simpler in the measurement of behavioral variables than it is in the measurement of physical variables like temperature, and, therefore, few ratio scales are as yet available in the behavioral sciences. Fortunately for our purposes, however, nearly all the statistical methods which may be applied to ratio scales may also be applied to interval scales.

To illustrate

Suppose a psychologist wished to measure people's attitudes toward nuclear bomb testing. The simplest measuring device would involve a *nominal* scale with two categories, "for" and "against." The number of people in each category could be counted, but the analyses of the data could not be pressed very far because of the crude form of measurement. If, however, the psychologist were to measure such attitudes by means of an *ordinal* scale, the people whose attitudes were measured could be ordered along a continuum with respect to the extent to which they were "for" or "against" nuclear bomb testing; their attitudes could, for example, be categorized as "very much against," "moderately against," "undecided," "moderately for," or "very much for." Still another method of scaling their attitudes would be to let 0 represent the bitterest possible opposition to testing and 100 represent the most wholehearted approval of it and then to ask each person to choose a number representing his position. Though the result in this last instance would be at best an ordinal scale, because no fixed unit of distance exists, such ordering would permit more and better analyses of the data than would have been the case if a nominal scale had been used. It would, for example, be possible to discover whether college students have a stronger attitude toward nuclear testing than high school students—that is, whether they were more extreme in their attitudes. Or it could be determined whether amount of education is related to the strength of attitudes toward nuclear testing. Ordering makes a closer analysis possible, because it permits a categorization of the measured objects along a continuum.

Suppose, however, that an *interval* scale were, by some means, developed to measure attitudes toward nuclear bomb testing. To the subject answering the questions the procedure might appear to be exactly like that when an ordinal scale was employed, for the difference would lie in the questions used. In the case of the interval scale the questions would be so chosen (on the basis of careful research) that the numerals representing the subject's test scores would have equal distances between them. Therefore, it would be possible to discover not only whether college students held stronger attitudes than high school students, but *how much* stronger one group's attitude toward nuclear testing was than another's; that is, it would be possible to ascertain the extent to which one group was for or against nuclear testing compared with another by noting that the average score in one group was so many units higher than the average score in the other. Because the units all along the scale are equal in size, such a comparison would be meaningful and important.

Much the same situation holds with respect to the use of a *ratio* scale. Again, the difference between a ratio scale and any other scale would not be apparent to the person answering the questions. But if a ratio scale were to be developed to measure attitudes toward nuclear bomb testing, an absolute zero point would have to be established through research procedures. If this were accomplished, then it would be meaningful to state that one group was *two* or *three* times as opposed to nuclear bomb testing as another, because the units all along the scale would have a common origin below which no score is theoretically or experimentally possible. (As might be expected, such scales require a great deal in the way of research.)

More refined measurement makes possible closer analysis of the data, more extensive statistical analyses, and, therefore, better understanding of the problem under investigation.

BY WAY OF SUMMARY

The purpose of this chapter is to expand the student's conception of measurement. Because of our long acquaintance with the foot rule, all of us are familiar with the most refined type of measuring scale, the ratio scale. But it is important to grasp the fact that there are at least three other types of measurement: the interval scale, the ordinal scale, and the nominal scale. Each of these has certain properties; that is, certain mathematical operations are appropriate for each. The principal operation applied to the nominal scale is simply that of counting the objects or events in each of the mutually exclusive categories. Ordinal scales involve not only classification, but an order-relation among the categories—that is, direction. Since this fact permits the ranking of categories, certain statistical methods which cannot be applied to nominal scales may therefore be applied to ordinal scales. Interval scales indicate distance as well as direction, the distances between categories on interval scales are themselves measurable in fixed units, and most of the usual arithmetical operations are thus applicable to the numerals of interval scales. Additional arithmetical operations are applicable to ratio scales (such as the foot rule) which involve not only measurable intervals but an absolute zero as well.

MATHEMATICS

Because measurement involves the representation of objects by symbols, it concerns both a world of symbols and a world of things. The world of symbols is, of course, mathematics—a system in which the relations among the symbols are governed by known rules. It is worthwhile to examine somewhat more closely the use of mathematical symbols to represent objects, for this step not only allows us great gains in our effort to analyze and interpret behavior but also exacts a price for these gains. What are the gains, and what is the price?

The gains

One gain from the use of mathematics in the representation of objects is perfectly clear. If objects are represented by symbols, it becomes possible to manipulate the symbols instead of the objects—obviously a far easier task. It is easier to manipulate objects in a make-believe world—as, for example, on the blackboard—than in the real one. However, if we are to gain anything by this procedure, the symbols must not be manipulated capriciously—that is, without regard to rules. And, of course, the rules should be clear, obvious, and public, so that scientists may understand what exactly their colleagues are doing. At this juncture it is only fair to ask, Who is going to provide the rules? Fortunately, scientists need not concern themselves much about this, because mathematicians have for centuries made it their business to formulate rules—or, better, systems of rules—for manipulating symbols. Naturally, these mathematical rules have been subject to study, to criticism, and to reformulation. Therefore—and this is of crucial importance—when the scientist uses mathematical symbols (when he moves from the world of things into the world of mathematics, so to speak), he reaps the benefits of hundreds, actually thousands, of years of work already done. Moreover, the systematic structure of mathematics provides us with a perfectly clear and easy set of rules for manipulating and thinking about real objects in symbolic terms. Deep and subtle relations between objects emerge clearly and easily with the aid of mathematics.

The rules of mathematics have three important assets: they are widely agreed upon, they are quite stable, and they are practically faultless. Because mathematical rules (such as those for adding, subtracting, and so on) have been agreed upon, we have a universal system of symbols and rules for manipulating them; in short, we have at our service a universal language. Mathematics, therefore, helps to take any mystery due to privacy and idiosyncrasy out of symbolic manipulation, because mathematical rules are public and well known. Because the rules of mathematics are stable, we are able to manipulate and think about our data with confidence. We can be certain that rules for adding and subtracting will not be changed overnight, and we know that we may compare our work directly with that of others—in the past or foreseeable future.

But most important is the fact that mathematics provides us with a *logical system* which, so far as this book is concerned, is virtually faultless. The logical character of mathematics, its rigorous system of reasoning, is its greatest asset. And, of course, if objects or events can be symbolized so that they can be properly translated into this logical system, then the manner in which we think about them is aided enormously, for most of our mistakes will have been made and corrected for us by scholars of the past.

The costs

But entrance into the system of mathematics exacts a price. If scientists wish to take advantage of the gains to be made by using a well-developed system of symbol manipulation, they must respect the rules of the system. More specifically, if scientists wish to use such mathematical concepts as zero, addition, subtraction, and averages, they cannot pluck these concepts from mathematics and use them without regard to the mathematical context in which the concepts were developed and given their meaning. That is why it was important to describe the four types of measuring scales discussed above. Each scale is a different type of connection, or translation, between the world of objects or events and the world of mathematics. And, because each translation is different, each provides a different set of advantages and, in turn, exacts a different price from the scientist. It is as if each scale were a railway ticket. Some tickets cost the scientist little; they ask him to be no more than a natural historian, a collector and classifier of objects and events. In return, however, these tickets do not take him very far. Other tickets cost a great deal: they require the scientist to develop highly refined data. However, these tickets are valuable ones, for they take the scientist far beyond the distance he could have traveled by himself and permit him much in the way of new vistas and high adventure. Thus, as one proceeds from the lowest level of measurement to the most refined, he pays a higher price in the form of participating in a more exacting system, but in return he enjoys the power of rigorous analysis and the reward of fresh insights.

But the scientist needs mathematical concepts that are more than simply *appropriate* to his measurements; he needs *useful* concepts—concepts which help him solve his problems. Thus, although mathematics demands the price of refined measurement in return for its rigorous logic, the scientist must find the logic pertinent to his problems. To carry the analogy of the railway ticket a bit further, the scientist must be certain that the ticket takes him in the general direction he wishes to go. In brief, the scientist has *requirements* as well as *needs*. And apparently Whitehead thought the gains well worth the price when he said "if only the schoolmen had measured instead of classifying, how much more they might have learnt!"

Mathematics and reality—a word of caution

At this point a caution is in order: the translation of objects and events into symbols which can be mathematically manipulated is, of course, a great advantage, but one should never be confused with the other. It must always be borne in mind that the manipulations *are* symbolic and that the mathematical operations performed on the symbols may result in forms, or descriptions, which have *no* physical analogy. This important point is worth developing further by means of an example.

Consider the formula $\dfrac{n^2 - 3n}{2}$, which gives the number of diagonals that can be drawn in a regular polygon of n sides. If $n = 2$, the number of diagonals is $\dfrac{4 - 6}{2} = -1$. But there is no polygon of two sides, and hence the mathematical model goes beyond the physical model which it is designed to describe. Every mathematically predicted relation must be verified experimentally before it can be asserted to exist in the phenomena being studied.

The numerical data used to describe objects or events are not extracted from the objects or events but exist outside of them. Confronted with a set of observations, the scientist draws out of the body of existing mathematics the numbers, operations, and concepts which best describe his observations. This mathematical description forms a model of the actual problem, a model which lends itself easily and extensively to complicated, subtle elaboration and study. Whatever properties the mathematical model is found to have may or may not have analogues in the phenomena of which it is a model. *Each such property of the mathematical model must be studied to see whether or not it has meaning in the relevant physical situation.* To construct a mathematical model all of the properties of which have physical analogues is practically impossible. Thus, for example, the arithmetic mean must be interpreted in the light of what it is—a mathematical concept whose analogue exists, not in the individual objects represented by the data, but in a relationship among all the objects represented. It is a mistake to insist on looking for a specific object corresponding to the mean in every case; such insistence is responsible for much of the nonsense written about the average man who has 2.53 children and 1.3 suits. All too frequently such expressions reflect nothing more than a writer's insistence on finding exact physical analogues for relations found in a mathematical model. The mean number of children in a family has no analogue among particular children or families; it merely gives some information about the distribution of children in families. To construe such a mean as describing either an actual or hypothetical family is to extrapolate far beyond what is justified by actual observation of families.

The same considerations hold throughout all the sciences. Einstein, for example, deduced from his mathematical model that light should be deflected by a large mass. Not knowing whether this property of the model had a physical analogue, he announced the discovery only as a hypothesis. After an experiment showed the hypothesis to be correct, he was acclaimed for a great discovery—a discovery which in fact he did not make or claim to make. It was made by the scientists who conducted the successful experiment. Einstein, with the guidance of his mathematical model, had uncovered the possibility of such a discovery and some of the conditions under which it might be made, but he did not confuse his mathematical model with reality. Neither must any other scientist using mathematics as a tool make this mistake. Mathematical results should be extrapolated into physical analogues only when such extrapolation can be experimentally verified. No experiment can verify the existence of a family with 2.53 children. In short, symbols must not be confused with the entities they symbolize.

⟨ Mathematically . . .

Having seen that symbols must be assigned to objects and events according to rules if the symbols are to be manipulated according to the logic of mathematics, we now turn to the problem of organizing and arranging the symbols so they can be made useful.

First of all, we shall refer to the symbols (nearly always numerals) as "data." ("Data" is a *plural* noun; thus, "these data were collected too early." The singular form is "*datum*"; thus, "this is a datum of great importance.") Once the type of measuring scale has been developed—that is, once the scientist has decided what sort of scale he will use and the measurements have been made—then a set of data is at hand; it is these data which are to be analyzed by the statistical method. For example, a social psychologist who has measured attitudes toward nuclear bomb testing may have interviewed fifty subjects, given them attitude tests, and so forth. Having made his measurements, he has at hand a group of data to be analyzed, and at this point he must *organize* the data.

THE NEED FOR ORGANIZING DATA

The necessity for organizing data arises out of the same phenomenon that created the necessity for the statistical method—variability. Variability is almost always present in the data of the behavioral scientist, and it is variability among the data which is the main obstacle to their direct interpretation. Without some form of organization, too many contradictory interpretations of the data will be made. In brief, if the data are not somehow organized, they can hardly be used, and, therefore, the measurements which constitute the data are wasted. As an illustration, contrast the unorganized data in Table 1 with the same data presented in Table 2. Note that it is the variability among the individuals which makes it difficult to make any immediate sense of the data of Table 1. However, when the data

TABLE 1

56 Test Scores Recorded Without Regard for Organization

51	88	31	87	47	56	69	43
59	71	93	92	73	38	82	77
69	50	85	51	63	64	58	68
84	51	72	56	50	96	45	42
27	62	67	59	74	40	45	74
66	20	79	45	39	87	64	63
85	35	63	69	42	80	71	71

are organized according to one or more criteria, as they are in Table 2, the data suggest interpretations upon simple inspection.

THE REQUIREMENTS

The scientist needs methods for organizing data, but he has certain requirements also. Two requirements are quite simple: good methods of organizing data should (1) provide a ready means for interpreting results and (2) be applicable to a wide variety of data. The methods currently in use (to be discussed in detail below) meet both requirements.

However, all organizational methods are not always used in such a fashion that they meet a third requirement: namely, that they should (3) permit further statistical analysis. This point should always be kept in mind for the reason that the organization of the data is one of the early steps in statistical analysis. Because it is not always possible to foresee with perfect accuracy the entire future analyses at the time the data are organized, it is

TABLE 2

The Organization of the Same 56 Test Scores in Table 1 into
Categories of Decades and Rank-Ordered within Decades

20	31	40	50	62	71	80	92
27	35	42	50	63	71	82	93
	38	42	51	63	71	84	96
	39	43	51	63	72	85	
		45	51	64	73	85	
		45	56	64	74	87	
		45	56	66	74	87	
		47	58	67	77	88	
			59	68	79		
			59	69			
				69			
				69			

important to organize the data at the outset in a fashion that anticipates and makes possible a wide variety of statistical analyses. Although pictorial arrangements of data, such as charts, are highly useful for scientists as well as laymen, such arrangements of data normally cannot be analyzed further. The scientist, however, must present his data in such a fashion that not only he but others may analyze the data further, or in different ways.

A final requirement exists: (4) data must be organized so that they convey their full meaning accurately. This seems self-evident, but, because data usually can be organized in many different ways, a choice as to the amount of information to be presented (as well as degree of precision) normally exists. Data *should* be organized so that the whole truth of the matter is presented accurately and efficiently, but it is possible to organize and present data so as to *suggest* a false interpretation without actually falsifying the data. The "huckster," the advertiser, the promoter, the propagandist—all of these and others are likely to choose to present partial data which will serve their special purposes rather than the purposes of honest communication. It is these groups, of course, which have created in the layman's mind a certain suspicion of the statistical method. (See Box 7.)

In short, the scientist must organize data in order to facilitate accurate interpretations of them. He requires methods which allow many comparisons of the data, methods which make further statistical analyses possible, and methods which convey their full meanings accurately.

METHODS OF ORGANIZING DATA

There are a great many methods of organizing data. Only those in common use in the behavioral sciences will be discussed here. Each method will be discussed in connection with the four types of measuring scales described in the first part of this chapter. In each case a tabular form and a graphic form of organization will be presented.

Organizing nominal-scale data

The graphic representation of statistical data takes various forms, according to the kind of scale being used, the nature of the data, and the aspect of the data which is to be emphasized.

The *bar graph*, illustrated in Figure 3, is the basic method of graphically representing data measured on nominal or ordinal scales. A vertical bar or rectangle is drawn for each category of data, with the height of each bar proportional to the number of data in the category represented by the bar. If the width of each bar is identical, it is easy to perceive the relative differences between categories by comparing these heights.

There are many variations of the simple bar graph. Most of these are pictorial; instead of rectangular bars of equal width, pictures of men, animals, factories, or other objects are used. Such graphic displays are usually, and often intentionally, misleading. When the height of a picture is in-

---

B O X 7

"Figures don't lie, but . . ."

No one who has lived in the twentieth century needs to be reminded that statistics have been badly misused by the advertisers, public relations men and the writers of TV and radio "commercials." Darrel Huff's *How to Lie with Statistics* provides a lighthearted treatment of the more commonly used techniques of deception.

"THE SEMIATTACHED FIGURE

"In America the semiattached figure enjoys a big boom every fourth year. This indicates not that the figure is cyclical in nature, but only that campaign

time has arrived. A campaign statement issued by the Republican party in October of 1948 is built entirely on figures that appear to be attached to each other but are not:

'When Dewey was elected Governor in 1942, the minimum teacher's salary in some districts was as low as $900 a year. Today the school teachers in New York State enjoy the highest salaries in the world. Upon Governor Dewey's recommendation, based on the findings of a Committee he appointed, the Legislature in 1947 appropriated $32,000,000 out of a state

---

creased, its width is increased proportionately. The area of a picture is increased fourfold if its height and width are doubled. Those who wish to emphasize a trend from small to large or large to small frequently use this technique, because they know that most readers will compare areas rather than confine their attention to comparative heights. To observe this tendency, compare two pictures of an automobile, one $\frac{1}{4}$ inch high and the other $2\frac{1}{2}$ inches high. One is ten times the height of the other, but the smaller would fit within the larger 100 times. (See the discussion of the one-dimensional figure in Box 7.)

Because nominal-scale data merely indicate the number of objects or events which have been placed in mutually exclusive categories, both tabular and graphic forms of organization are easily applied. Table 3, for example, presents a set of nominally scaled data. Figure 3 presents the same data graphically.

It is worthwhile to note three things about Table 3 and Figure 3. First, since neither *direction* nor *distance* is involved in a nominal scale, the cate-

---

surplus to provide an immediate increase in the salaries of school teachers. As a result the minimum salaries of teachers in New York City range from $2,500 to $5,325.'

"It is entirely possible that Mr. Dewey has proved himself the teacher's friend, but these figures don't show it. It is the old before-and-after trick, with a number of unmentioned factors introduced and made to appear what they are not. Here you have a before of $900 and an after of $2,500 to $5,325, which sounds like an improvement indeed. But the small figure is the lowest salary in any rural district of the state, and the big one is the range in New York City alone. There may have been an improvement under Governor Dewey, and there may not."

"THE GEE-WHIZ GRAPH

". . . the method is far from new, and its impropriety was shown up long ago—not just in technical publications for statisticians either. An editorial writer in *Dun's Review* in 1938 reproduced a chart from an advertisement advocating advertising in Washington, D.C., the argument being nicely expressed in the headline over the chart: GOVERNMENT PAY ROLLS UP! The line in the graph went along with the exclamation point even though the figures behind it did not. What they showed was an increase from about $19,500,-000 to $20,200,000. But the red line shot from near the bottom of the graph clear to the top, making an increase of under four percent look like more than 400. The magazine gave its own

(*continued on next page*)

---

gories need not have been arranged as they were. Any other arrangement would be just as correct. Convenience alone determines the arrangement of the data.

Second, the measurements of a nominal scale are *discrete* data rather than a series of *continuous* data. In general, when a datum cannot fall between categories, the data are said to be "discrete." However, when more refined measurement can theoretically produce a datum between any two different categories, however close together they may be, the data are said to be "continuous." Thus, male and female are usually treated as discrete categories, whereas length is a continuous variable. To illustrate this difference further, consider a study in forestry which requires a count of the trees in certain areas as well as a measurement of the annual rainfall there. The number of trees will be a whole number in every case; such data are discrete because they are accurate representations of the exact number of

graphic version of the same figures alongside—an honest red line that rose just four percent, under this caption: GOVERNMENT PAY ROLLS STABLE." was to show how the industry's steelmaking capacity had boomed between the 1930s and the 1940s and to indicate that the industry was doing such a job on its own

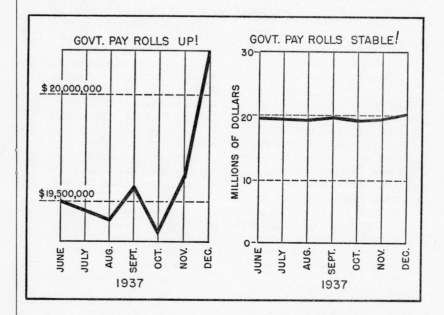

GOVT. PAY ROLLS UP!

$ 20,000,000

$19,500,000

JUNE JULY AUG. SEPT. OCT. NOV. DEC.

1937

GOVT. PAY ROLLS STABLE!

MILLIONS OF DOLLARS

30
20
10
0

JUNE JULY AUG. SEPT. OCT. NOV. DEC.

1937

"THE ONE-DIMENSIONAL FIGURE"

The person who wishes to deceive takes advantage of the fact that a figure which is twice as tall as another is four times its size in area.

"The American Iron and Steel Institute has done it, with a pair of blast furnaces. The idea

hook that any governmental interference was uncalled for. There is more merit in the principle than in the way it was presented. The blast furnace representing the ten-million-ton capacity added in the '30s was drawn just over two-thirds as tall as the one for the fourteen and a trees. On the other hand, the rainfall measurements will not be discrete data, because they will at best be estimates of the true amount of rainfall; that is, any fraction of an inch of rain may fall, but the measurement that is made will only be an estimate of the true amount. This estimate will be

quarter million tons added in the '40s. The eye saw two furnaces, one of them close to three times as big as the other. To say 'almost one and one-half' and to be heard as 'three'—that's what the one-dimensional picture can accomplish."

"Some of this may be no more than sloppy draftsmanship.

But it is rather like being short-changed: When all the mistakes are in the cashier's favor, you can't help wondering."

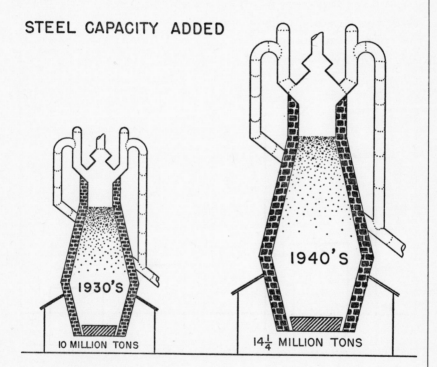

STEEL CAPACITY ADDED

1930'S

10 MILLION TONS

1940'S

14¼ MILLION TONS

Reprinted from *How to lie with statistics* by Darrell Huff. Pictures by Irving Geis. By permission of W. W. Norton & Company, Inc. Copyright 1954 by Darrell Huff and Irving Geis.

expressed on a discrete scale graduated to hundredths of an inch, but the rainfall could, in principle, be measured in terms of thousandths of an inch, or in even smaller units.

TABLE 3

Classification of 125 Students of Foreign Languages According to Their Major Field of Study

	GERMAN	FRENCH	ITALIAN	RUSSIAN
NUMBER OF STUDENTS	27	62	21	15

It is characteristic of continuous data that they can never be measured with perfect accuracy (see Box 5) and of discrete data that they should and can always be recorded with perfect accuracy. Nominal scales always involve discrete data, for continuity implies direction (an attribute of ordinal scales). Therefore, the points of a graph of nominal-scale data should not

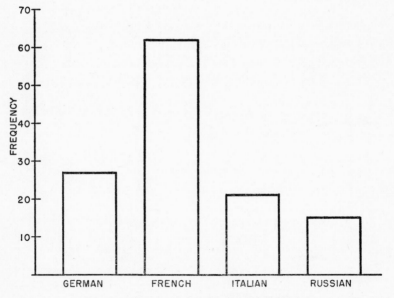

FIG. 3. A bar graph for the data of Table 3.

be joined by lines the purpose of which is to indicate where intermediate but unmeasured values would fall. Such lines imply continuity and direction, and, of course, objects or events classified by nominal scales do not possess either. Furthermore, the bars of a graph of nominally scaled data should be separated, rather than placed adjacent to one another, so that they do not imply continuity.

Organizing ordinal-scale data

Ordinal scales indicate direction. Thus, the categories into which the data are classified must be arranged according to their order, as, say, from small to large. Table 4 presents a set of ordinal-scale data, and Figure 4 pictures the same data.

TABLE 4

Distribution of Students' Grades

GRADE	FREQUENCY (number of cases)
A	10
B	15
C	23
D	5
F	2

The data in Table 4 and Figure 4 happen to be continuous, but ordinal-scale tables or graphs may represent either discrete or continuous data. The reason for this is that, since ordinal scales imply nothing about the intervals between the categories, a discontinuity may occur between cate-

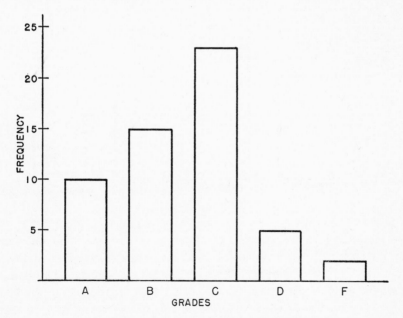

FIG. 4. A bar graph for the grades listed in Table 4.

gories, or the break between categories may be made for the sake of convenience. When the data are continuous, it is, of course, legitimate to draw
lines connecting the points in the graph if that is desirable, but any implication that the intervals between categories are equal in length or extent
should be avoided. This is rather difficult to do in practice, but separating
the bars as in Figure 4 seems to meet the requirement better than placing
the bars contiguously. The same rule concerning the proportionality of
areas holds for ordinal- as well as nominal-scale bar diagrams.

A second and more detailed example is provided by the data of Table
5. We begin the organization of these data by grouping them into *class*

TABLE 5

48 Measurements Recorded Without Regard to Organization

19	26	29	34	38	47	54	19
28	30	39	45	5	22	32	35
44	9	25	30	40	51	21	32
41	53	26	35	50	27	38	11
31	48	29	42	30	51	35	24
16	14	18	36	47	33	40	41

intervals and tallying the number of cases which fall into each class interval,
as illustrated in Table 6.

TABLE 6

The Frequency Distribution of the Measurements
Listed in Table 5

CLASS INTERVAL	TALLY	FREQUENCY
52–55	//	2
48–51	////	4
44–47	////	4
40–43	/////	5
36–39	////	4
32–35	days //////	7
28–31	days //////	7
24–27	/////	5
20–23	//	2
16–19	////	4
12–15	/	1
8–11	//	2
4–7	/	1
		$\overline{48}$

These data range from a low of 5 to a high of 54. The *range* is said to be $54 - 5 = 49$. The classification of the data consists of subdividing the *range interval* of 50 (which is one more than the range) into subintervals of equal length and determining the number of data that fall into each such subinterval. These subintervals are called *class intervals*, and the number of data in any one of them is called the *class frequency*. The set of all the class intervals with their corresponding class frequencies constitutes the *frequency distribution* of the data.

Choosing the class interval

The choice of how many class intervals to use will depend mainly on the number of data to be classified. The more numerous the data, the larger will be the number of intervals. Using fewer than ten intervals usually produces insufficient detail for adequate analysis, while dividing data into more than twenty intervals often has the opposite effect of obscuring the general outline by too much detail. Ten class intervals of length 5 just manage to span the range of the data in Table 6, but thirteen intervals of length 4 would be a good choice for classification. So also would be seventeen intervals of length 3. Having chosen the number and length of the class intervals, they should be listed as in the first column of Table 6.

The second column contains a tally mark for each datum and represents its assignment to one of the class intervals. The third column contains the class frequencies obtained from the distribution of tally marks. If the tally marks are spaced uniformly as they accumulate in the various rows of the table, a clear visual picture of the frequency distribution emerges.

For illustrative purposes, the data of Table 5 can be treated as though they were exact measurements—that is, discrete data such as the number of correctly answered test questions. The gaps of length 1 between class intervals in Table 6 would then be of no importance, since no datum could fall between consecutive whole numbers (for example, we could not have a value of 7.5).

The data of Table 5 may also be treated as though they were scores on a psychological test. Then, while appearing to be discrete measurements, they are actually approximations of true magnitudes lying on a continuous scale. In reading any datum, such as 11, one must realize that it is a rounding off of a true measurement that may lie anywhere between 10.5 and 11.5. For this interpretation of the data, class intervals without intervening gaps must be used. Such a set of class intervals is shown in Table 7. The

TABLE 7

A Frequency Distribution Using Class Intervals
Suitable for Continuous Data

CLASS INTERVAL	FREQUENCY
51.5–55.5	2
47.5–51.5	4
43.5–47.5	4
39.5–43.5	5
35.5–39.5	4
31.5–35.5	7
27.5–31.5	7
23.5–27.5	5
19.5–23.5	2
15.5–19.5	4
11.5–15.5	1
7.5–11.5	2
3.5–7.5	1

lack of gaps between class intervals makes it necessary to begin each interval at the ending point of the preceding one. If any datum falls on such an endpoint, there is a question as to which interval the datum should be assigned. This ambiguity is resolved by using fractional end points so chosen that no datum can have an endpoint value. Had the data been rounded off to the nearest half-unit instead of to the nearest whole unit, it would have been necessary to use class intervals beginning and ending with quarter-unit accuracy.

When data are to be classified, the method which corresponds most closely to the phenomena being studied should be selected. The classification of data is a substitute for the classification of the actual subjects of study. A choice of interval design not in consonance with the type and accuracy of the measurements being made will result in some data being placed in class intervals adjacent to their proper locations, with a corresponding loss in accuracy of representation. Thus, the two interpretations given above for the data of Table 5 require different methods of class-interval construction.

As a further example, suppose that each datum of Table 5 represents the age in years of a subject. Since ages are usually rounded off to the age at the last birthday, the class intervals of either Table 6 or Table 7 would be inappropriate. The age of a subject who is eleven years and eight months old would be classified in the third class interval, along with other ages in the interval $11\frac{1}{2}$–$12\frac{1}{2}$ years. A more appropriate system of class intervals would be 4–8, 8–12, and so on. For such intervals, it is necessary to state that initial endpoints are inclusive but final endpoints are not. An eight-year-old would thus fall into the interval 8–12 rather than in 4–8.

Organizing interval- and ratio-scale data

If the data are taken from an interval or ratio scale, the graphic representation can be made to display more information than in the case of nominal or ordinal scales. The bars of a bar graph (used with nominal scales) are necessarily separated because they represent categories based on kind or order rather than on relative numerical value. And, because the intervals between categories of an ordinal scale are of indeterminate length, the bars are separated rather than contiguous. Interval and ratio scales do specify determinate, equal intervals, however, and, for data so scaled the *histogram* replaces the bar graph.

The histogram

The histogram is similar to the bar graph in that a rectangular bar is constructed for each category of the classification. The categories in this case are called "class intervals." The width of each bar is equal to the length of the class interval containing the data to be represented by that bar, and the height of the rectangular bar for a given class interval is fixed by dividing the number of data in that class interval by the length of the class interval. Thus, if the class interval is five units long, and forty-seven data are included in it, then the corresponding bar of the histogram will have a width of 5 units and a height of $^{47}/_5 = 9.4$ units. This method of determining the heights of the bars insures that each bar will have an area equal to the number of data represented. It is then clear that the completed histogram will have a total area equal to the number of data in the entire sample; in the above example the bar width (5) times the bar height (9.4) is exactly 47.

Unlike bar graphs, histograms should be constructed without gaps between the bars. The histogram differs from the bar graph also in that the bars need not be of uniform width. The rule for determining the heights of bars was designed especially to allow for bars of different width while preserving the area characteristics of the diagram. It is thus possible to construct histograms for data that have been classified into class intervals of unequal length. An example of such unequal widths is given in Figure 6 below.

The vertical scale against which the bars of the histogram are to be viewed should be marked off at equal intervals, beginning with zero and extending up to slightly above the largest number obtained as a bar height. (For an illustration of what can happen when the vertical scale does *not* begin with zero, see Huff's discussion of the truncated or "Gee Whiz" graph in Box 7.) The bar heights are computed by dividing class frequencies by class-interval lengths, and thus the units on this vertical scale are "numbers of data per unit of class interval length." The labeling of the vertical axis will depend on the units in which the class intervals (and the data) are measured: if, for example, the horizontal scale is in dollars, the vertical scale measures "frequency per dollar."

TABLE 8

*A Set of 48 Test Scores Classified
into Intervals of Equal Length*

CLASS INTERVAL	MIDPOINT	FREQUENCY
51.5–55.5	53.5	2
47.5–51.5	49.5	4
43.5–47.5	45.5	4
39.5–43.5	41.5	5
35.5–39.5	37.5	4
31.5–35.5	33.5	7
27.5–31.5	29.5	7
23.5–27.5	25.5	5
19.5–23.5	21.5	2
15.5–19.5	17.5	4
11.5–15.5	13.5	1
7.5–11.5	9.5	2
3.5–7.5	5.5	1

The horizontal scale may be marked off in three different ways. The class marks (interval midpoints) may be placed at the centers of the bottoms of the corresponding bars; this method is illustrated in Figure 5. Instead of using the class marks to indicate the centers of the bars, the endpoints of the class intervals can be used to indicate the right and left extremities of the bars; this method is illustrated in Figure 6. The third method is to mark off conveniently sized equal intervals over the whole length of the horizontal axis without regard for whether or not these marks coincide with the beginnings, centers, or ends of the bottoms of the bars; this method may be illustrated by marking only multiples of 5 or 10 on the horizontal axis of Figure 5 instead of the values actually shown there. This last method usually gives a neater and more readable scale. The nature of the data and the aims of the investigator will usually suggest which of these methods is best for a particular histogram.

Table 7 is reproduced as Table 8 with an additional column giving the class marks (midpoints) for each class interval. Each midpoint was obtained by taking half the sum of the interval endpoints. The data are considered here as test scores, and the histogram is given in Figure 5.

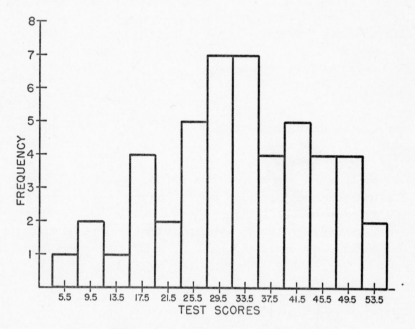

FIG. 5. A histogram for the test scores listed in Table 8.

Table 9 illustrates the classification of data into unequal class intervals. The third column of this table is obtained by dividing the entries of the second column by the corresponding lengths of the class intervals shown in the first; that is, the entries of the third column represent numbers of employees per age year. Thus, the number 20 in the third column indicates that for each one-year interval in the class interval 21–28 there are presumed to be twenty persons.

Note that the 131 employees of the 35–45 year interval outnumber the 123 in the 28–35 year interval. Reference to the histogram in Figure 6 shows that this excess is only apparent, having been caused by the difference in class-interval lengths. The histogram shows that there are more employees of a given age in the 28–35 class than there are of a given age in the 35–45 class.

The best proportions for histograms have been found to be those of

T A B L E 9

A Classification of Employees According to Age

AGE	NUMBER OF EMPLOYEES	NUMBER OF EMPLOYEES PER YEAR OF AGE
18–21	56	18.67
21–28	140	20.00
28–35	123	17.57
35–45	131	13.10
45–55	126	12.60
55–65	95	9.50

the diagrams above. The height of each one is about three fourths of its width.

The frequency polygon

The histogram may easily be converted into another kind of graphic representation called a *frequency polygon*. To construct a frequency polygon, it is only necessary to join the midpoints of the tops of adjacent bars in a histogram with straight-line segments. If the lines which compose the histogram are now erased or ignored, the several joining lines form the

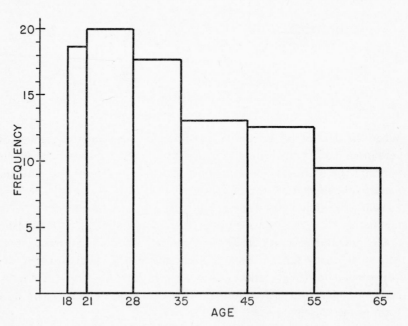

Fig. 6. A histogram for the data of Table 9.

frequency polygon. The frequency polygon obtained from Figure 5 is shown in Figure 7. It is, of course, not necessary to draw a histogram before constructing a frequency polygon: if only the frequency polygon is desired, it is sufficient to place dots where the tops of the bars would be if fully drawn and then to join the dots.

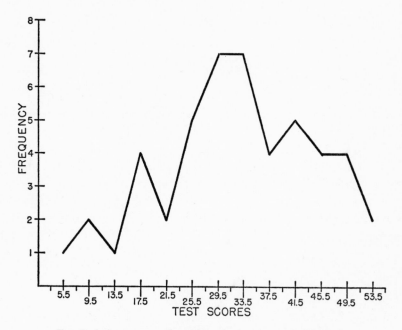

FIG. 7. A frequency polygon for the test scores in Table 8.

THE SHAPE OF FREQUENCY DISTRIBUTIONS

When the data of the behavioral sciences are organized and graphed, it very often happens that the data approximate to a well-known form—the "normal curve" (see Figure 8). *Although the normal curve has a specific mathematical definition*, any curve which is roughly bell-shaped is likely to be confused with a normal curve. The reason for this, and for the sense of familiarity which the normal curve produces in most people, is that school grades are often given on the assumption that they follow a normal curve. Moreover, many familiar biological characteristics, such as height, are "distributed normally"—that is, present themselves in normal curve form. And, of course, intelligence tests provide data that are represented by a form of the normal curve.

There are two general reasons why the normal curve has a prominent

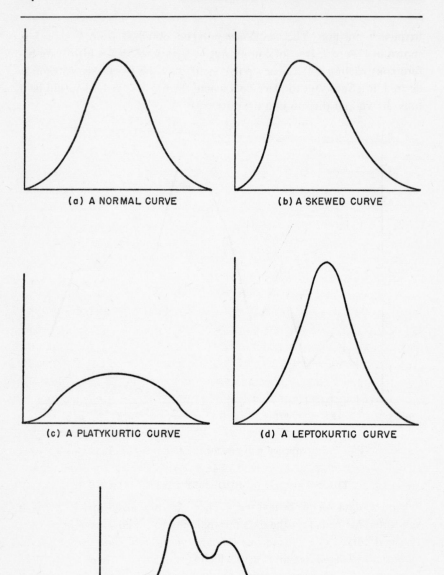

FIG. 8. Some commonly occurring frequency curves.

place in the behavioral sciences. One is that the behavioral sciences have a very close tie with the biological sciences, and, as noted above, many biological phenomena may be fairly accurately represented by the normal curve. The other reason is a mathematical one and will be discussed in detail in Part II. Because the data of the behavioral sciences very often appear to approximate this normal curve in form, and because the normal curve has some very useful mathematical properties, all of the remaining chapters will include explanations of various aspects of the normal curve.

Furthermore, the fact that data do appear in the form of a normal curve so frequently makes departures from "normality" interesting in themselves. For this reason and for the sake of completeness, various forms of departure from normality are given names. Thus, for example, if a frequency distribution has a series of cases piled up at one end, as in Figure 8b it is referred to as a *skewed* distribution, "skewness" referring to the fact that a distribution is asymmetrical.

Frequency distributions may differ from the normal in a number of ways. The distribution may be skewed, as in Figure 8b. The curve may be too flat, as in Figure 8c, or it may be too peaked, as in Figure 8d. Curves that are too flat to be normal curves are called *platykurtic*, and those that are too peaked are called *leptokurtic*. The term "platykurtic" is derived from the Greek "platy" (meaning broad, wide, flat) and "kyrtos" (curved). Similarly, "leptokurtic" means finely or thinly curved. Among the many other curves which are non-normal are the *bimodal curves*, as illustrated in Figure 8e. Such curves are called "bimodal" because they appear to be the overlapping of two different distributions having different maxima. A bimodal distribution of examination grades occurs when the examination is quite easy for those who have read the material covered by the test but very difficult for those who have not read it. The result is many low grades and many high grades, with very few grades near the mean.

Suggestions for Further Reading

NEWMAN, J., 1956. *The world of mathematics*. New York: Simon & Schuster.

Four volumes of excellent reading which will prove exciting to the intellectually curious and indispensable to the student of science and mathematics. (See especially Part XII of Vol. III for material relevant to this chapter.)

SENDERS, V. 1958. *Measurement and statistics.* New York: Oxford.

> Chapter 2 provides a discussion of "Numbers, things and measurement."

BLALOCK, H. 1960. *Social statistics.* New York: McGraw-Hill.

> Also provides a good discussion of measurement in Chapter 2.

WALKER, H., and LEV, J. 1958. *Elementary statistical methods.* New York: Holt.

> A good introduction to elementary statistics. Several chapters in the beginning of this book provide detailed discussions of tables, and charts.

PROBLEMS

1. List the four measurement scales in such a way that if a set of data is appropriate to a scale, it will also be appropriate to all prior scales in the list. Such a list of the scales of measurement may be called a "hierarchy of precision."

2. Suppose that a group of licensed drivers is tested for driving ability by means of a test consisting of twenty different episodes in each of which the driver is rated "satisfactory" or "unsatisfactory," the score given a driver being the number of "satisfactory" ratings given to him. In the hierarchy of problem 1 what is the most advanced scale appropriate to these driving-ability scores?

3. For each scale prior to that chosen in problem 2, explain what information contained in the driving ability data would be sacrificed if such a prior scale were to be used to interpret the data.

4. Contestants in a race are usually rated "first," "second," "third," . . . , "last." The scale applied is clearly an ordinal scale of measurement. What are a few of the questions that might be answered by devising a nominal scale by which to interpret such data?

5. What other or additional information about the racers in problem 4 would be required in order that a more advanced scale in the hierarchy of precision might be used?

6. The hierarchy of precision constructed in problem 1 constitutes a scale of measurement itself. Where does this scale lie in the hierarchy of precision?

7. The income of a certain man depends on his salary and on his business investments.
   (a) What scale of measurement should he use to measure his salary with maximum precision?
   (b) What scale of measurement should he use to measure with maximum precision the contribution of his investments to his income?
   (c) What scale will provide the most precision in measuring his net income?
8. (a) What scale of measurement is being used by a teacher if it is his practice to mark every paper and every performance with a percentage between 0 and 100 inclusive?
   (b) What scale of measurement is represented by the A-B-C-D-F system of grading?
   (c) What are some of the difficulties standing in the way of the development of a more precise scale for grading?
9. (a) If the price of a loaf of bread rose from $.10 in 1932 to $.30 in 1952, is it proper to assert that the price in 1952 was three times the price in 1932?
   (b) What scale of measurement is being improperly applied in (a) if the answer given there is yes?
   (c) What scales can be used to measure bread prices over a period of time?
10. It is a common practice in contests to award ten points for a first place, five for a second, and two for a third. The purpose is obviously to improve the possibility of comparing performances. What scale is being discarded in this process, and what scale is being used instead? Is this a proper use of this latter scale?
11. What are the advantages of the mathematical *lingua franca* that exists throughout the world today?
12. What is the mathematical advantage to be gained by refining measurement methods?
13. The familiar mathematical model for finding areas of rectangles is represented by the formula $LW = A$, where L, W, and A denote length, width, and area, respectively. Does this formula produce a value of A that can be interpreted as an area no matter what numbers are used for L and W? What kinds of numbers must be used for L and W in order for the formula to be meaningful as a method of computing area?

14. Find two or three applications of the formula $LW = A$ which have nothing to do with length, width, or area. You may find it convenient to use other letters in place of L, W, and A. Will doing so result in any actual change in the mathematical model being used?

15. Because the organization of data occurs early in any experiment, the methods of organization are conditioned more by future requirements of the scientist than by other considerations. What are these future requirements?

16. The grades received by 100 students were as follows:

GRADE	A	B	C	D	F
NO. OF STUDENTS	15	20	40	15	10

   (a) Make a bar graph of these data using bars 1 inch wide, with one inch on the vertical scale representing fifty students.

   (b) Repeat (a) using bars $\frac{1}{2}$ inch wide, one inch on the vertical scale representing twenty-five students.

   (c) Repeat (a) using bars $\frac{1}{4}$ inch wide and a vertical scale of ten students to the inch.

   (d) Which bar graph do you think best displays the data? What changes in the proportions would you make to improve the representation?

17. Which of the following are discrete measures and which are continuous?

   Amount of rainfall
   Grades on a true-false test
   Salaries of executives
   Grades on an essay test
   Average annual rainfall
   Temperature
   Time since 8 a.m. today
   Grains of sand on earth

18. Use the graphs of problem 16 to make an estimate of the number of students who were borderline cases between grades of B and C. What assumptions about the data must be made to justify this kind of calculation?

19. Classify the data of Table 1 using

   (a) sixteen intervals each of length 5.
   (b) eleven intervals each of length 7.
   (c) twenty intervals each of length 4.

   These classifications will be used again for later problems.

20. Classify the data of Table 5 using thirteen class intervals which, unlike those of Table 6, have endpoints which cannot coincide with a datum.

21. Let each of the data in Table 5 be divided by 10, and classify the resulting data in each of the following ways:
    (a) Use thirteen intervals of length .4 such that no datum may fall on any interval endpoint.
    (b) Use ten intervals of length .5 such that data may fall at one end of the interval but not at the other.

22. Make a histogram for each of the three classifications made in problem 19. Let all three histograms have the same height and width.

23. Make frequency polygons for each of the three classifications made in problem 19. (The results of problem 22 may be used here.)

. . . an experiment to determine the average number of sides to a question.

JOHN C. POLYANI

CHAPTER

3

CENTRAL TENDENCY

THIS CHAPTER is concerned with what is called an "average." And, just as we have seen that the term "measurement" involves more complex and interesting features than we might expect, we shall find that "average" also has more connotations for the behavioral scientist than it has for most people. For the word "average" has a technical meaning quite different from that intended in the ordinary use of the word. Technically, an average is a value which lies at the center of the range of the data. This center may be defined in many different ways, and there are, therefore, many different averages. Because the word "average" is so closely associated in ordinary language with a particular definition of the center of a distribution, *measure of central tendency* will be used to denote a value around which a distribution tends to center. First we turn our attention to the scientists' *need* for a concept such as average, and to the requirements such a concept must meet if it is to be useful.

THE NEED FOR DESCRIBING CENTRAL TENDENCY

Previous chapters dealt with the matters of measurement and mathematics, as well as ways and means for organizing data. The organization of data is clearly a preliminary step, for, although the events may have been counted and organized in the form of a frequency distribution, all the variability among the events remains. A frequency distribution organizes the data, but it does not in itself sufficiently describe the set of data so that exact quantitative comparisons may be easily made. There is, therefore, a clear need for a procedure that will do more than simply organize the data in tabular or graphic form.

In the effort to go beyond mere organization of the data, statisticians have taken advantage of the fact that at least two features of most frequency distributions stand out rather clearly: (1) the tendency of the data to cluster around some value lying between the smallest and largest data and (2) the tendency of the data to be dispersed around this central value. The first of these features—*central tendency*—will be discussed in this chapter, and the matter of dispersion, or variability, will be discussed in the next chapter.

Being able to specify the location of a point of central tendency is very useful, for, once the point on which the data center has been specified, it may be used to represent the entire set of data in the distribution. (This kind of representation of a large set of data by a single number which indicates the point of central tendency is particularly useful, as we shall see, when it is accompanied by a measure of the dispersion or variability about this point.) Because a measure of central tendency may be used to represent the entire set of data, it serves a very important need of the scientist—*reduction of the confusing and cumbersome detail of many data to a single number which is readily understood and communicated and which, therefore, permits quantitative comparison.*

The value of being able to make quantitative comparisons—despite variation among the events being compared—can hardly be overestimated. Averages (measures of central tendency) are constantly used to make comparisons in daily life and are, of course, so used in the behavioral sciences. Without such a technique, our daily lives would be far different, and any scientific effort which has to cope with variability would be vastly more difficult, if not impossible.

REQUIREMENTS

The requirements for a measure of central tendency are these: (1) fairness, or adequate representation of all the data, (2) location of the "center" of the distribution, and, (3) ease of understanding and communication. The latter requirement is particularly important, because it is almost always necessary to report some measure of central tendency, and because a measure of central tendency is often the only descriptive measure reported. A good measure of central tendency should also be widely applicable and useful for comparing many types of data. As we shall see, present methods of measuring central tendency meet all these requirements, but only if they are correctly applied.

METHODS OF DESCRIBING AND LOCATING CENTRAL TENDENCY

Because there is more than one method of describing and locating the central tendency of a distribution, it is necessary to study each of the methods in order to discover which one is appropriate to various conditions. And, because the measurement of central tendency is fundamental, it is of great importance that the method used be appropriate to the problem. As might be expected, some methods are appropriate on certain occasions and other methods are preferable at other times; for example, different methods are applied when the data are measured in terms of a nominal scale (categorization without ordering) than when the data are measured in terms of an ordinal scale (categorization plus ordering). Each method for describing central tendency will be discussed in terms of the scale to which the method is appropriate.

Central tendency of nominal scales

As we have seen, a nominal scale indicates only that certain numbers of cases fall in each of the categories. Under these circumstances a measure of central tendency also tells us very little, for all that such a measure can signify is which category contains the largest number of events. The measure of central tendency indicating the category that contains the largest number of events is the *mode*.

The mode is seldom used in the behavioral sciences, least of all in psychology. In economics the mode is used more frequently—for example, to identify the city which contains the largest number of retail stores, or car loadings, and so on. In general, the mode is used in connection with statistical *records* rather than with the attempt to make *inductive inferences*.

Central tendency of ordinal scales

A measure of central tendency appropriate to ordinal scales should take advantage of the fact that the categories are arranged in order from small to large, low to high, and the like. The *median* is a measure of central tendency which does take account of order, for the median is a point on the scale which divides the distribution of events precisely in half; one half of the cases lie *above* the median, and one half lie *below* it. For example, consider the data 20, 25, 26, 30, and 32, which are arranged in order. Since an equal number of cases lie above and below the value 26, this value (26) is the median of this distribution. In the above example the number (N) of observations was odd—five. When the number of observations is even, the median is half the sum of the two center, or middle, values; thus, in the distribution 50, 51, 56, 58, 61, 62 the median is $\dfrac{56 + 58}{2} = 57$.

The median has a clear meaning in the above two cases as the "center" of the distribution, but these examples do not illustrate how the median indicates the point of central tendency in a distribution with a larger number of cases. This property of the median may be seen by considering Table 10.

TABLE 10

Data Used to Illustrate the Location of the Median

(1) CLASS INTERVAL	(2) FREQUENCY	(3) CUMULATIVE FREQUENCY
99.5–109.5	6	100
89.5–99.5	9	94
79.5–89.5	12	85
69.5–79.5	14	73
59.5–69.5	18	59
49.5–59.5	13	41
39.5–49.5	10	28
29.5–39.5	8	18
19.5–29.5	6	10
9.5–19.5	4	4
	$n = 100$	

Although the explanation of procedures for computing the median are deferred to the mathematical section of this chapter, the student will see that the median, the point that divides the distribution in half $\left(\dfrac{n}{2} = \dfrac{100}{2} = 50\right)$, lies in the interval 59.5–69.5. (The method for determining precisely where it lies in this interval is explained later.) The main point to be observed here does not concern the procedure for locating the median (that is discussed in full on pages 86–89); rather, it should simply be noticed that the median is so defined as to give a different interpretation of central tendency than does the mode.

Although the median is a very useful measure of central tendency, it is seldom used, except by statisticians, simply because few others are acquainted with it, and because the arithmetic mean (to be discussed below) is so familiar to everyone. But the median deserves to be much more widely used than it is. The reasons for this will become apparent after the following discussion of the arithmetic mean.

Central tendency of interval scales

As we have seen, it is characteristic of interval scales that the intervals between the data are comparable. A measure of central tendency which, unlike the mode and median, takes this information into account would be a more appropriate measure than either of those previously described. The *arithmetic mean* (often referred to simply as the *mean*) is such a measure; its computation not only makes use of but wholly depends on the numerical comparability of the data.

Unlike the median, the mean is a familiar concept: it is what the layman has in mind when he speaks of "the average." Curiously, despite the widespread use of the mean, it is difficult to present a concise, accurate, but *nonmathematical* definition of this familiar concept. Mathematically, however, the arithmetic mean is easy to define, simply by referring to its computation, and very likely the reader has been able to do this for some time. The arithmetic mean is calculated, quite simply, by adding the data and dividing the sum by the number of data. Thus, the mean of the data, 11, 13, 16, 24, 25, and 31 is 20, arrived at by adding the above values and dividing by the number of data, as in

$$\text{Mean} = \frac{11 + 13 + 16 + 24 + 25 + 31}{6}$$

$$\text{Mean} = \frac{120}{6} = 20$$

The arithmetic mean meets the general requirements for a measure of central tendency very neatly. It is certainly useful for comparing sets of data (see Box 8). It is common to observe that one group of students has a higher "average" (mean) test score than another, that one group has a higher "average" (mean) income than another, and so forth. And it is obvious that it can be applied, and has been applied, to a wide variety of situations. In fact, the widespread use of the arithmetic mean makes superfluous a discussion of its general application.

However, it is important to note that, despite its widespread use and easy calculation, the arithmetic mean does not fully deserve the popularity it has achieved. Although it is applicable to a great many situations, there are many others in which its use not only is likely to result in confusion but actually may be misleading. Three cases are discussed below: Case I involves the inappropriate calculation of the arithmetic mean from data taken from an ordinal scale; Case II involves the appropriate calculation of the arithmetic mean from a symmetrical distribution; and Case III involves the inappropriate calculation of the arithmetic mean from an asymmetrical distribution.

Case I—Ordinal scales

When the data have been measured by means of an ordinal scale, the mean is not an appropriate measure of central tendency. The reason for this is simple: the mean involves the addition of numbers which represent categories which are assumed to have numerically comparable intervals between them, but that is precisely the feature an ordinal scale lacks. If, for example, a mean is calculated for the data in Table 11, a mistake is made.

TABLE 11

A Frequency Distribution of Grades

GRADE	FREQUENCY
A	18
B	32
C	60
D	16
F	14

Every student, if not every instructor, knows that the interval between a grade of A and a grade of B cannot be demonstrated to be equal to the interval between the grades B and C, nor can the interval between B and C be demonstrated to be equal to that between C and D; that is, the amount

B O X 8

A Comparison of Two Distributions

As an example of clarity of presentation and interpretation of data which illustrates both central tendency and variability, as well as for its historical interest, we present in the figure below a classified into two groups which we have designated as rural and urban. The urban group is here defined to include all subjects from areas having a population density of 1,000 or more per

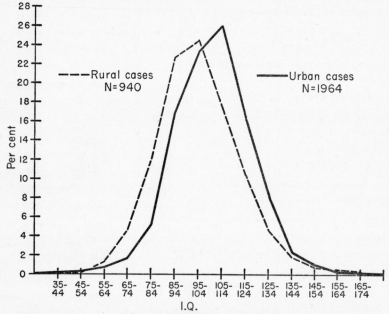

Distributions of I.Q.'s of Rural and Urban Groups. Reprinted from *Measuring intelligence* by Lewis M. Terman and Maud A. Merrill. Copyright 1937 by Houghton Mifflin Company and reprinted with their permission.

graph from Terman and Merrill's *Measuring intelligence* (which contains the 1937 revision of the Stanford-Binet Intelligence Test) together with the passage in the text which comments on the graph.

"Our subjects have been square mile, and the rural group all others. [The figure] shows the I.Q. distributions for the two groups. The respective means are 105.7 and 99.2."

Terman, L. and Merrill, M. 1937. *Measuring intelligence.* Boston: Houghton Mifflin.

of improvement indicated by a change in grade from B to A cannot be demonstrated to be equal to the amount of improvement indicated by a change from C to B. When the mean is computed, however, each score is added exactly as if the increments were equal. If the letter grades were known to be related to one another by some known numerical measure— that is, if an A were 1 times, or 1.5 times, or 2.672 times a B, and so on— then the mean could be taken. But this is not the case: the usual (and *incorrect*) practice is to take 1 as the unit and assign four units to A, three units to B, two units to C, one unit to D, and no units to F; the mean is then computed—sometimes to four decimal places!

Since it is obviously harder to move from B to A than it is from C to B, there would be more equity, but just as little accuracy, in assigning 10, 6, 3, 1, and 0 instead of 4, 3, 2, 1, and 0 to the letter grades. The basic unit of measurement remains a guess with which nearly all will disagree, and the mean is an inappropriate measure of the central grade tendency. Grade-point averages illustrate a most common, yet inappropriate, application of the arithmetic mean to ordinally scaled data.

Case II—Symmetrical distributions

Table 12 shows the frequency distribution of thirty-four scores which range from 11 to 19 inclusive. Column (2) gives the frequency (f) with which each score value (X) occurred. The distribution is said to be "symmetrical" because the lowest and highest scores occurred with equal frequency, the next to lowest and next to highest scores occurred with equal frequency, and so on, throughout the whole range of the scores. As a result of this symmetry, column (2) reads the same from bottom to top as it does from top to bottom. Figure 9 illustrates this symmetry geometrically.

From our earlier discussion of the median, it is clear that 15 is that score below which and above which an equal number of data lie; hence, 15 is the median. But 15 is also the arithmetic mean. The computation of the mean is accomplished by dividing 36 (the number of scores) into the sum of all the 36 scores. This sum is computed in column (3) of Table 12, where each entry fX represents the contribution of the f instances of the score X to the sum. That the result, 15, is equal to the median is no accident. *The mean and median are always the same for symmetrical distributions, and if a symmetrical distribution has just one mode, then the mode is also equal to the median and the mean.*

Because all the commonly used measures of central tendency are equal for a symmetrical distribution, any one of these statistics represents the data as well as any other. The question as to which may be most appro-

TABLE 12

A Symmetrical Frequency Distribution

(1)	(2)	(3)
		FREQUENCY $\times$ SCORE
SCORE	FREQUENCY	VALUE
X	f	fX
19	1	$(19 \times 1) = 19$
18	2	$(18 \times 2) = 36$
17	4	$(17 \times 4) = 68$
16	7	$(16 \times 7) = 112$
15	8	$(15 \times 8) = 120$
14	7	$(14 \times 7) = 98$
13	4	$(13 \times 4) = 52$
12	2	$(12 \times 2) = 24$
11	1	$(11 \times 1) = 11$
	$n = 36$	540

$$\text{Mean} = \frac{540}{36} = 15$$

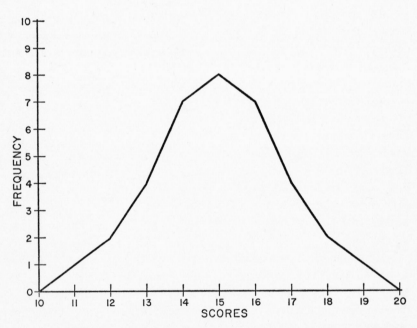

FIG. 9. A frequency polygon for the data of Table 12 illustrating a symmetrical distribution.

priately used is settled by choosing that one which best yields itself to further study and analysis. The arithmetic mean meets this criterion more
completely than any of the other measures of central tendency. It does so
because it is the most familiar such measure to most readers, and because
there exists an extensive mathematical development by which the mean
may be further studied.

The various measures of central tendency become less and less in
agreement as the distribution becomes less and less symmetrical.

Case III—Distributions which are not symmetrical

The behavioral scientists' data by no means always appear in the form
of a symmetrical distribution. The shape of the distribution is frequently
asymmetrical, or skewed—as, for example, are the data in Table 13. Note
how the majority of the cases are clustered at one end of the distribution
(see column (2)).

As in the previous example, the value and frequency of each score enter
into the computation of the arithmetic mean. Indeed, the very fact that
both value and frequency enter into the calculation of the mean results in
an ambiguity when the distribution is not symmetrical. And this ambiguity
is the root of the likelihood of misinterpretation.

The ambiguity is this: When the distribution is asymmetrical, one
cannot be certain whether frequency *or* value is the principal factor in
determining the location of the mean. For in a skewed distribution a small
frequency of cases which are a large distance from the mean will have the
same weight in determining the location of the mean as a large frequency
of cases near the mean.

As an example, assume that two cases are added to the distribution of
Table 13, with each of the two new cases having a score of 10. (Note that
this is a large distance from the mean.) What effect would these two new
cases have on the mean? The answer is made clear by computing the new
sum, which would equal 161 (the two new scores of 10 would add 20 to
141), and N would be increased to 44. Since $161/44 = 3.65$, it is clear that
adding two cases with scores of 10 would move the mean higher—from
3.36 to 3.65.

Now suppose that, instead of two cases which have scores of 10, two
cases with scores of 5 are added—that is, two cases which are closer to the
mean (3.36). These two cases will have almost no effect on the location of
the new mean, it will be $151/44 = 3.43$, instead of 3.36. Thus, adding two
cases with scores of 10 changes the mean .30 points, whereas adding two
cases with scores of 5 changes the mean only .07 points. How many cases

T A B L E   1 3

An Asymmetrical Frequency Distribution

(1)	(2)	(3)
X	f	fX
10	0	0
9	1	9
8	1	8
7	2	14
6	3	18
5	5	25
4	6	24
3	8	24
2	7	14
1	5	5
0	4	0
	N = 42	141

$$\text{Mean} = \frac{141}{42} = 3.36$$

The asymmetry of Table 13 is illustrated in Figure 10.

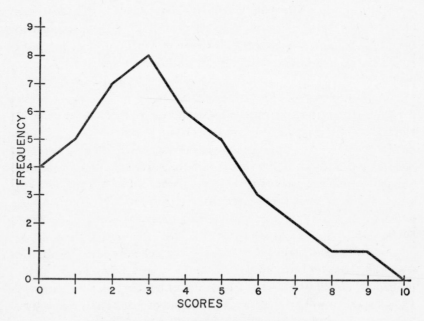

Fig. 10. A frequency polygon for the data of
Table 13 illustrating an asymmetrical distribution.

with scores of 5 would have to be added to the distribution in order to move the mean from 3.36 to 3.65 (the distance which two cases with scores of 10 moved the location of the mean)? It would take an additional ten cases with scores of 5 to move the mean from 3.36 to 3.65 ($^{191}\!/_{52} = 3.65$). In short, a mean of 3.65 could have arisen because of a small number of cases (two) at the extreme of the distribution (score value of 10) or because of a large number of cases (ten) with scores quite close (5) to the center distribution.

The main point to be learned from the above illustration is this: The arithmetic mean of an asymmetrical or skewed distribution always conceals an ambiguity. One cannot know whether the specific location of the mean is due mainly to the factor of frequency or value. The following simple example will illustrate the importance of this ambiguity. Suppose the distribution of income in two nations is represented by the mean, and that Nation A reports a higher mean than Nation B. If we were unable to inspect the shape of the distribution, however, the reported means would be difficult to interpret, for the distribution might very well be asymmetrical or skewed, and the higher mean of Nation A may be due almost entirely to the extremely large income of a very few individuals. (See Box 9.) Moreover, the majority of the people in Nation A may have lower incomes than the majority of people in Nation B. This fact would become apparent if the *median* income in each nation were represented. For, it will be remembered, the median is simply that point which divides the distribution in half.

Furthermore, although the mean and median are identical when the distribution is perfectly symmetrical, these two methods of locating the central tendency of the distribution become progressively different as the distributions become progressively more asymmetrical. As an illustration, consider the data 4, 5, 6, 7, 8; here the mean and median are identical (6). Suppose we add two cases of value 14 and 16: the data are now 4, 5, 6, 7, 8, 14, 16, and the median is now 7, but the mean has increased to 8.57. Adding two more cases of value 40 and 50, the data become 4, 5, 6, 7, 8, 14, 16, 40, 50: the median is now 8, but the mean is now 16.7. The mean is being highly affected by the new cases being added at the extreme of the distribution.

Note, however, that the change in the value of the median is independent of the values of the new data. It depends only on how many data are added and on the values of the data just above the original median. This does not mean that adding additional data at the extremes always leaves the median only slightly changed. For example, the median of the numbers 5, 7, 10, 85, and 90 is 10. Adding 92 and 94 to the data makes the median 85. Note that the increase of 75 in the median was due to the datum 85, however, and not to the values 92 and 94 of the new data; in this example the increase in the mean amounts to less than 16, while the median increased by 75.

In brief, the differently defined measures of central tendency coincide for symmetrical distributions but differ for asymmetrical distributions.

B O X 9

Imposter in the Robes of an Average

Moroney, the English statistician, illustrates the fact that one must always scrutinize very carefully the relation between the average, a concept in the world of ideas, with the entity it may be supposed to represent in the world of things.

"The idea of an average is common property. However scanty our knowledge of arithmetic, we are all at home with the idea of goal averages, batting and bowling averages, and the like. We realize that the purpose of an average is to represent a *group of individual values* in a simple and concise manner so that the mind can get a quick understanding of the general size of the individuals in the group, undistracted by fortuitous and irrelevant variations. It is of the utmost importance to appreciate this fact that the average is to act as a *representative*. It follows that it is the acme of nonsense to go through all the rigmarole of the arithmetic to calculate the average of a set of figures which do not in some real sense constitute a single family. Suppose a prosperous medical man earning £3,000 a year had a wife and two children none of whom were gainfully employed and that the doctor had in his household a maid to whom he paid £150 a year and that there was a jobbing gardener who received £40 a year. We can go through all the processes of calculating the average income for this little group. Six people between them earn £3,190 in the year. Dividing the total earnings by the number of people we may determine the average earnings of the group to be 531 13s. 4d. But this figure is no more than an imposter in the robes of an average. It represents not a single person in the group. It gives the reader a totally meaningless figure, because he cannot make one single reliable deduction from it. This is an extreme example, but mock averages are calculated with great abandon. Few people ask themselves: What conclusions will be drawn from this average that I am about to calculate? Will it create a false impression?"

Moroney, M. J. 1956. *Facts from figures.* Harmondsworth: Penguin Books.

The differences between the two measures make possible a choice as to which is most appropriate to the kind of information sought by the investigator and to the amount of further mathematical elaboration planned by the investigator.

Choosing the proper measure

Unfortunately, there is no rule of thumb for deciding whether the mean or median is the more appropriate measure of the central tendency of a distribution. The general rule, if it may be so called, is simply this: *think of the consequences.* If the distribution is symmetrical, or nearly so, there will ordinarily be no problem, since the mean and median will be nearly alike. If the distribution is skewed, the mean and the median will, of course, differ, and the researcher will face a choice: the mean should be used if it is appropriate for the measure of central tendency to reflect extreme cases, and the median should be used when the measure of central tendency should not reflect the values of extreme cases. (See Box 10.) (If both the mean and median are presented, their difference conveys to the reader at least a rough measure of the asymmetry of the distribution.) If the distribution is skewed, and if the researcher computes only the mean, he is apt to mislead—not only others but himself. At the least, the reader deserves to know when the mean is computed from a skewed distribution. The researcher who prepares the data and the person who reads the data must decide which is appropriate in light of the nature of the problem.

On purely technical grounds, however, the mean has an advantage, for it is more susceptible to further mathematical and statistical treatment. Therefore, the researcher who intends to carry out further and more detailed statistical analyses of his data will probably choose to calculate the mean, perhaps in addition to reporting the median. However, the researcher must take into account the statistical knowledge of those who read his report: the mean will ordinarily be a familiar concept to the layman, while the median will not.

In addition to the arithmetic mean, the median, and the mode, there are other measures of central tendency. These include the geometric mean, the harmonic mean, and others. They will not be discussed here because they are seldom employed in research in the behavioral sciences.

BY WAY OF SUMMARY

Large amounts of variability are found among the phenomena included within the behavioral sciences. The first step in coping with variability is organization of the data, and the second is description of the central tendency of data organized into some form of frequency distribution. Comparison, the *sine qua non* of the scientific method, would be difficult to the

---

BOX 10

A letter to the Editor from Sir Francis Galton

"A certain class of problems do not as yet appear to be solved according to scientific rules, though they are of much importance and of frequent recurrence. Two examples will suffice. (1) A jury has to assess damages. (2) The council of a society has to fix on a sum of money, suitable for some particular purpose. Each voter, whether of the jury or of the council, has equal authority with each of his colleagues. How can the right conclusion be reached, considering that there may be as many different estimates as there are members? That conclusion is clearly *not* the *average* of all the estimates, which would give a voting power to cranks in proportion to their crankiness. One absurdly large or small estimate would leave a greater impress on the result than one of reasonable amount, and the more an estimate diverges from the bulk of the rest, the more influence would it exert. I wish to point out that the estimate to which least objection can be raised is the *middlemost* estimate, the number of votes that it is too high being exactly balanced by the number of votes that it is too low. Every other estimate is condemned by a majority of voters as being either too high or too low, the middlemost alone escaping this condemnation. The number of voters may be odd or even. If odd, there is one middlemost value; thus in 11 votes the middlemost is the 6th; in 99 votes the middlemost is the 50th. If the number of voters be even, there are two middlemost values, the mean of which must be taken; thus in 12 votes the middlemost lies between the 6th and the 7th; in 100 votes between the 50th and the 51st. Generally, in $2n - 1$ votes the middlemost is the nth; in $2n$ votes it lies between the nth and the $(n + 1)$th.

I suggest that the process for a jury on their retirement should be (1) to discuss and interchange views; (2) for each juryman to write his own independent estimate on a separate slip of paper; (3) for the foreman to arrange the slips in the order of the values written on them; (4) to take the average of the 6th and 7th as the verdict, which might be finally approved as a substantive proposition. Similarly as regards the resolutions of councils, having regard to the above $(2n - 1)$ and $2n$ remarks."

FRANCIS GALTON

Galton, F. 1907. One Vote, One Value. *Nature,* 75, 414.

point of impossibility without the information provided by a description of central tendency. Indeed, the use of "averages" is such an integral part of everyone's method of making comparisons that it is hard to imagine what it would be like to live without such a concept.

But neither the informed citizen nor the scientist can be satisfied with the vagueness in the term "average." Both need to push beyond this imprecise concept. The scientist in particular has a special reason for being dissatisfied with "average." His problems and methods are such that he has a need for more clarity than the concept of average affords, and he has a definite need for a technique for making quantitative comparisons despite the variation in the data.

What are the behavioral scientists' requirements for mathematical concepts or devices for measuring central tendency? A good measure of central tendency should have wide applicability and be useful for making comparisons. It should provide a number which, by representing the center of the distribution, represents the whole distribution more accurately than would any other single number. Two mathematical concepts, the median and the arithmetic mean, meet these requirements rather well. A third, the mode, meets them poorly and is useful only under special conditions.

On the other hand, what do these mathematical concepts require of the empirical phenomena? Certain concepts require very little from the data which they represent. The mode, for example, requires only that the data be separated into categories. And, in turn, the mode conveys little information: it merely indicates which category contains the largest number of events. The median requires that the data be categorized and ordered from small to large and, in turn, indicates that half of the cases lie to one side of it and half on the other; it is not, however, affected by *how far* to one side or the other extreme cases lie. The arithmetic mean requires that the data be categorized in order and that the intervals between the scale categories be comparable to one another; in turn, the mean reflects and is affected by the *distance* as well as the direction of every datum in the distribution. Furthermore, the mean fits more readily into more complex mathematical systems than does either the mode or median. Because it lends itself more readily to further mathematical manipulation, it both *requires* more information and *provides* more information than does the mode or median.

In general, then, the scientist must be certain that the concepts he selects from mathematics are appropriate to his method and problem. Specifically, the method of describing central tendency should fit the researcher's problem and his method of analyzing it. More than one scientist has been lured into such a meaningless effort as "an experiment to determine the average number of sides to a question" merely because of the existence of the concept of the average.

❰ Mathematically . . .

Having discussed in a general way the various measures of central tendency, we turn now to the methods of computing the mode, median, and mean.

THE MODE

It is a simple matter to compute the mode. For unclassified data the mode is that datum which occurs most frequently; thus, in the series 4, 8, 10, 10, 10, 12, 12 the mode is 10. For data classified into a frequency distribution the mode is taken to be the midpoint of the class interval having the greatest frequency. For interval and ratio scales the mode described here is actually an approximation to what is known as the *true mode*—that point which corresponds to the highest point on the theoretically perfect frequency polygon of the population involved. Approximations to this theoretically perfect frequency polygon are obtained by greatly increasing the number of data, the accuracy of measurement, and the number of class intervals. Then the lengths of the class intervals become very short, and the line segments composing the frequency polygon become short also. The further this process is carried, the more the frequency polygon resembles a smoothly turning curve. This limiting curve, the theoretically perfect frequency polygon, is called the "frequency curve." A vertical line through its highest point cuts the horizontal axis in the true mode.

The approximations to the mode are almost always sufficiently close to the true mode for practical purposes. The great multiplication of data and the refinement of measure required to get a closer approximation are seldom justified by any added usefulness of the result.

THE MEDIAN

The median is most easily determined by reference to the frequency distribution. If the data are ordered according to size and are counted individually, the median is the center datum. There will, of course, be a "center datum" only if the number of data is odd. If the number of data is even, there will be two "center data" and the median is defined to be the point midway between them, obtained by taking half their sum.

The data of Table 14 are used to illustrate the computation of the median. Since there are 100 data, the median accordingly lies between the

TABLE 14

Data Used to Illustrate the Computation of the Median

11	36	43	50	53	56	60	64	69	78
18	36	43	50	53	56	60	65	70	79
20	37	44	51	53	57	62	66	71	79
23	37	44	51	54	57	62	67	72	82
23	39	45	51	54	58	62	67	73	83
25	39	46	51	54	58	63	67	74	84
30	40	47	51	54	58	63	68	74	87
31	41	48	52	55	59	63	68	75	92
33	41	48	52	55	59	63	68	76	93
34	42	48	53	55	60	64	69	77	99

fiftieth and fifty-first data when all are ordered from small to large. Note that there are forty-nine data below and forty-nine data above these two "center data." When so ordered, as in Table 14, $X_{50} = 55$ and $X_{51} = 56$; the median is therefore $\dfrac{55 + 56}{2} = 55.5$.

TABLE 15

The Data of Table 14 Classified to Illustrate the Computation of the Median

INTERVAL	FREQUENCY	CUMULATIVE FREQUENCY
94.5–100.5	1	100
88.5–94.5	2	99
82.5–88.5	3	97
76.5–82.5	5	94
70.5–76.5	7	89
64.5–70.5	11	82
58.5–64.5	14	71
52.5–58.5	18	57
46.5–52.5	13	39
40.5–46.5	9	26
34.5–40.5	7	17
28.5–34.5	4	10
22.5–28.5	3	6
16.5–22.5	2	3
10.5–16.5	1	1

If the data are classified into intervals, the computation is as follows. The sum of the frequencies for all class intervals up to and including each interval is placed opposite that interval. The data of Table 14 have been classified in Table 15 and such a cumulative-frequency column included. The median is defined as that point above which and below which half the data lie. If there are n data, the median point is taken to lie midway between the $\left(\dfrac{n}{2}\right)^{nd}$ and the $\left(\dfrac{n}{2}+1\right)^{nd}$ data. The midpoint between the ordinal numbers $\dfrac{n}{2}$ and $\left(\dfrac{n}{2}+1\right)$ is $\dfrac{n+1}{2}$ or $\dfrac{n}{2}+\dfrac{1}{2}$.

To find the median, look up the cumulative frequency column until a number equal to or greater than $\dfrac{n}{2}+\dfrac{1}{2}$ is encountered. If the number thus found is exactly equal to $\dfrac{n}{2}+\dfrac{1}{2}$, take as the median the upper endpoint of the class interval in which the number was found. If the number found in the cumulative frequency column is larger than $\dfrac{n}{2}+\dfrac{1}{2}$, compute what percentage of the frequency of the class interval in which the number was found would be required to make the cumulative frequency exactly $\left(\dfrac{n}{2}+\dfrac{1}{2}\right)$. The median will be equal to the initial endpoint of the class interval in which $\dfrac{n}{2}+\dfrac{1}{2}$ was found plus the above percentage of its length. (The procedure is reversed if the frequencies are accumulated from the top to the bottom of the frequency distribution.)

An inspection of the cumulative frequency column of Table 15 shows that the number $\dfrac{100}{2}+\dfrac{1}{2}=50.5$ is first equaled or exceeded in the cumulative frequencies opposite the interval 52.5–58.5. The median lies somewhere in this interval; its exact location depends on how many of the eighteen data in the class interval are needed to raise the cumulative frequency to 50.5. Since the cumulative frequency for the previous interval is 39, $50.5-39=11.5$ cases are needed to raise the cumulative frequency to 50.5. The median is then $11\frac{1}{2}/18$ of the way through the interval 52.5–58.5. The fraction $\dfrac{11.5}{18}$ reduces to .64 or 64 per cent, and the class interval length is 6; hence the median lies at 64 per cent of 6 past the beginning of the interval 52.5–58.5. Thus, $52.5+(.64)(6)=56.3$ is the median.

This result agrees to within .6 of the median obtained by a direct counting of the data. If it could be correctly assumed that all the data in any class interval are uniformly distributed over that interval, then errors such as this .6 would not occur. Such a false assumption is implicit in the definition of the median for grouped data, but the error is usually negligible if the number of class intervals is well chosen. The method of computation used also makes it clear that if all the data below those in the interval 52.5–58.5 were changed to *any* other numbers all below 52.5, the median would remain the same. A similar change could be made in the data in the intervals above 52.5–58.5, with a similar result. This is because the median depends only on the direction of the observations, not on their distance from one another. This makes the median an excellent measure of centrality whenever circumstances make frequency a more important consideration than the data values.

THE MEAN

When the data are recorded in an interval scale, the information implied by the data is much more specific and extensive, and the mean may be used as the measure of central tendency. Since the mean is a function of both direction and distance (unlike the mode and the median), it is admirably suited to mathematical manipulation and development. A highly refined and extensive area of statistical operation is based upon this fact. Coupled with its fairness as a measure of centrality in most cases, this mathematical suitability makes the mean the most used of all measures of central tendency.

Assuming that the size of the sample is n and that each datum is represented by X with a suitable subscript, the mean $\bar{X}$ (note the bar over the X) is defined to be

(1)
$$\bar{X} = \frac{1}{n} \sum_{i=1}^{n} X_i$$

This formula is a concise set of symbols used to express the idea that the mean is equal to $\dfrac{X_1 + X_2 + \cdots + X_n}{n}$, where each datum has been assigned a symbol to represent it; that is, each of the X's stands for one of the n data being studied. The subscripts and the limits of summation are frequently omitted when to do so results in no ambiguity. Equation (1) thus often appears in the form

$$\bar{X} = \frac{1}{n}\sum X$$

To illustrate the application of this formula, the data in Table 14 will be used. The sum of the 100 numbers is 5600, and, hence,

$$\bar{X} = \frac{1}{100}\sum X$$
$$= \frac{5600}{100}$$
$$= 56$$

The mean may also be computed from the classified data if the assumption is made that each datum in an interval has the value of the midpoint of that interval. Although this assumption is clearly false in almost every actual case, for well-chosen intervals the error introduced is nevertheless very small and, for practical purposes, may be ignored. Using this assumption, the formula for the mean becomes

(2) $$\bar{X} = \frac{1}{n}\sum_{i=1}^{h} f_i p_i$$

where h is the number of intervals used, p_i is the midpoint of the ith interval and f_i is the frequency associated with the ith interval. If it is well understood from the context of the work that there are h intervals and that p and f run over their corresponding values for the various intervals, then h and the subscripts may be omitted. The formula then is

(3) $$\bar{X} = \frac{1}{n}\sum fp$$

Written this way, the formula is superficially simpler than equation (2). Actually it assumes from its context all that is explicitly stated in (2). In this formula each X is replaced by a p representing the midpoint of the interval in which X lies. The f is introduced to indicate that such a p must be taken f times to obtain the total of the data for that particular class interval. The sum of all the X's is then replaced by the sum of the products fp, there being one such for each of the h class intervals.

The computation using (3) and the frequency distribution in Table 15 is then

$$\bar{X} = \frac{1}{n}\sum fp$$

$$= \frac{1}{100}[(1)(13.5) + (2)(19.5) + \cdots + (1)(97.5)]$$

$$= \frac{5604}{100}$$

$$= 56.04$$

which differs from the actual mean by .04. This difference is due to the assumption that each datum is equal to the midpoint of the class interval in which it lies. These computations of the mean are at best laborious, however, and they are carried out here only to illustrate the basic rules and assumptions which define the mean.

The short method

It is possible to make the computation of the mean quite short without sacrificing any more accuracy than is the case with the method used above. The rationale of the short method depends on two properties of the mean, the use of which enables the statistician to work with easily handled small numbers instead of with the actual data. These two properties will be stated in the form of theorems. Each theorem will be proved and then employed in an example to show its usefulness.

Theorem 1. If a constant is added to each datum, the mean is increased by the value of the constant.

Letting the constant be denoted by c, the theorem in symbols is

(4) $$\frac{1}{n}\sum(X + c) = \bar{X} + c$$

The constant may be either positive or negative. (If it is negative, the phrase "increased by the value of the constant" in the theorem actually implies a decrease.)

To prove the theorem, the left side of (4) must be shown to equal the right side. Thus

$$\frac{1}{n}\sum(X+c) = \frac{1}{n}\sum X + \frac{1}{n}\sum c \qquad \text{(by distributing the summation symbol over } (\bar{X}+c). \text{ See page 24)}$$

$$= \bar{X} + \frac{1}{n}(nc) \qquad \text{(by summing over the constant } c. \text{ See page 25)}$$

$$= \bar{X} + c \qquad \text{(by canceling } n\text{'s in second term)}$$

and the proof is complete. The value of this theorem lies in the fact that it makes possible the substitution of a much easier problem for the one at hand in many instances. For example, the sum of the numbers, 63, 64, 66, 69, and 72 is 334, and the mean is 66.8. If the constant -63 is added to each of them, the result is 0, 1, 3, 6, and 9. The mean of these numbers is $19/5 = 3.8$. According to the theorem, this is the original mean with -63 added to it. To obtain the true mean, $+63$ must be added to 3.8 in order to offset or cancel out the effect of altering the data. The result is $3.8 + 63 = 66.8$, which is correct. This theorem also has value in the case of a set of mixed positive and negative numbers: the mean of the numbers -25, -20, -4, 6, 12, 21, and 24, for example, is 2; if 25 is added to each of the numbers, the result is 0, 5, 21, 31, 37, 46, and 49, and the mean is $189/7 = 27$, which is exactly 25 more than 2. Here the theorem has been used to make all the data non-negative and thus simplify the arithmetic.

Another method of reducing data to smaller, more easily handled numbers is that of multiplying each datum by a constant. If the constant is a fraction, the results will be smaller numbers. The second theorem on the mean has to do with such a multiplicative constant and is as follows: *Theorem 2. If each datum is multiplied by a constant, k, the new mean will be k times the original mean.* In symbols, the theorem is

(5)
$$\frac{1}{n}\sum kX = k\bar{X}$$

To prove the theorem, it is necessary to show that the left member of (5) is equal to $k\bar{X}$. Factoring the constant k out of the summation gives

$$\frac{1}{n}\sum kX = \left(\frac{1}{n}\right)k\sum X$$

$$= k\left(\frac{1}{n}\sum X\right)$$

$$= k\bar{X}$$

The second step here is merely a reversal of the factors k and $\frac{1}{n}$ so that $\frac{1}{n}\sum X$ can be replaced by $\bar{X}$ in the last step. Only the principle of factoring a constant out of a sum and the definition of the mean are needed to justify the steps of the proof. This result also allows the substitution of simpler numbers in many problems. As an example, consider the numbers 6, 15, 21, 33, and 42, the mean of which is $\frac{1}{5}(117) = 23.4$. If each number is multiplied by $k = \frac{1}{3}$, the result is 2, 5, 7, 11, and 14, the mean of which is $\frac{1}{5}(39) = 7.8$. According to the theorem, 7.8 is one third of the actual mean sought because each datum was multiplied by $\frac{1}{3}$. To obtain the actual mean, 7.8 is multiplied by 3; and the correct result is thus 23.4.

By applying *both* theorems on the mean to this example, the mean may be computed as follows. First, multiply each of 6, 15, 21, 33, and 42 by $\frac{1}{3}$, obtaining 2, 5, 7, 11, and 14. Then add -7 to each, obtaining -5, -2, 0, 4, and 7. The mean of these is $\frac{1}{5}(4) = .8$. Now .8 is the mean of the original data *after* they have been first multiplied by $\frac{1}{3}$ and then reduced by 7. According to the theorems, then, .8 is the actual mean multiplied by $\frac{1}{3}$ and decreased by 7. To obtain the actual mean, it is necessary to increase .8 by 7 and then to take three times the result; thus, $3(.8 + 7) = 23.4$ which is correct.

Extension to classified data

As will be seen from the following example, these theorems on the mean can be used to greatly shorten the work of computing the mean from a frequency distribution.

The frequency distribution of the data of Table 15 is repeated in Table 16. To take advantage of the properties of the mean just established, columns (2), (3), (4), and (6) have been added to the frequency distribution. Column (2) consists of the midpoints of the class intervals. These may always be computed by adding half the length of the class intervals to the initial points of the various class intervals. The assumption that each datum in a given class interval is equal to the midpoint of that interval is an essential part of the computation to be described. Column (3) is formed by subtracting from each midpoint, the midpoint of any arbitrarily chosen interval. In the present case the interval 52.5–58.5 is chosen (merely because it was estimated to contain the mean) and its midpoint 55.5 is subtracted from each of the midpoints listed in column (2). Note that, because the class intervals are regularly distributed and all of the same length, 6,

TABLE 16

Data of Table 14 Classified to Illustrate a Simplified Method of Computing the Mean

(1) INTERVAL	(2) MIDPOINT	(3) MIDPOINT LESS 55.5	(4) COLUMN (3) $\times \frac{1}{6}$	(5) FREQUENCY	(6) COLUMN (4) $\times$ COLUMN (5)
94.5–100.5	97.5	42	7	1	7
88.5–94.5	91.5	36	6	2	12
82.5–88.5	85.5	30	5	3	15
76.5–82.5	79.5	24	4	5	20
70.5–76.5	73.5	18	3	7	21
64.5–70.5	67.5	12	2	11	22
58.5–64.5	61.5	6	1	14	14
52.5–58.5	55.5	0	0	18	0
46.5–52.5	49.5	−6	−1	13	−13
40.5–46.5	43.5	−12	−2	9	−18
34.5–40.5	37.5	−18	−3	7	−21
28.5–34.5	31.5	−24	−4	4	−16
22.5–28.5	25.5	−30	−5	3	−15
16.5–22.5	19.5	−36	−6	2	−12
10.5–16.5	13.5	−42	−7	1	−7
			TOTALS	100	+9

the numbers of column (3) form a sequence running both ways from 0 in multiples of 6. Column (4) is obtained by multiplying each entry in column (3) by $\frac{1}{6}$, and the result is a sequence in column (4) running both ways from 0 in steps of one unit.

It is the numbers of column (4) that will be used in lieu of the actual data for the computation of the mean. Each number in column (4) represents a midpoint to which −55.5 has been added and the result multiplied by $\frac{1}{6}$. Since the midpoints represent the data, so also do the numbers in column (4). Column (5) gives the class frequencies. Column (6) is the product of matching entries in columns (4) and (5). The total of column (6), which is 9, is the sum of all the numbers used to represent the data, of which there are 100. The mean of these numbers is then $\frac{9}{100} = .09$. According to the theorems on the mean, this figure .09 is the result that would be obtained if the true mean were to be decreased by 55.5 and the result multiplied by $\frac{1}{6}$. To obtain the true mean, it is necessary to multiply by 6 to offset or cancel out the multiplication by $\frac{1}{6}$ and then to add 55.5 to cancel out the effect of the former subtraction of 55.5. The result is $\bar{X} = (.09)(6) + 55.5 = 56.04$.

The two theorems on the mean thus make possible a computation which involves only small whole numbers in lieu of the data. The selection of proper additive and multiplicative constants always results in a consecutive run of small whole numbers, as in column (4). The proper additive constant is the negative of the midpoint estimated to represent the mean. The proper multiplicative constant is the reciprocal of the class interval length. Expressed as a formula, the mean as computed in this example is

$$\bar{X} = C_e + \frac{I}{n} \sum_{i=1}^{h} \frac{(C_i - C_e)f_i}{I}$$

where C_e is the midpoint estimated to represent the data in the neighborhood of the mean, I is the length of the class intervals, and the expressions $C_i(i = 1, 2, \ldots, h)$ represent the h midpoints of the frequency distribution.

Combining two samples

Sometimes it is desired to combine two samples into a single sample. The mean of the combined sample may, of course, be computed in the usual way after the sample has been formed. If the means of the two constituent samples are known, however, they may be combined in a simple relationship to produce the mean of the combined sample. Suppose that the first sample is composed of n_1 data and has a mean of $\bar{X}_1$, while the second sample contains n_2 data with a mean of $\bar{X}_2$. Then $n_1 + n_2$ is the number of data in the combined sample, and its mean is

$$\bar{X} = \frac{n_1 \bar{X}_1 + n_2 \bar{X}_2}{n_1 + n_2}$$

This formula depends on the fact that

$$\bar{X}_1 = \frac{1}{n_1} \sum X$$

and
$$n_1 \bar{X}_1 = \sum X$$

Similarly, for the second sample, denoted by Y's,

$$n_2 \bar{X}_2 = \sum Y$$

Then

$$\sum X + \sum Y = n_1 \bar{X}_1 + n_2 \bar{X}_2$$

is the sum of the data in the combined sample.
The mean is then

(6)
$$\bar{X} = \frac{n_1 \bar{X}_1 + n_2 \bar{X}_2}{n_1 + n_2}$$

The numerator of (6) is then simply the sum of all the data in the combined
sample, and the denominator is the number of data. The formula may be
generalized to cover the combination of more than two samples into a
single larger one. For a combination of four samples, it is

$$\bar{X} = \frac{n_1 \bar{X}_1 + n_2 \bar{X}_2 + n_3 \bar{X}_3 + n_4 \bar{X}_4}{n_1 + n_2 + n_3 + n_4}$$

This formula may be written more briefly as

$$\bar{X} = \frac{\sum_{i=1}^{4} n_i \bar{X}_i}{\sum_{i=1}^{4} n_i}$$

The data of Table 17 illustrate this formula. The mean of the X's is

TABLE 17

*Data Used to Illustrate the Computation of
the Mean of Two Samples Combined*

X	Y
24	78
20	58
18	46
11	34
7	26
80	22
	16
	280

$\bar{X}_1 = 16$, and n_1 is 5. The mean of the Y's is $\bar{Y} = 40$ with $n_2 = 7$. According
to formula (6), the mean of the combined sample is

$$\frac{n_1 \bar{X} + n_2 \bar{Y}}{n_1 + n_2} = \frac{5(16) + 7(40)}{5 + 7}$$

$$= \frac{80 + 280}{12}$$

$$= \frac{360}{12}$$

$$= 30$$

which is obviously the mean to be obtained if both samples are combined into a single sample.

Deviations from the mean

The difference between each datum and the mean is the *deviation* of that datum from the mean. These deviations have two very important properties, both of which are employed frequently in further chapters. The first of these is that, for any frequency distribution, the sum of the deviations from the mean is always zero. In symbols, and stated as a theorem, this result is

Theorem 3.
$$\sum_{i=1}^{n} (X_i - \bar{X}) = 0$$

Each of the addends $X_i - \bar{X}$ is a deviation of a datum X_i from the mean $\bar{X}$ of all the X's. To prove the theorem, distribute the summation symbol over the addend $(X_i - \bar{X})$ so that

$$\sum (X_i - \bar{X}) = \sum X_i - \sum \bar{X}$$

Now $\sum X_i$ is $n\bar{X}$, as may be seen by dividing each of these expressions by n. Also, summing over the constant $\bar{X}$ gives $\sum \bar{X} = n\bar{X}$. Consequently,

$$\sum (X_i - \bar{X}) = n\bar{X} - n\bar{X} = 0$$

and the theorem is proved.

To illustrate, consider the numbers 2, 7, 9, 12, and 20. The mean is 10; the deviations from the mean are -8, -3, -1, 2, and 10, respectively; and the sum of these deviations is 0. The proof given for Theorem 3 makes it clear that, no matter what set of numbers had been chosen, the result would have been the same. The mean of a frequency distribution is the only number the deviations from which have the property of adding up to 0.

The second important and unique property of the mean is that the *sum of the squares of the deviations from the mean* is less than the sum of the squares of the deviations from *any* other number. Stated as a theorem, the result is

Theorem 4. $\displaystyle\sum_{i=1}^{n} (X_i - A)^2$ assumes its least value when $A = \bar{X}$

Proof: (1) $\sum(X_i - A)^2 = \sum(X^2 - 2AX + A^2)$

(2) $\qquad\qquad = \sum X^2 - \sum 2AX + \sum A^2$

(3) $\qquad\qquad = \sum X^2 - 2A\sum X + nA^2$

(4) $\qquad\qquad = \sum X^2 - 2nA\bar{X} + nA^2$

(5) $\qquad\qquad = \sum X^2 - n\bar{X}^2 + n\bar{X}^2 - 2nA\bar{X} + nA^2$

(6) $\qquad\qquad = \sum X^2 - n\bar{X}^2 + n(\bar{X} - A)^2$

In this sequence of algebraic manipulations, step (1) is the result of expanding $(X - A)^2$, and step (2) shows the distribution of the $\sum$ symbol over the resulting three terms. Step (3) is the result of factoring the constant $2A$ out of the second sum in (2) and of summing over the constant A^2 in the third sum. The only change in step (4) is the substitution of $n\bar{X}$ for $\sum X$ in in the second term. Step (5) consists of adding $n\bar{X}^2$ in one place and of subtracting it in another. The net change in value is 0, but the form has been changed so that, in step (6), the last three terms can be factored into $n(\bar{X} - A)^2$.

The problem is now reduced to finding a value of A for which $(X - A)^2$ is least. But this is clearly $A = \bar{X}$, because any other value of A will make $(\bar{X} - A)^2$ greater than 0. The proof is thus complete.

As an example of the effect of this theorem, consider the numbers 2, 7, 9, 12, and 20, the mean of which is 10.

Note that the sum of the deviations is 0 only when they are taken from the mean 10. Note also that the sum of the squares is greater for deviations taken from 9 and 11 than is the case when the mean 10 is used. Theorem 4 proves that similar results will be obtained for any set of data. The minimum property proved in Theorem 4 is of fundamental importance in the mathematical theory of statistics.

						SUMS
Data	2	7	9	12	20	50
Deviations from 10	8	3	1	−2	−10	0
Squares of the Deviations from 10	64	9	1	4	100	178
Deviations from 9	7	2	0	−3	−11	−5
Squares of the Deviations from 9	49	4	0	9	121	183
Deviations from 11	9	4	2	−1	−9	5
Squares of the Deviations from 11	81	16	4	1	81	183

Finally, the student should be aware of the fact that the vast majority of statistical work done in the sciences is carried out on desk computing machines, not by the procedures indicated above. The above remarks concerning the computation of the mean and median are, for the most part, intended to enable the student to understand the nature of these two concepts. That, of course, is of utmost importance. Details concerning machine computation will be presented in Chapter 4, because the machine computation of the mean and of measures of variability go hand in hand.

PROBLEMS

1. The representation of a set of data by a single number which indicates the point of central tendency may be a better representation in some cases than in others. Under what circumstances will the representation be good and under what circumstances will it be bad?
2. It has been said that the "average" family with 2.3 children and 1.2 cars does not exist in fact. What can be said as to the existence of the "median" family?
3. Write a short paragraph discussing the extent to which the median meets the requirements of a measure of central tendency.
4. Repeat Problem 3 replacing median with arithmetic mean.
5. What in each of the following three cases can be said about the distribution?

    (a) The mean is much less than the median.

    (b) The mean is equal to the median.

    (c) The mean is much more than the median.

6. In a class of twenty-nine students there were five A's, four B's, nine C's, eight D's, and three F's. Compute the measures of central tendency described below.

    (a) Let A, B, C, D, and F be assigned respectively the values 4, 3, 2, 1, and 0. Then compute the arithmetic mean and the median.

    (b) Repeat part (a) with the values 15, 10, 6, 3, and 1 assigned respectively to A, B, C, D, and F.

7. The mean always equals the median in a symmetrical distribution. To show that the converse is not true, find a set of five numbers which are not symmetrically distributed but for which the mean and median are equal. Such distributions are easily obtained by modifying symmetric distributions.

8. The mean annual income of carpenters in both Aville and Beeville is $5400. The median in Aville is $5200, and in Beeville the median is $3000. Would a carpenter contemplating a move to Aville or Beeville be more interested in the means or more interested in the medians? Do both taken together give him a good basis for choosing between the two towns? Why?

9. The mean of the numbers 2, 5, 6, 9, and 13 is 7. If 19 is added to the set, the mean is increased to 9. How many 1's must be added to the set then to reduce the mean to 7? How many 6's must one add to the set to reduce the mean to 7? How many 7's?

10. The arithmetic mean requires more information for its compilation than the other measures of centrality studied, and it usually conveys more information than do the others. What property of the mean lies behind this assertion?

11. Find the mode of the data in Table 14. What will the mode be if a 62 and a 64 are each changed to 63? What if only a 62, but not a 64 is changed to 63?

12. Find the median of the data of Table 11.

13. Find the median for the classified data in Table 7.

14. If groups A, B, and C contain respectively 3, 10, and 5 persons, and if group B is to be absorbed by groups A and C so that A and C will then be equal, what fraction of group B must be shifted to group A?

15. If groups 1, 2, 3, and 4 have respectively 3, 9, 13, and 19 members, and if it is desired to eliminate group 3 by shifting its members so

that groups 1 and 2 will together have as many as group 4, what fraction of group 3 should be shifted to group 4?

16. Write a short paragraph explaining the similarity between the process carried out in problems 15 and 16 and in computing the median from classified data.

17. (a) Find the mean of the numbers 1, 2, 3, . . . , 9.
    (b) Find the mean of the numbers 1, 2, 3, . . . , 11.
    (c) Make a conjecture as to the mean of the numbers 1, 2, 3, . . . , n where n is an odd number.

18. Repeat problem 17 using the numbers from 1 to 10 and from 1 to 12, and make a conjecture as to the mean of 1, 2, . . . , n where n is even.

19. Find the mean of the data in Table 1 using formula (1) (page 89).

20. If formula (2) (page 90) is used to compute the mean from the classification completed by you in problem 20, Chapter 2, what will the values of the f_i and p_i be, and how many of each will there be?

21. Repeat problem 20 for the classifications completed by you in problem 21, Chapter 2.

22. Find the mean of the classified data referred to in problem 20.

23. Find the mean of the classified data referred to in problem 21.

24. To what do you attribute the difference between the results in problems 22 and 23?

25. Formula (3) (page 90) is an apparently simpler form of formula (2) (page 90). Explain in detail what must be gathered from the context to complete the formula.

26. Use Theorem 1 (page 91) to show that if your age is one year under the class mean today, it will be one year under the mean age of the same group fifty years hence.

27. A statistics instructor wants two sets of data having the same mean. He is aware that by using Theorem 1 to increase the mean and Theorem 2 (page 92) to decrease the mean, he can alter a set of data while leaving its mean fixed. Starting with the data 2, 3, 8, 11, 15, 16, 18, 23, 25, and 29, he added 5 to each datum. What must he then multiply the new data by in order to bring the mean down to what it was before?

28. If the data were first multiplied by 5 in problem 27, what would have to be added (or subtracted) from each result to restore the original mean?

29. Discuss the advantages of the two methods described in problems 27

and 28 from the viewpoint of ease of arithmetic, avoidance of fractions, and avoidance of negative "data."

30. Use Theorems 1 and 2 on the mean in the computation of the mean of the classified data of problem 20 of Chapter 2.

31. Repeat problem 30 for the data of problem 21 of Chapter 2.

32. Combine the data of Tables 12 and 13 into a single frequency distribution and compute the mean. Then compute the mean of the combined sample by means of formula (6) (page 96).

33. The mean of 100 measurements taken by one operator was 28.31, and the mean of 150 measurements taken by a second operator was 30.27. Is the mean of the combined 250 measurements less than, equal to, or greater than the mean of the two means?

34. What would have been the answer in problem 33 if the two operators each made 125 measurements and reported means of 28.00 and 29.50?

35. What would be the result in problem 33 if the numbers of measurements made by the two operators were interchanged?

36. Using -8, -2, 11, 15, and 24, show that the sum of the deviations from the mean is 0.

37. Compute the deviations of the numbers in problem 36 from 7, and find the sum of the squares of these deviations.

38. Repeat problem 37, using 9 instead of 7.

39. Repeat problem 37 using the mean 8 instead of 7, and explain what bearing Theorem 4 (page 98) has on these calculations.

40. Let $X_1 = 2$, $X_2 = 5$, $X_3 = 6$, and $n = 3$ in Theorem 4. Write out each step of the proof using these numbers, their sum, mean, and so forth, to provide a detailed example of the structure of the proof.

Suggestions for Further Reading

GUILFORD, J., 1956. *Fundamental statistics in psychology and education* (3rd ed.). New York: McGraw-Hill. Chapter 4.

McNEMAR, Q., 1955. *Psychological statistics* (2nd ed.). New York: Wiley. Chapter 3.

WALLIS, W., and ROBERTS, H., 1956. *Statistics: a new approach.* Glencoe: Free Press. Chapter 7.

All of the above are introductory texts used by students in the behavioral sciences. They present material on measures of central tendency as well as other descriptive statistics. For further readings of a more mathematical nature the student may consult the following:

DIXON, W., and MASSEY, F., 1957. *Introduction to statistical analysis* (2nd ed.). New York: McGraw-Hill.

HOEL, P., 1954. *Introduction to mathematical statistics* (2nd ed.). New York: Wiley.

CHAPTER

4

VARIABILITY

THE ORGANIZATION OF DATA into frequency distributions was shown to be
a preliminary step toward describing data. And computing the central
tendency of a frequency distribution was shown to be a further step toward
making the description more informative. However, knowledge of the
location of the mean, or median, alone, ordinarily is not completely satisfactory, for there are other important features of the distribution which
need to be described. Specifically, it is quite important to describe data in
terms of their *variability*.

THE NEED FOR DESCRIBING VARIABILITY

It can readily be perceived, for example, that two distributions may have
exactly the same mean but differ significantly with respect to the amount
of variation among the objects or events measured. Consider the following
situation. A teacher is asked to teach reading to one of two classes of
third-grade students. She is told that each class has the same number of
students and that intelligence test results show that the classes are equal in
intelligence; that is, the *mean* I.Q. of the classes is the same—100. What the

teacher is not told, however, is that the range of I.Q. scores in class A is from 95 to 105 while the range in class B is from 80 to 120. Clearly, the teacher of class A will have an easier time than the teacher of class B. Other things being equal, class A will move at a much more uniform pace than class B, for the teacher of class A will not have to talk to exceptionally bright and exceptionally dull children at the same time. In short, when the teacher is asked to make her choice, an important item of information—the range of variation among the I.Q. scores—is not being provided here. This simple example is intended to show that, although distributions may have equal means, the unequal range of variation among the events may prove to be very important.

A situation almost directly opposite to the one just described may also occur; that is, two distributions may have *different* means, but the variability among the objects or events may be so large as to make the difference in means in fact trivial. Suppose the teacher mentioned above was given a different choice, this time between class A, which has a mean I.Q. of 104, and class B, which has a mean I.Q. of 101. It appears that it would be prudent to choose class A, and without further information it would be. But if it became known that the range of scores in each class was very large—say, from 80 to 125—a sensible conclusion would be that there was little if any significant difference between the two classes. In short, a large *range* of variation may very well make differences between means of little practical importance.

The above examples show only the need for knowledge about the range of variation present in distributions. But an index of the *average amount* of variation is also necessary. Consider the situation in which the mean I.Q. scores of children in class A and class B are equal—say, 100. Suppose it is discovered that the range of class A is from 80 to 120 and the range of class B from 95 to 105. The information about the range of scores is informative, but not very, for class A may contain only one child who has an I.Q. of 80 and only one child who has an I.Q. of 120. All others in class A may have an I.Q. of exactly 100. In class B there may be none with an I.Q. of 100; one half the children may have I.Q.'s of 95 and the other half I.Q.'s of 105. This example shows that the variation of *all* the scores in the distribution can be more informative than the variation of the two most extreme scores—the highest and lowest.

Another need for a measure of variation lies in the fact that change in the behavior of a group is often reflected in a change in variation rather than a change in central tendency. Suppose, for example, that a group of

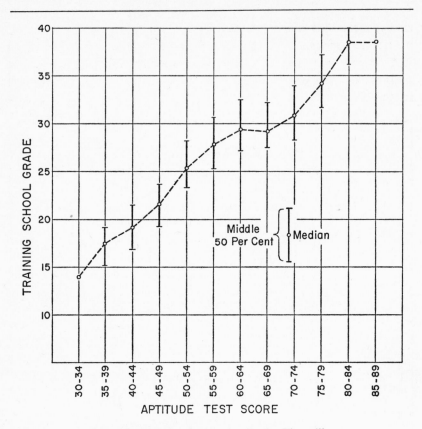

From *Personnel selection* by R. L. Thorndike.
Copyright 1949 by John Wiley & Sons, Inc., and
used with their permission.

children is given training in a specific skill while such training is withheld
from a second group. The effect of the training might very well be to eliminate the variation in the work of the individuals in the trained group without having the over-all effect of general improvement. If this were the case,
the variation of the trained group relative to that of the untrained group
would be decreased, although the mean scores might not change. And, of
course, a single individual's performance on a skill test or other behavioral
measure might become more or less variable, even though his mean performance score remained the same.

The above examples show in a rather simple illustrative manner the
need for a measure of the variability among the scores in a frequency distribution. The need stems mainly from the fact that distributions may have

similar means but differ widely in the amount of variation present. Or distributions may have different means, but the variation among the scores in the distributions may be so large as to make the difference between the means trivial. (See Box 11.) Also, it may be important to compare changes in variability.

B O X 1 1

Don't Overlook Overlap

The omission of data on the variability of scores may give rise to wrong interpretations.

Consider, for example, the data in the table below.

Median Training-School Grade
for Each Level of Aptitude Test Score

APTITUDE TEST SCORE	NUMBER OF CASES	MEDIAN ACADEMIC GRADE
85–89	43	38.5
80–84	120	38.5
75–79	85	34.2
70–74	18	30.9
65–69	5	29.3
60–64	2	29.4
55–59	12	27.9
50–54	43	25.4
45–49	90	21.6
40–44	147	19.2
35–39	230	17.5
30–34	205	14.0

Thorndike, from whose book the above table was adapted, comments as follows: ". . . this form . . . of presentation is misleading in the extreme. The tabulation and plotting of means (or medians) ignores entirely the variability within a given score group. It conveys the impression of an almost one-to-one relationship between test and criterion score (grades). This impression may be corrected by also giving some measure of variability of the criterion scores (grades) for each test score category."

See the figure on p. 106, which shows the large amount of overlap between categories.

Thorndike, R. L. 1949. *Personnel selection.* New York: John Wiley & Sons, Inc. Copyright 1949. Reprinted by permission of the publishers.

REQUIREMENTS

A good measure of the amount of variation in a frequency distribution should, of course, meet the general and technical requirements of all statistical methods, as well as the requirements specific to the problem of measuring variation; that is, a good measure of variation should (1) be applicable to a wide range of statistical problems and be useful for making comparisons of scientific data, (2) be fitted easily into a system of mathematics, and (3) be appropriately sensitive to variation. "Appropriately sensitive" means that a good measure of variation will reflect the variability in the distribution but will not be so markedly affected by one or two extreme cases that it conveys little information about the variability among the vast majority of cases in the distribution. (This point will be illustrated below.)

Another special requirement of a measure of variability is that it be independent of the value of the measure of central tendency; that is, it should be possible to compare the amount of variation in one distribution with that in another without regard for the value of the mean. It clearly would be unfortunate if a measure of variation were to take on a large value when the mean was large and a small value when it was small. It would be impossible to compare amounts of variation if this were the case. A good measure of variation will be independent of the value of the mean or other measure of central tendency in order to facilitate comparison. As we shall see below, at least one of the three methods of measuring variation meets nearly all of the above requirements rather well.

METHODS OF MEASURING VARIABILITY

There are three common methods of measuring amounts of variability: the *range*, the *mean deviation*, and the *standard deviation*. These are all appropriate for data taken from interval or ratio scales but not for data taken from nominal or ordinal scales. The reason for this is that the computations of these measures require that the data be related with respect not only to order but also to distance. Each is discussed below. (Measures of variability which apply to nominal and ordinal scales will not be discussed in detail.)

The range

As indicated earlier, the *range* denotes the scale distance between the lowest and highest numerical values in the distribution. Although this information may sometimes be interesting and useful, the fact that the range can be changed by a change in a single score when that score is either the highest or lowest but remain unchanged by the addition of many new scores when they fall between the highest and lowest sharply limits the usefulness of this method. It simply does not use much of the available information provided by the data with respect to variability. Although the range is applicable to all forms of frequency distributions (except "open-ended" ones—that is, those few which do not report highest and lowest values), and although it is independent of the numerical value of the mean, its sensitivity to the placement of the two end (extreme) scores makes it such an unstable, inefficient measure for making comparisons that it is rarely used in the behavioral sciences.

But the range does have some implicit importance and common-sense value in everyday thinking about statistics. For example, a mean is often quoted in the hope that readers will automatically assume a small range of variation above and below the value given; that such hopes are occasionally justified makes the mean a favorite tool of those who seek to convince rather than inform. A mean is never a meaningful statistical measure unless there is present also, either explicitly or implicitly, some indication of the variation of the data around the mean. For example, consider two businesses each of which employs 100 people and each of which pays a mean salary of $10,000. The range of the salaries in one of the firms is $5,000 and that in the other is $92,000. Without the ranges the means would imply that the two firms pay approximately the same salary scale.

The mean deviation

The mean deviation takes into account every score in the distribution. It derives its name from the manner in which it is computed: the difference, or *deviation*, of each score from the mean of the distribution is determined (without regard for the direction of the difference—that is, whether the score is larger or smaller than the mean). These deviations are then added and the sum is divided by the number of scores. The result is the *mean of the deviations of the scores from their mean*, but this phrase is usually shortened to the *mean deviation*. For example, the mean of the numbers 4, 6, 10, 14, and 16 is 10. The deviations of these numbers from 10 are 6, 4, 0, -4, and -6. Adding the deviations *without regard for their signs* gives 20. The mean deviation is then $20/5 = 4$.

The mean deviation does not have a wide range of application, nor is it very useful for making comparisons among sets of data. The main reason for this is that the absolute values of the deviations of the scores from the mean are used in the computation; that is, all negative as well as positive deviations are added as though positive. This is always easy to do with specific data, but the mathematical development of general properties of the mean deviation is hindered by the use of absolute values. It is not so readily fitted into further statistical analyses as the standard deviation, the next measure of variability to be discussed.

The standard deviation

The most widely employed technique for measuring variability is known as the *standard deviation*. This method is employed in the vast majority of statistical analyses which include a report on variability.

Mathematically, *the standard deviation is defined as the square root of the mean of the squared deviations from the mean of the distribution.* (For a discussion of the squared deviations from the mean, see page 98 of Chapter 3.) This rather formidable statement can be written very simply by using algebraic symbols with *s* for standard deviation:

$$s = \sqrt{\frac{\Sigma(\bar{X} - X)^2}{n}}$$

The lower-case letter *s* is a commonly accepted symbol for the standard deviation. (Sometimes the lower-case Greek letter sigma (σ) is used, but we shall reserve σ for a special meaning in Part II.) The expression under the square root sign is a mean, because it indicates that all the squared deviations (from the mean of the distribution) are added and then divided by the total number of deviations. Thus, the formula indicates that *s* is equal to the square root of the mean of the squared deviations.

As may be seen from the above, the computation of the standard deviation from the formula is straightforward but lengthy. (Simpler computational procedures will be presented in the mathematical section of this chapter.) The student will be curious, of course, as to why deviations from the mean should be squared, summed, and divided by *n*, and why the square root should be extracted from the resultant number. The rationale for these procedures is given in the mathematical section of this chapter, where each part of the formula is related to some desirable property of the standard deviation. It suffices now to state that the behavioral scientist needs a measure of variability and that mathematicians have provided him with the standard-deviation technique—a procedure which satisfies his needs very well because it meets several requirements for a good measure of variability. (See Box 12.)

B O X   1 2

Why not just guess?

How good are one's intuitive guesses at the principal characteristics of a frequency distribution? Suppose that you glance at a line of trees—a windbreak, say. How accurately can you guess the standard deviation of the distribution of tree heights? How good are we as intuitive statisticians?

Only one study has been carried out with respect to man's ability to estimate standard deviations. Hoffstätter, a European psychologist, found that estimations of the standard deviation were strongly influenced by the value of the mean of the distribution; the larger the mean, the larger the estimate of s. In other words, the intuitive statistician does not meet one of the more important requirements of a good measure of variability—independence of the value of the

mean. Even trained statisticians seem subject to this distortion and are no better at this task than children. Most interesting is Hoffstätter's finding that, when reconstructing the formula the intuitive statistician uses for "calculating" the standard deviation, the exponent of the deviation $(\bar{X} - X)$ is not 2 as in $s = \sqrt{\dfrac{(\bar{X} - X)^2}{n}}$ but is closer to 1, or even ½. In short, we had better not guess.

Hofstätter, P. R. 1939. Über die Schätzung von Gruppeneigenschaften. *Zeitschrift f. psychol.,* 145, 1–44.
(Also described in Brunswik, E. 1956. *Perception and the representative design of experiments.* Berkeley: University of Calif. Press.)

Comparing variabilities

Because comparison is one of the most fundamental aspects of the scientific method, a prime requirement of a good measure of variability is that it facilitate comparison. The standard deviation meets this requirement well, for the larger the variability in a frequency distribution, the larger the value of the standard deviation; therefore, it greatly facilitates the comparison of amounts of variation between groups. Furthermore, it not only makes it possible to compare the performance of different individuals on the same test, but it is also used to compare the performance of the same individual on different tests. (These latter forms of comparison will be discussed in detail in the next chapter.)

Comparing different groups in terms of their variabilities is a straightforward matter. In Table 18 the standard deviations are computed for two groups. Inspection of the scores in Group I and Group II makes it clear

TABLE 18

Standard Deviations for Two Groups Differing in Variability

GROUP I

SCORES X	DEVIATIONS $\bar{X} - X$	DEVIATIONS SQUARED $(\bar{X} - X)^2$
15	$-.4$	.16
19	-4.4	19.36
15	$-.4$	.16
13	1.6	2.56
16	-1.4	1.96
20	-5.4	29.16
15	$.4$	.16
10	4.6	21.16
12	2.6	6.76
11	3.6	12.96

$$\Sigma(\bar{X} - X)^2 = 94.40$$

$(\bar{X} = 14.6)$
$(n = 10)$

$$s = \sqrt{\frac{\Sigma(\bar{X} - X)^2}{n}} = \sqrt{\frac{94.40}{10}} = 3.07$$

GROUP II

15	-1	1
17	-3	9
14	0	0
11	3	9
15	-1	1
14	0	0
12	2	4
14	0	0

$$\Sigma(\bar{X} - X)^2 = 24$$

$(\bar{X} = 14)$
$(n = 8)$

$$s = \sqrt{\frac{\Sigma(\bar{X} - X)^2}{n}} = \sqrt{\frac{24}{8}} = 1.73$$

that Group I is the more variable. This fact is represented by the difference in the size of the two standard deviations.

As an example of the utility of the standard deviation as a method of comparing variabilities, consider the data in Table 19.

TABLE 19

Raw Score Means and Standard Deviations on Various Scales of the
California Psychological Inventory *

FOR THREE GROUPS OF MALES

SCALE	HIGH SCHOOL STUDENTS (n = 3,572)		COLLEGE STUDENTS (n = 680)		MEDICAL SCHOOL APPLICANTS (n = 70)	
	(1)	(2)	(3)	(4)	(5)	(6)
	$\bar{X}$	s	$\bar{X}$	s	$\bar{X}$	s
1	23.2	6.0	28.5	6.0	31.6	4.4
2	15.3	4.4	21.4	4.0	23.9	3.0
3	21.5	6.5	25.4	5.3	28.8	3.7
4	32.7	5.7	37.6	6.6	40.2	5.2
5	18.7	4.1	20.6	6.3	24.2	2.9
6	33.5	5.6	37.2	4.9	39.7	2.8
7	26.7	5.7	31.5	4.7	34.0	3.9
8	36.3	6.0	37.5	5.2	39.3	4.8
9	25.3	8.0	29.2	7.1	31.3	5.8
10	17.8	5.3	24.0	4.8	27.2	3.6
11	15.1	6.2	18.1	6.3	20.5	5.7
12	25.2	2.8	25.3	2.2	26.4	1.4
13	22.3	5.3	28.6	4.6	31.4	3.1
14	14.6	4.1	21.6	4.1	23.7	3.3
15	33.6	6.3	40.8	5.2	44.3	3.1
16	9.2	2.6	11.9	3.1	13.8	2.4
17	9.1	3.4	11.4	3.8	11.9	3.5
18	15.4	3.6	16.8	3.8	16.4	3.6

* Reproduced by special permission from *California psychological inventory,* by Harrison G. Gough. Copyright, 1957. Published by the Consulting Psychologists Press, Inc., Palo Alto, California.

In this comparison we shall ignore the values of the various means. Note first the values of the standard deviations in columns (2) and (4) and observe how closely the values in these two columns approximate one another. From this fact we would draw the conclusion that there is very nearly the same amount of variation among college students on these personality scales as there is among high school students. Closer inspection shows that in eleven of the eighteen scales the college students are less variable (that is, their standard deviations are smaller). Now, observing the standard deviations for the medical school applicants, note how much smaller than the standard deviations for college students these are. In fact, the standard deviations of *all* eighteen scales are smaller for the medical school applicants. From these data we draw the conclusion that those students who apply for admission to medical school are much more alike in their personalities than are college students (or high school students) in general. The point to notice here is the utility of the standard deviation in quantifying "variety, . . . the most obtrusive character of the universe."

A further comparison may be made from the data of Table 19. Note, for example, that the various test scales which make up the California Psychological Inventory do not by any means have the same standard deviation. The standard deviation for Scale 9 in column (2), for example, is 8.0, compared with the standard deviation of only 2.8 for Scale 12. High school students, it appears, are much more heterogeneous with respect to the psychological dimension represented by Scale 9 than with respect to the dimension represented by Scale 12.

It will be obvious from the above illustration that the standard deviation is a useful device for comparing the variability of different groups. What is not obvious from these illustrations is that the standard deviation is also highly useful for making scores on different tests comparable to one another (to be discussed in the next chapter). Furthermore, as will be shown in Part II of this book, the standard deviation also has a key function in the solution of problems of sampling and of inductive inference and in the analysis of cause and effect in experimentation. The standard deviation is one of the most useful concepts employed in the statistical method. (See Boxes 13 and 14.)

(Mathematically . . .

The remainder of this chapter will discuss in more mathematical detail the methods of measuring variability. The range is simply the numerical distance between the least and greatest data. In symbols,

$$R = X_{max} - X_{min}$$

There is a further mathematical development of the range, but it is beyond the scope of this book.

THE MEAN DEVIATION

The *mean deviation* is a statistical measure designed to measure variability on a more detailed basis than is possible with the range. The mean deviation uses all of the data rather than only the two at the extremes, as is the case with the range. To compute the mean deviation, the distance of each datum from the mean is used. A datum that is much larger or much smaller than the mean is a greater contributor to variability than is a datum that lies near the mean. The distance from the mean to a given datum is called the "deviation" of that datum. The mean of all such deviations is called the "mean deviation" and is used as a measure of variability. The deviation of a datum from the mean is always considered to be a positive number no matter on which side of the mean it lies. To see the reason for this, consider the following example, in which the deviations will first be taken as

---

B O X   1 3

Intra-Individual Variability

Standard deviations ordinarily are computed for frequency distributions in which every separate datum in the distribution represents a different subject's score. But standard deviations may also be computed in the effort to describe the variability in just one subject's performance. An interesting illustration of an analysis of the variability within an individual's score may be found in a study of interpersonal perception by Wayman J. Crow, working in the Behavior Research Laboratory at the University of Colorado.

The problem was to discover whether medical students who participated in a special clinical program were able to perceive the personality characteristics of patients more accurately than those medical students who did not have the benefit of the special program. In other words, did participation in the special program produce doctors who were better able to appraise the personality characteristics of patients?

In the main, the results indicated that participation in the special program did not markedly affect the accuracy with which the students perceived their patients. But an analysis was made of the frequency distribution of each individual student's set of responses on a test which required him to appraise the personality characteristics of a number of patients. And it was found that the *standard deviations* of these frequency distributions tended to increase as a result of participation in the special program. This result was interpreted as indicating that such participation resulted in the students becoming more aware of individual differences among patients. This outcome was found through an analysis of intra-individual variability—the analysis of the standard deviation of each student's frequency distribution of responses.

Hammond, K. R., Kern, F., *et al.* 1959. *Teaching comprehensive medical care: a psychological study of a change in medical education.* Cambridge: Harvard University Press.

positive or negative according to whether the data involved lie to the right or left of the mean. Let the data be $X_1 = 2, X_2 = 5, X_3 = 11$, and $X_4 = 22$. The mean is 10; the deviations are $10 - 2 = 8$, $10 - 5 = 5$, $10 - 11 = -1$, and $10 - 22 = -12$; and the sum of the deviations is $(8) + (5) + (-1) + (-12) = 0$.

This result would have to be interpreted as meaning that very little variability was present in the data, were it not for the fact that such sums are zero (see Theorem 3, page 97) no matter what the data may be. The positive deviations always exactly cancel the negative deviations.

Absolute values

To avoid this difficulty, the numerical or absolute values of the deviations are used, and the mean deviation is

$$MD = \frac{1}{n} \sum_{i=1}^{n} |X_i - \bar{X}|$$

Applying this formula to the example above gives

$$MD = \frac{|2 - 10| + |5 - 10| + |11 - 10| + |22 - 10|}{4}$$

$$= \frac{1}{4}(8 + 5 + 1 + 12)$$

$$= 6.5$$

If the data are extensive, the computation of the mean deviation is quite laborious because of the absolute value signs in the formula. To illustrate the computation of the mean deviation for a set of data large enough to be classified into a frequency distribution, the data of Table 20

TABLE 20

I.Q.'s of Eighty Students

75	78	79	82	86	86	88	91
94	98	106	69	75	79	82	87
88	90	93	98	107	73	80	82
84	87	90	95	99	71	78	81
86	88	91	97	119	75	81	85
92	95	104	74	84	88	92	103
79	84	89	96	72	82	90	110
77	87	100	77	91	69	85	102
83	96	81	99	86	74	80	89
87	92	76	85	70	80	94	80

will be used. The computations will be carried out first in detail for the data in unclassified form and then for the classified case. Table 20 represents the I.Q.'s of eighty students assigned to a remedial reading class. The sum of these scores is

$$\sum_{i=1}^{80} X_i = 6947$$

and the mean is therefore $6947/80 = 86.84$. The deviations from the mean corresponding to the data above are given in Table 21.

TABLE 21

Data from Table 20 Expressed As Deviations
from the Mean ($\bar{X} = 86.84$)

11.84	8.84	7.84	4.84	.84	.84	−1.16	−4.16
−7.16	−11.16	−19.16	17.84	11.84	7.84	4.84	−.16
−1.16	−3.16	−6.16	−11.16	−20.16	13.84	6.84	4.84
2.84	−.16	−3.16	−8.16	−12.16	15.84	8.84	5.84
.84	−1.16	−4.16	−10.16	−32.16	11.84	5.84	1.84
−5.16	−8.16	−17.16	12.84	2.84	−1.16	−5.16	−16.16
7.84	2.84	−2.16	−9.16	14.84	4.84	−3.16	−23.16
9.84	−.16	−13.16	9.84	−4.16	17.84	1.84	−15.16
3.84	−9.16	5.84	−12.16	.84	12.84	6.84	−2.16
−.16	−5.16	10.84	1.84	16.84	6.84	−7.16	6.84

If these deviations are summed with the minus signs taken into account, the sum should be 0, as noted above. The sum of the positive terms is 315.44 and that of the negative terms is -315.24. (The fact that these numbers are not numerically equal is due to the use of the two-place approximation, 86.84, for the mean instead of the true value, 86.8375.) For the mean deviation, however, it is evident that

$$MD = \frac{1}{80}\Sigma|X - 86.84|$$

$$= \frac{1}{80}(315.44 + 315.24)$$

$$= 7.88$$

Obviously, the mean deviation has been obtained here only after a large amount of detailed work. To achieve an easier computation, the above data have been classified in Table 22 and the mean deviation computed from the grouped data.

The frequency distribution of the data consists of columns (1) and (3) only; all the other columns have been included as aids to the computation that is to be made. Column (2) contains the midpoints of the class intervals (q_i). These are important to the present problem, because every datum is assumed to be equal to the midpoint of its interval.

Steps in computation

The first step is to compute the mean. For this purpose, the p_i in column (4) replace the q_i in column (2) and are formed by subtracting 86.5 from each number in column (2) and dividing the results by 4, which is the length of the class intervals. Column (5) contains the products of corresponding pairs of numbers in columns (3) and (4). The result is to

---

BOX 14

A Fish Story about the Mean and Standard Deviation

The following story about eels provides a nice example of how careful attention to means and standard deviations led to a search and a rather remarkable discovery. The story was told by Sir Ronald Fisher, an eminent British statistician.

"Johannes Schmidt of the Carlsberg Laboratory in Copenhagen was not only an ichthyologist, but also an assiduous biometrician, particularly interested in the numbers of vertebrae and finrays of the various species of fish he studied. Usually he was able to establish statistical differences between samples of the same species drawn from different localities; often even from different parts of the same fjord. With the eel, however, in which the variation in vertebra number

is large, Schmidt found sensibly the same mean, and the same standard deviation, in samples drawn from all over Europe, from Iceland, from the Azores, and from the Nile. He inferred therefore that the eels of all these different river systems came from a common breeding-ground in the ocean, and it was a major triumph of the research vessel "Dana's" expedition to secure the young eel larvae from a limited region in the Western Atlantic, not far from the breeding-grounds of the different species of eel which inhabits the Eastern rivers of North America and the Gulf of Mexico."

Fisher, R. A. 1954. The expansion of statistics. *American Scientist, 42*, 275–282.

TABLE 22

Data from Table 20 in Group Form

(1)	(2)	(3)	(4)	(5)	(6)	(7)
INTERVAL	INTERVAL MIDPOINT	FRE- QUENCY	$p_i = \dfrac{q_i - 86.5}{4}$		DEVIATIONS	
	q_i	f_i		$p_i f_i$	$|d_i|$	$f_i|d_i|$
68.5–72.5	70.5	5	−4	−20	16.25	81.25
72.5–76.5	74.5	7	−3	−21	12.25	85.75
76.5–80.5	78.5	11	−2	−22	8.25	90.75
80.5–84.5	82.5	11	−1	−11	4.25	46.75
84.5–88.5	86.5	15	0	0	.25	3.75
88.5–92.5	90.5	11	1	11	3.75	41.25
92.5–96.5	94.5	7	2	14	7.75	54.25
96.5–100.5	98.5	6	3	18	11.75	70.50
100.5–104.5	102.5	3	4	12	15.75	47.25
104.5–108.5	106.5	2	5	10	19.75	39.50
108.5–112.5	110.5	1	6	6	23.75	23.75
112.5–116.5	114.5	0	7	0	27.75	0
116.5–120.5	118.5	1	8	8	31.75	31.75
		80		5		616.50

obtain numbers in column (5) which represent the combined effect of the values of the data in each class interval and the number of data in the class interval. The total of column (5) is 5 and the mean is obtained by first multiplying $\frac{5}{80}$ by 4 and then adding 86.5; the result is 86.75.

So far, all the operations performed have been merely those of finding the mean of classified data. Column (6) is peculiar to the problem of the mean deviation. It consists of the absolute deviations of the class interval midpoints from the mean 86.75. Strictly speaking, the differences between the actual data and the mean should be taken. But the class interval midpoints are replacing the actual data in this computation. Column (7) consists of the products of corresponding pairs of numbers in Columns (3) and (6). To proceed with column (6) alone would be to assume that each class interval contains but a single datum. The total of column (7) is 616.50, and the mean deviation is then $MD = 616.50/80 = 7.71$, which differs by .17 from the more accurate value previously determined. An error such as this, which amounts to about one forty-fifth of the true value, is not often important enough to justify long calculations for its removal. The error of .17 was caused by the fact that all the data in any interval are assumed to be concentrated at the midpoint of that interval, but it is this assumption also which is responsible for all the saving in computational effort. The value 7.71 has been obtained at the cost of two additional columns in the frequency classification; all the other columns are required for the computation of the mean. For well-chosen intervals the advantages of the assumption will always outweigh the disadvantage of a small error. The intervals in the example under discussion are well chosen for all except the last four or five data which are scattered quite sparsely over a wide interval. It is these last data which are mainly responsible for such error as exists. The longer such a sparsely populated "tail" of a distribution is, the more difficult is the choice of proper intervals for accurate computation— that is, the more difficult it is to make the assumption of midpoint concentration fit the facts.

The contribution of each datum to the mean deviation is proportional to the distance of that datum from the mean; that is, if X_1 is twice as far from $\bar{X}$ as X_2 is, then $|X_1 - \bar{X}|$ is twice as large as $|X_2 - \bar{X}|$. Any measure constituted of such contributions is said to be a linear measure.

In summary, the computation of the mean deviation—a much finer measure of variability than is the range (see Box 15)—can be reduced to a reasonable amount of work by using the grouped frequency distribution. The mean deviation is, moreover, a linear measure of variability, which means that the contribution of each datum to the result is directly proportional to its distance from the mean. This, of course, may be considered a valuable property in some investigations. If an analysis of the experiment in question indicates that a linear measure of variability is highly desirable, the mean deviation is a very good one. The deviations from the *median* may also be used to form a similar measure.

THE STANDARD DEVIATION

Mathematically, the standard deviation, represented by s, is

$$s = \sqrt{\frac{1}{n} \sum_{i=1}^{n} (\bar{X} - X_i)^2}$$

Notice that, by definition, s is never negative. The radical sign indicates that the principle square root (the positive square root) is to be taken. The radicand is $\frac{1}{n} \sum (\bar{X} - X_i)^2$, from which it can be seen that each datum X_i makes a contribution to the value of the radicand. As in the case of the mean deviation, these contributions are based on the deviations $\bar{X} - X_i$ of the data from the mean. Also, as in the case of the mean deviation, each of the contributions must be nonnegative to avoid a canceling out of the con-

BOX 15

The Range of the Mean Deviation

The mean deviation is, of course, a much finer measure of variability than is the range. The numbers 2, 3, 12, and 13 have a range of 11, as does also the set of numbers 2, 7, 8, and 13. The mean deviation of the first set is 5, and for the second set it is 3. The implication is that the more even distribution of the second set is reflected in a smaller mean deviation. In general, if the range is R, the mean deviation will be some place between R/n and $R/2$. If the range is R and the data are widely dispersed, the mean deviation will be very close to $R/2$, which is the maximum possible. If most of the data are closely concentrated, the mean deviation will be near R/n, which is the least value possible.

The implication of these observations on the mean deviation is that the mean deviation has a definite range of possible values, and this range is related to the range and number of the data. This provides a means of comparing the variability of two sets of data even though the numbers of data and the ranges may be different for the two sets. A formula for such a comparison may be derived as follows. The mean deviation, M, will lie between the minimum value R/n and the maximum value $R/2$. The fraction

$$M_p = \frac{M - R/n}{R/2 - R/n}$$

has for its denominator the length of the interval from minimum to maximum possible values. The numerator represents the length of the interval from minimum to actual values. The fraction thus varies from 0, when M is as small as possible, to 1, when M is as large as possible. The fraction reduces to

$$M_p = \frac{2(Mn - R)}{R(n - 2)}$$

If this fraction is computed for two sets of data, that which yields the higher value will be the set whose mean deviation is the closest to its maximum.

An example will show that the largest value of M does not always lead to the largest value of M_p. The mean deviation, M, of the test scores of a certain thirty-two students was found to be 8 and the range was 35. Twenty-nine of the same students were tested again one year later over the same material; the mean deviation was found to be 10 and the range was 48. Which set of scores is characterized by the most variability? The computation of $\dfrac{2(8 \cdot 32 - 35)}{35 \cdot 30} = .421$ and $\dfrac{2(10 \cdot 29 - 48)}{48 \cdot 27} = .373$ shows that $M = 8$ is 42.1 per cent of the way from the least possible to the maximum possible values. The corresponding proportion for $M = 10$ is 37.3 per cent. The value $M = 8$ thus indicates more variability than does $M = 10$ when the ranges and sample sizes are also taken into account.

tributions. This is accomplished by squaring the deviations from the mean instead of using absolute value signs, for the square of a real number cannot be negative. The squaring of the deviations also causes extreme data to have a greater effect on s than do the data near the mean. To observe this, note that if $\bar{X} - X = 2$, then $(\bar{X} - X)^2 = 4$, whereas if $\bar{X} - X = 5$, then $(\bar{X} - X)^2 = 25$. The second datum is only three units farther from the mean than the first one, but its contribution is over six times as large as that of the first. This makes s quite sensitive to extreme values.

The factor $1/n$ is used so that the value of s will depend on the size but not on the number of the individual contributions; that is, the value of s depends on the mean of the squared deviations rather than on whether there are few or many of them. The square root is taken so that s will have the same units as the original data. If the X_i are measurements in feet, the $(\bar{X} - X_i)^2$ will be quantities of "feet squared" (so also will the sum), but taking the square root will reduce the units to feet again.

Thus, each part of the formula is the mathematical expression of some intention concerned with the data or the measure being considered: (1) Each $(\bar{X} - X_i)$ is used to *insure contributions from every datum*, (2) squares are used to *insure positive contributions and to emphasize those of the extreme data*, (3) $1/n$ is used to *make the contributions independent of sample size*, (4) the square root is used to *make the units of s and X the same*. Because of the emphasis placed on extreme data, the standard deviation is a nonlinear measure of variability.

In situations in which all of the data have a single value—that is, when all of the X's are equal, and the common value is the mean—then all deviations from the mean will be zero, and, consequently, s will equal zero. Conversely, the value of s will differ from zero to the extent that the data are dispersed out of the maximum concentration. The maximum of dispersion is illustrated by the case in which half the data have one value—say, a—and the other half a larger value—b. The mean is then $\dfrac{a+b}{2}$, and all the deviations are either $\dfrac{b-a}{2}$ or $\dfrac{a-b}{2}$. The result is $s = \dfrac{b-a}{2}$, or half the range. The standard deviation must then fall between 0 and $R/2$, where R is the range.

Computation of the standard deviation

The computation of the standard deviation from its basic definition is no less laborious than that for the mean deviation. This section, therefore, will be devoted to the development of three different forms of the standard deviation, each suited to conditions under which the investigator may be working. Form I assumes a small array of data. Form II assumes a larger number of data and a desk calculator. Form III has been developed to deal with grouped data. The various computational forms are derived in complete detail so that the student may be fully persuaded that each of these different forms is a paraphrase of the basic definition of the standard deviation. The use of formulas without a full knowledge of their source leads inevitably to their application in situations inappropriate to their design and purpose.

Computational Form I

By means of the three rules for manipulating the $\sum$ symbol (see page 21), the first form can be obtained. This form is simple to apply to problems involving few (less than thirty-five or forty) data. In developing this form, the *variance*, s^2 (the square of the standard deviation, s), will be used so that numerous radical signs will not complicate the calculations. The variance is

$$s^2 = \frac{1}{n}\sum(\bar{X} - X)^2$$

(1)
$$= \frac{1}{n}\sum(\bar{X}^2 - 2\bar{X}X + X^2)$$

(2)
$$= \frac{1}{n}\sum\bar{X}^2 - \frac{1}{n}\sum 2\bar{X}X + \frac{1}{n}\sum X^2$$

(3)
$$= \frac{1}{n}(n\bar{X}^2) - (2\bar{X})\frac{1}{n}\sum X + \frac{1}{n}\sum X^2$$

(4)
$$= \bar{X}^2 - 2\bar{X}^2 + \frac{1}{n}\sum X^2$$

(5)
$$= \frac{1}{n}\sum X^2 - \bar{X}^2$$

which is the desired simplified form of the variance. The first step of the derivation replaces $(\bar{X} - X)^2$ by its algebraic equivalent, $(\bar{X}^2 - 2\bar{X}X + X^2)$. The second step distributes the summation symbol over these three terms. The third step consists of summing over the constant $\bar{X}^2$ in the first sum and of factoring the constant $2\bar{X}$ out of the second sum. The next step performs the obvious multiplication in the first term and replaces $\frac{1}{n}\sum X$ by $\bar{X}$ in the second term. The final step is obvious. The result may be summed up in the phrase "the variance is the mean of the squares less the square of the mean."

It has been established, then, that

$$s = \sqrt{\frac{1}{n}\sum(\bar{X} - X)^2} = \sqrt{\frac{1}{n}\sum X^2 - \bar{X}^2}$$

The latter form is easy to compute, since it involves only adding the squares of the data, dividing by n, subtracting the square of the mean, and extracting the square root. Tables are available for the last step.

Table 23 shows examples of the computation of s using the defining formula and the alternative form just developed.

TABLE 23

Calculation of the Standard Deviation by Computational Form I

(1)	(2)	(3)	(4)
DATA	DEVIATIONS		
X	$x = \bar{X} - X$	x^2	X^2
10	42.4	1797.76	100
71	−18.6	345.96	5041
21	31.4	985.96	441
90	−37.6	1413.76	8100
82	−29.6	876.16	6724
51	1.4	1.96	2601
31	21.4	457.96	961
42	10.4	108.16	1764
14	38.4	1474.56	196
92	−39.6	1568.16	8464
39	13.4	179.56	1521
61	−8.6	73.96	3721
41	11.4	129.96	1681
53	−.6	.36	2809
88	−35.6	1267.36	7744
$\Sigma X = 786$	$\Sigma x = 0$	$\Sigma x^2 = 10681.60$	$\Sigma X^2 = 51868$

$$\bar{X} = \frac{\sum X}{n} = \frac{786}{15} = 52.4 \qquad \bar{X}^2 = 2745.76$$

(defining formula)   (computational Form I)

$$s = \sqrt{\frac{1}{n}\sum(\bar{X} - X)^2} \qquad s = \sqrt{\frac{1}{n}\sum X^2 - \bar{X}^2}$$

$$= \sqrt{\tfrac{1}{15}(10681.60)} \qquad = \sqrt{\tfrac{1}{15}(51868) - 2745.76}$$

$$= 26.69 \qquad\qquad = 26.69$$

Column (2) is obtained by subtracting each datum in column (1) from the mean $\bar{X} = 52.4$. Column (3) gives the squares of the deviations thus obtained, and the calculation on the left produces $s = 26.69$. Column (4) consists of the squares of the data in column (1). These are simpler and easier to obtain than the squares of the deviations in column (3). The calculations on the right, using the derived formulas, give the same result for s.

Computational Form II

If a desk calculator is available, a variation of the first computational form will be found useful. That is, beginning with Form I,

$$s = \sqrt{\frac{1}{n}\sum X^2 - \bar{X}^2}$$

$$= \sqrt{\frac{n}{n^2}\sum X^2 - \frac{n^2\bar{X}^2}{n^2}}$$

$$= \frac{1}{n}\sqrt{n\sum X^2 - (n\bar{X})^2}$$

$$= \frac{1}{n}\sqrt{n\sum X^2 - (\sum X)^2}$$

The first step of this derivation consists of multiplying the first term of the radicand by $n/n = 1$, and the second term by $n^2/n^2 = 1$. This changes the value of neither term, but it does permit the factor $1/n^2$ of the radicand to be moved outside the radical as $1/n$ in the second step. The equality $n^2\bar{X}^2 = (n\bar{X})^2$ is also used in the second step. The last step consists of replacing $n\bar{X}$ by its equivalent, $\sum X$. Though this form of s appears to be more complicated than its other forms, it actually is simpler, having been reduced to an expression involving only the sum of the data and the sum of the squares of the data. Since any modern desk calculator will accumulate both of these sums simultaneously, simply entering the data into the calculator *once* will provide both sums.

As an example of the computation of s by means of Form II, the data of Table 23 will again be used. Form II is

$$s = \frac{1}{n}\sqrt{n\sum X^2 - (\sum X)^2}$$

$$= \frac{1}{15}\sqrt{15(51868) - (786)^2}$$

$$= \frac{1}{15}\sqrt{160224}$$

$$= 26.69$$

Note that this computation requires only the sums of columns (1) and (4) of Table 23 and the value of n. It is not necessary to compute any deviations or even to compute the mean in order to obtain s.

Computational Form III

The above forms for computing s are not appropriate for grouped data. The computation of s from grouped data can be made quite easy if two properties of s analogous to those shown for the mean are first established. These properties will be stated as theorems and proved.

Theorem 1. If a constant is added to each datum, s is unchanged.

PROOF: Consider the expression $(\bar{X} - X_i)^2$ in the definition

$$s = \sqrt{\frac{1}{n}\sum_{i=1}^{n}(\bar{X} - X_i)^2}$$

If a constant, c, is added to each datum, X_i, then the mean, $\bar{X}$, will be increased, or decreased, to $\bar{X} + c$. The addenda, $(\bar{X} - X_i)^2$ will then be of the form $\{(\bar{X} + c) - (X_i + c)\}^2$; but this is $(\bar{X} + c - X_i - c)^2 = (\bar{X} - X_i)^2$. Hence, since the addition of a constant to each datum results in no change in any of the addenda entering into the computation of s, it must remain the same.

On the basis of this theorem, the standard deviation computed above could have been arrived at much more easily by first adding -50 to each datum. The use of smaller numbers also decreases the probability of arithmetic errors. The most interesting and important aspect of this theorem, however, is that it demonstrates that s is independent of the magnitude of the data. This is a primary technical requirement of a measure of variability (see page 108). The contributions of the data to the measure should be based on their relative distances from one another and not on their numerical sizes. The mean deviation also has this valuable property.

Theorem 2. If each datum is multiplied by a constant, then s is changed by the same constant factor.

PROOF: If each datum is multiplied by c, so is the mean according to the second theorem on the mean (see page 92). Now,

$$\sum_{i=1}^{n}(c\bar{X} - cX_i)^2 = \sum_{i=1}^{n}\{c(\bar{X} - X_i)\}^2$$

$$= \sum_{i=1}^{n} c^2(\bar{X} - X_i)^2$$

$$= c^2 \sum_{i=1}^{n} (\bar{X} - X_i)^2$$

The first step consists of factoring c out of the expression $c\bar{X} - cX_i$. The second step makes use of the exponent rule that $(ab)^2 = a^2b^2$ for any numbers a and b. The last step factors the constant c^2 out of the sum.

The standard deviation of data multiplied by a constant c is then

$$s = \sqrt{\frac{1}{n} \sum_{i=1}^{n} (c\bar{X} - cX_i)^2} = \sqrt{\frac{c^2}{n} \sum_{i=1}^{n} (\bar{X} - X_i)^2}$$

$$= c\sqrt{\frac{1}{n} \sum_{i=1}^{n} (\bar{X} - X_i)^2}$$

$$= cs$$

The first step consists of the result proved above. In the second step c^2 is taken out of the radical as c; the result is c times the formula for s with the data unaltered. The conclusion is that multiplying all the data by c changes the standard deviation from s to cs.

That s should be changed by applying a multiplicative constant is to be expected, not because it changes the size of the data, but because it alters the distances between the data. The pattern of dispersion is magnified if the constant c is greater than 1 and is shrunk if c is a fraction less than 1.

These two theorems may be combined to produce an easier computation of s. The method of computation to be derived is particularly suited to grouped data. It consists of adding some fixed (usually negative) number, c_1, to every datum so that smaller numbers that may more easily be handled result. After this has been done, each altered datum is multiplied by another constant, c_2, to simplify further the numbers to be dealt with. After s has been computed for the simplified numbers, it is only necessary to multiply it by $1/c_2$ in order to obtain s for the original data.

The method will be applied to the computation of s for the data in Table 20. These data have been classified in Table 22, the first three columns of which are reproduced in Table 24. Column (2) contains the class interval midpoints. It is these numbers, repeated according to the several frequencies in column (3), whose standard deviation is sought; that is, each interval midpoint is made to stand in the place of each datum in that particular class interval.

According to the first theorem on the standard deviation, it will not affect s if a constant is added to each of the midpoints of column (2). The constant to be chosen is -86.5, because 86.5 seems to be rather centrally located in the distribution. Column (4) is obtained by adding -86.5 to each number in column (2). The smaller numbers of column (4) may be used to compute s. A further simplification can be obtained by using the second theorem on the standard deviation. Column (4) consists of consecutive multiples of 4, the length of a class interval; this is no coincidence,

TABLE 24

*Calculation of the Standard Deviation
from Grouped Data by Computational Form III*

(1) INTERVAL	(2) INTERVAL MIDPOINT q_i	(3) FREQUENCY f_i	(4) $q_i - 86.5$	(5) $p_i = \dfrac{q_i - 86.5}{4}$	(6) p_i^2	(7) $f_i p_i$	(8) $f_i p_i^2$
116.5–120.5	118.5	1	32	8	64	8	64
112.5–116.5	114.5	0	28	7	49	0	0
108.5–112.5	110.5	1	24	6	36	6	36
104.5–108.5	106.5	2	20	5	25	10	50
100.5–104.5	102.5	3	16	4	16	12	48
96.5–100.5	98.5	6	12	3	9	18	54
92.5–96.5	94.5	7	8	2	4	14	28
88.5–92.5	90.5	11	4	1	1	11	11
84.5–88.5	86.5	15	0	0	0	0	0
80.5–84.5	82.5	11	−4	−1	1	−11	11
76.5–80.5	78.5	11	−8	−2	4	−22	44
72.5–76.5	74.5	7	−12	−3	9	−21	63
68.5–72.5	70.5	5	−16	−4	16	−20	80
		80				5	489

$$s = \frac{1}{n} \sqrt{ n \sum_{i=1}^{h} f_i p_i^2 - \left(\sum_{i=1}^{h} f_i p_i \right)^2 }$$

$$= \frac{4}{80} \sqrt{80(489) - (5)^2}$$

$$= 9.89$$

but a consequence of the uniform length, 4, of the class intervals chosen. If each number in column (4) is multiplied by $\frac{1}{4}$, the result is the simple series of consecutive whole numbers in column (5). These may be used to compute s, if it is remembered that the s computed will be just one fourth of the proper value ($+9.89$) for the original data. Column (5) will be used for the computation, then, and the resulting s multiplied by 4 to obtain the standard deviation of the original data.

The interval midpoints have been reduced here to the numbers -4, $-3, -2, \ldots, 6, 7$, and 8 by use of the constants -86.5 and $\frac{1}{4}$. Under the assumption of concentration at the interval midpoints, these numbers stand in the place of the original data. Column (7) gives the sum

$$\sum_{i=1}^{13} f_i p_i = 5$$

of the transformed data, and column (8) gives the sum

$$\sum_{i=1}^{13} f_i p_i^2 = 489$$

of the squares of the transformed data. The formula

$$s = \frac{1}{n} \sqrt{n \sum_{i=1}^{n} X_i^2 - \left(\sum_{i=1}^{n} X_i \right)^2}$$

becomes for grouped data

$$s = \frac{I}{n} \sqrt{n \sum_{i=1}^{h} f_i p_i^2 - \left(\sum_{i=1}^{h} f_i p_i \right)^2}$$

where I is the length of the intervals used and the reciprocal of the multiplicative constant used to reduce the data, and h is the number of intervals. Using the results obtained above, this becomes

$$s = \frac{4}{80} \sqrt{80(489) - 5^2}$$
$$= .05 \sqrt{39120 - 25}$$
$$= .05 \sqrt{39095}$$
$$= 9.89$$

which differs by .1 from the actual standard deviation computed directly from the data, 9.99. This error is entirely due to the midpoint concentration assumption and to no other cause. A small amount of experience usually enables one to judge whether or not a sparsely populated "tail" such as occurs in this case is sufficiently thin to make the use of the concentration assumption unwise.

The computation just completed is quite short and simple in view of the complexity of the definition of s and the size of the data involved.

Since the mean is used in the computation of s, it may appear that the value of s depends on the value of the mean. Actually these two statistics are independent of one another. If s depended on the mean, any change in the data that changed the mean would automatically change s. But this is not the case, since it has already been shown that increasing every datum by a constant does not change s. Such a change in the data does change the mean, however. Thus, it follows that s is independent of the mean.

(*Note:* It will be left to the reader as an exercise to prove that if each datum is multiplied by a constant c and $(1 - c)$ times the mean added to each result, then the new mean will be the same as the former one, and the new standard deviation will be c times the former one.)

The relation between the range and the standard deviation

The range fixes limits over which s may take its value. For a fixed range $X_n - X_1 = R$ the standard deviation will be minimum if all the other data are concentrated at the point $\dfrac{X_1 + X_n}{2} = \bar{X}$. The only nonzero deviations from the mean will be those for X_1 and X_n.
Then

$$s^2 = \frac{1}{n}\left(\frac{-R}{2}\right)^2 + \frac{1}{n}\left(\frac{R}{2}\right)^2$$

$$= \frac{R^2}{2n}$$

and

$$s = \frac{R}{\sqrt{2n}}$$

Given a fixed range $X_n - X_1 = R$, the value of s will be maximum if half the data are equal to X_1 and the other half equal to X_n. Then all the deviations from the mean are equal to $R/2$ or $-R/2$. Hence,

$$s^2 = \frac{1}{n}\Sigma\left(\frac{R}{2}\right)^2 = \frac{1}{n}\cdot n\left(\frac{R}{2}\right)^2$$

$$= \frac{R^2}{4} \quad \left(\text{by summing over the constant }\left(\frac{R}{2}\right)^2\right)$$

and

$$s = \frac{R}{2}$$

It follows that the standard deviation must always be equal to or greater than $R/\sqrt{2n}$ and that it must be equal to or less than $R/2$. *These limits serve as rough checks on the computation of s.* They also serve to indicate whether a given standard deviation indicates a dispersion which is nearer to the minimum possible for the range or nearer to the maximum possible for the range. If for a given fixed range the standard deviations for every possible population were to be computed and plotted, the result would be a smooth curve symmetrical about the point midway between $R/2$ and $R/\sqrt{2n}$. This point is $\frac{1}{2}\left(\frac{R}{2} + \frac{R}{\sqrt{2n}}\right) = \frac{R}{4}\frac{\sqrt{2n}+2}{\sqrt{2n}}$. If for a given range, R, s is less than this value, then s is nearer to its minimum than to its maximum for distributions having the range R. The expression $\frac{R}{4}\frac{\sqrt{2n}+2}{\sqrt{2n}}$ is very close to $R/4$, and this value may be used to judge whether or not s is large or small as compared to other distributions having the range R.

To illustrate the use to which this relation between R, n, and s may be put, consider the following examples. In a sample of size 50 and range 64, it is found that $s = 7$. Now 7 is considerably less than $64/4 = 16$, and one concludes that among all distributions of size 50 this is one of those having least variability; the least that s could be in this case is $64/\sqrt{100} = 6.4$, and 7 is thus seen to be near the least possible value. Suppose, on the other hand, that the range is 15, while $n = 50$ and $s = 7$. Then 7 is larger than $15/4 = 3.75$, and the distribution is seen to be one of the more widely dispersed distributions of size 50. Here the maximum possible value of s is $15/2 = 7.5$, and $s = 7$ is near the maximum.

These examples show that, *although the two samples have the same n and the same s, the populations sampled are essentially different.*

The standard deviation and the normal curve

Almost everyone is familiar with the "bell shaped" curve of Figure 11. Frequency distributions of data obtained by social, biological, and physical scientists, as well as by educators, fall so often into this form that it is now a commonplace to talk of the "normal curve" (see page 63). When students ask if they are to be graded "on the curve," they are referring to the normal curve. The frequent occurrence of the distribution in nature and society has motivated an extensive mathematical analysis and development of the curve's properties. One of the most useful of these properties is the part played by the standard deviation in the structure of the curve. While at this point we wish only to develop the special significance of the standard deviation, it is necessary first to mention some of the other properties of the curve.

In Chapter 3 mention was made of the theoretically perfect frequency polygon or frequency curve of a frequency distribution (see page 77). The normal curve is such a frequency curve. The curve was first studied by Abraham DeMoivre (1733) who developed the expression

$$Y = \frac{1}{\sigma\sqrt{2\pi}}\, e^{-\frac{1}{2}\left(\frac{X-\mu}{\sigma}\right)^2}$$

If this equation is graphed with X on the horizontal axis and Y on the vertical axis, the resulting curve will be that of Figure 11.

This equation is too complex for complete or detailed analysis here. It is given only to indicate the quantities which enter into the shape of the curve. The value of π is approximately 3.1416 and will be recalled as having special significance in connection with circles. The value of e is approximately 2.7183; its most common use, among many elsewhere in mathematics, is as the base number for the system of natural logarithms. The symbols μ and σ in the formula represent, respectively, the mean and the standard deviation of the distribution.

Some properties of the normal curve

Mathematical analysis of the equation for the curve has shown that it has the following properties:

1. The curve is symmetrical about its mean. This means that, if a perpendicular to the X-axis is raised at the point $X = \mu$, it will divide the curve into two parts, one of which is the mirror image of the other. Such a perpendicular which starts on the X-axis and ends at the curve is called an *ordinate* of the curve. In Figure 11 the ordinate AB is the axis of symmetry for the curve.

2. The curve has only one "hump" or relative maximum. This single high point occurs, of course, at the center of the curve, directly above the mean on the X-axis. The symmetry of the curve and the existence of only

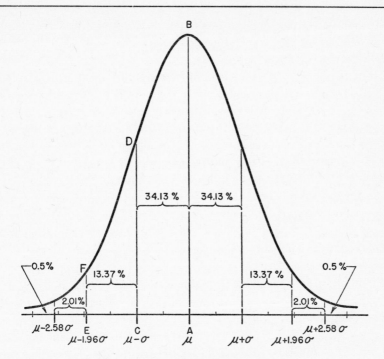

FIG. 11. A normal probability curve.

one relative maximum tell us that the mean, median, and mode of a normal distribution are all equal.

3. The curve flattens out as it extends to either side of its center. The greater the distance from the center, the more pronounced the flattening becomes. The curve gets closer and closer to the X-axis but never touches it. The curve is thus said to be *asymptotic* to the X-axis.

4. The area between the curve and the X-axis is exactly one square unit of area. This may appear to contradict property 3, but it does not. There are many regions treated in mathematics which, while having infinitely long boundaries, nevertheless have a finite area. This curve, taken with the X-axis, "encloses" such a region.

5. If two ordinates, such as CD and EF in Figure 11, are raised from the X-axis, they mark off a portion $CDFE$ of the area under the curve. Such an area will always, in view of property 4, be between 0 and 1. For this and for other reasons, it may be regarded as a measure of the probability that a randomly selected datum from the distribution will lie between the two values of X at which the ordinates are raised. Note that, since the total area

under the curve is one square unit of area, all areas found between pairs of ordinates must be between 0 and 1. The curve is so designed that these areas may be considered as probabilities associated with the values of X which lie along the lower boundary of the area.

Computing an area such as $CDFE$ requires the techniques of the calculus because of the curvilinear nature of part of the boundary of the area. Extensive calculations have been tabulated by mathematicians so that others may determine easily the height of *any* ordinate and the area between *any* pair of ordinates. Such a table is called a *normal probability table*. Appendix Table A is a normal probability table of adequate scope for this book. Instructions for its use will be given below.

6. For every different pair of numbers, μ and σ, there is a different normal curve. The significance of μ has already been noted in property 1. No matter what values μ and σ may have, the ordinates at the points $X = \mu$ and $X = \mu + \sigma$ enclose the same area as described in property 5. The amount of area between these two ordinates (AB and CD) is 34.13 per cent of all the area under the curve (see Figure 11). According to property 1, the same amount of area is included between the ordinates at $X = \mu - \sigma$ and $X = \mu$. The implication, according to property 5, is that in any normally distributed population 68.26 per cent of the distribution lies within plus or minus one standard deviation of the mean. The basic point of interest here is that this is a property of any normal distribution, no matter what the values of μ and σ may be. The area between the ordinates at $X = \mu$ and $X = \mu + 1.96\sigma$ is 47.50 per cent of the whole area, indicating that 95 per cent of a normal distribution lies within 1.96 standard deviations of the mean. Appendix Table A gives the proportions of the total area to be found between the ordinates $X = \mu$ and $X = \mu + z\sigma$ where z takes values from 0 to 3 in steps of .01; the table gives areas only for the right side of the curve, because the left side is a mirror image of the right side.

Normal probability table

The following example shows how the normal probability table may be read. Suppose that a population is known to be normal with $\mu = 6$ and $\sigma = 2$. Let it be asked, "What is the probability that a randomly selected datum will lie between 7 and 8?" To answer this question, it is necessary to know how far 7 and 8 are from the mean 6 in terms of standard deviations. Since the point $X = 7$ is $7 - 6 = 1$ unit from the mean, it must then be $\dfrac{7 - 6}{2} = \dfrac{1}{2}$ standard deviations from the mean. Similarly, the point 8 is two units, or one standard deviation, from the mean 6. The question then reduces to asking what area lies between the ordinates at $X = \mu + \frac{1}{2}\sigma$ and $X = \mu + \sigma$. Appendix Table A shows that the area between $X = \mu$ and $X = \mu + \frac{1}{2}\sigma$ is .1915, and that the area between $X = \mu$ and $X = \mu + \sigma$ is .3413. The required area is then the difference between these figures, .3413 − .1915 = .1498 (see Figure 12). The required probability is thus

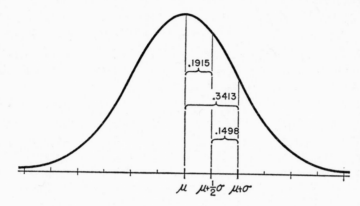

FIG. 12. An illustration showing the areas of the normal curve anchored by ordinates erected at the points μ, $\mu + \frac{1}{2}\sigma$, and $\mu + \sigma$.

.1498, which may be interpreted as indicating that 14.98 per cent of all the data in this distribution lies between 7 and 8. In the same distribution let it be asked, What is the probability that a randomly chosen datum will be between 4.5 and 7.6? The distance between 4.5 and 6 expressed as a number of standard deviations is computed by the formula

$$z = \frac{X - \mu}{\sigma}$$
$$= \frac{4.5 - 6}{2}$$
$$= -.75$$

Using $X = 7.6$, the formula yields $z = .8$. What then is the area between the ordinates at $X = \mu - .75\sigma$ and $X = \mu + .8\sigma$? Appendix Table A gives .2734 for $z = .75$ and .2881 for $z = .8$. Since the first of these represents an area to the left of the center and the other an area to the right of the center, the required area is obtained by adding them; the result is .5615, and hence 56.15 per cent of the population lies between 4.5 and 7.6. (See Figure 13.)

No matter where the two ordinates are located, one uses Table A to

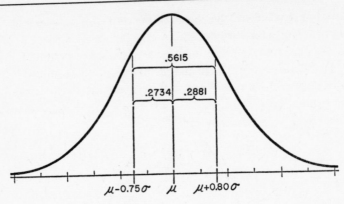

FIG. 13. Ordinates erected at the points μ, $\mu - 0.75\sigma$, and $\mu + .80\sigma$.

determine the area between the ordinate at the mean and each of the given ordinates. If the two ordinates are on one side of the mean, the lesser of these areas is subtracted from the greater to get the area between the two ordinates; if the two given ordinates are on opposite sides of the mean, then the two areas must be added to get the area between the two given ordinates. Table A can be used for any normal curve if $z = \dfrac{X - \bar{X}}{s}$ is used instead of X. The reason for this is that if X is normally distributed with mean $\bar{X}$ and standard deviation s, then $z = \dfrac{X - \bar{X}}{s}$ is also normally distributed and its mean and standard deviation are, respectively, 0 and 1. It is this "standard" normal curve for which Table A has been prepared. Instead of having a different table for every normal curve, we have a formula for converting every normally distributed variable into the standard normal variable, z. (See Box 16.)

THE INDEX OF DISPERSION—A MEASURE OF VARIABILITY FOR ORDINAL AND NOMINAL DATA

It should be pointed out that another kind of measure of variability can be based on the number of pairs of data the members of which are in different categories. Such pairs are said to contain "distinguishable members," whereas a pair of data from the same classification category is said to be "indistinguishable." Such a measure is particularly applicable to ordinally and nominally scaled data because the standard deviation and the mean deviation are not appropriate measures for such data. This raises the question of how many different pairs can be made up from a given set of data. To answer this question, let A_1, A_2, . . . A_n be any n objects. A_1 may be paired with any of the other $n - 1$ objects, among which will be the pair A_1, A_2. In order not to duplicate this pair, let A_2 be paired only with the objects following A_2. There are $n - 2$ of these, so that the number of pairs counted so far is $(n - 1) + (n - 2)$. Continuing with A_3, and the others in turn, the number of pairs is seen to be

$$(n - 1) + (n - 2) + (n - 3) + \cdots + (3) + (2) + (1)$$

Reversing the order of the terms in this sum gives

$$1 + 2 + 3 + \cdots + (n - 3) + (n - 2) + (n - 1) = \sum_{x=1}^{n-1} X$$

This sum is known to have the value $\dfrac{n(n - 1)}{2}$, the formula being sought. It gives the number of ways that n objects can be taken two at a time. For example, if $n = 2$, the number of pairs is $\dfrac{2(2 - 1)}{2} = 1$, as is to be expected. For $n = 3$ the formula gives $\dfrac{3(2)}{2} = 3$, which is correct. For $n = 100$ the formula gives $\dfrac{100(99)}{2} = 4950$ as the number of different pairs.

Suppose now that the n objects are classified into two categories, the first category having n_1 members and the second n_2. Then $n_1 + n_2 = n$. Any pair of objects both of which are in the same category is to be rejected as not containing members that are distinguishable. There are, by the formula just developed, exactly $\dfrac{n_1(n_1 - 1)}{2}$ such pairs from the first category, and there are exactly $\dfrac{n_2(n_2 - 1)}{2}$ such pairs in the second category. All of these pairs must then be deleted from the totality of all possible pairs; the result is

$$\frac{n(n - 1)}{2} - \frac{n_1(n_1 - 1)}{2} - \frac{n_2(n_2 - 1)}{2}$$

Now it is clear that if three, four, or more categories are used, it will be necessary to delete the sets of pairs that can be formed from each individual

BOX 16

The Normal Curve—Law of Nature, or Mathematical Fiction?

If recent signs are an indication of what the future holds, the dispute as to whether the normal curve is a law of nature or a mathematical fiction promises to achieve sharper focus. The argument is important, for the application of the normal curve reaches from educational policy (as every student knows) to chemistry and physics. And it is an argument on which nearly every educator, statistician, and scientist is willing to take a stand. The following brief sketch outlines the history of the dispute.

The equation for the curve was developed by DeMoivre (earliest record 1733) as a piece of pure mathematical reasoning —slightly tarnished by the fact that the initial stimulus for DeMoivre's work seems to have come from gamblers who occasionally sought his assistance. Much later, in the very early 1800's, the famous mathematician Gauss, while working on certain problems of astronomy relating to Newton's theory, found it necessary to record a large number of observations of planetary motions. But there were always annoying errors in plotting the true motion of a planet. It was in the effort to cope with these errors that Gauss further developed the mathematical properties of the normal curve and used it to describe the distribution of the errors. Gauss thus developed what came to be known as the "Normal Law of Error," which, of course, is the normal curve so familiar to us.

Now enter those who shift the application of the curve from a description (or theory) of *error* to a description (or theory) of social and biological *fact*. Quetelet, a Belgian astronomer, writing in approximately 1840, seems to have been the first to urge this shift (and to construct a table to simplify calculations). But it was Galton, in the latter part of the 1800's, who, with his customary vigor and insight, turned the Law of Error into a "Law of Nature." Galton's own words on this matter are instructive: "The primary objects of the Gaussian Law of Error were exactly opposed, in one sense, to those to which I applied them. They were to get rid of, or to provide a just allowance for errors. *But these errors or deviations were the very things I wanted to preserve and to know about* (italics ours)." And, Galton points out, it was for this reason he had difficulty in explaining to mathematicians his interest in applying the Law of Error to social and biological events. This shift is a prime example of a scientist putting a "new twist" on an older idea. And Galton and his followers, in biology, sociology, psychology, and education, have shown continued enthusiastic interest in wanting "to preserve and to know about" the *distribution* of various social and biological events.

But this shift in application has not gone untouched by criticism. Hogben, a well-known writer of books in science, mathematics, and statistics, presents a modern attack on Galton's "new twist." He argues that Galton's application of the Gaussian curve was fallacious, a *tour de force,* and that it has seduced mathematicians and behavioral scientists alike into thoughtlessly extending a mathematical concept to a matter of social and biological fact. Many other scientists simply argue that although distributions of events are frequently found to be normal in form, they are often found not to be—and they caution against elevating the normal curve to a "law of nature."

It would be unjust to leave this brief historical venture without pointing out that Galton was himself quite aware of the fact that he was reaching, perhaps, "beyond his grasp." He remarks, in 1888, "It has been objected . . . that I pushed the application of the Law of Frequency of Error somewhat too far. I may have done so . . . ; but I am sure that, with the evidence now before me, the applicability of that law is more than justified within . . . reasonable limits." And in the true spirit of scientific inquiry, Galton notes that "there is always room for legitimate doubt . . . [and] it is therefore exceedingly desirable to put the theoretical conclusions to frequent test." (see Walker).

Galton, F. 1908. *Memories of my life*. London: Methuen.
Hogben, L. 1957. *Statistical theory*. London: Allen and Unwin.
Walker, H. 1929. *Studies in the history of the statistical method*. Baltimore: Williams and Wilkins.

category. If h categories are used and the numbers of objects in these categories are $n_1, n_2, \ldots, n_h$, respectively, then the number of pairs wherein the elements are distinguishable is

$$\frac{n(n-1)}{2} - \sum_{i=1}^{h} \frac{n_i(n_i - 1)}{2} = \frac{n(n-1)}{2} - \frac{1}{2} \sum_{i=1}^{h} (n_i^2 - n_i)$$

$$= \frac{n^2}{2} - \frac{n}{2} - \frac{1}{2} \sum_{i=1}^{h} n_i^2 + \frac{1}{2} \sum_{i=1}^{h} n_i$$

$$= \frac{n^2}{2} - \frac{1}{2} \sum_{i=1}^{h} n_i^2$$

The first step factors the constant ½ out of the sum. Then the $\sum$ symbol is distributed over the general term, and, finally, it is observed that the sum of the n_i is n.

The formula

$$D = \frac{h\left(n^2 - \sum_{i=1}^{h} n_i^2\right)}{n^2(h-1)}$$

is mainly a consequence of these counting procedures for the enumeration of pairs. The ratio of the number of pairs whose members may be distinguished from one another to the totality of possible pairs is

$$\frac{\dfrac{n^2}{2} - \dfrac{1}{2} \sum\limits_{i=1}^{h} n_i^2}{\dfrac{n(n-1)}{2}} = \frac{n^2 - \sum\limits_{i=1}^{h} n_i^2}{n(n-1)}$$

The higher this ratio is, the more the variability in the data. The fewer the number of pairs of distinguishable elements, the lower the ratio will be and, consequently, the less the variability. The ratio will have its maximum value if each category contains an equal number of data. The ratio will have the value zero if all the data are in one category and all the others are empty. When each n_i is n/h, the ratio is

$$\frac{n^2 - \sum_{i=1}^{h} \left(\frac{n}{h}\right)^2}{n(n-1)} = \frac{n^2 - h\left(\frac{n}{h}\right)^2}{n(n-1)}$$

$$= \frac{n(h-1)}{h(n-1)}$$

This maximum value of the ratio corresponds to maximum variability in the data. If the ratio used to get this result is multiplied by $\frac{h(n-1)}{n(h-1)}$, then the maximum would be 1. So that the index of dispersion may vary from 0 to 1 no matter how many categories are used, the index is defined as

$$D = \frac{h(n-1)}{n(h-1)} \frac{n^2 - \sum_{i=1}^{h} n_i^2}{n(n-1)}$$

$$= \frac{h\left(n^2 - \sum_{i=1}^{h} n_i^2\right)}{n^2(h-1)}$$

To illustrate the use of D, suppose that fifty subjects are classified into four categories and that there are, respectively, twenty, twelve, eleven, and seven subjects in these categories. Then $n = 50, n_1 = 20, n_2 = 12, n_3 = 11, n_4 = 7$, and $h = 4$.

$$D = \frac{4[50^2 - (20^2 + 12^2 + 11^2 + 7^2)]}{50^2(3)}$$

$$= \frac{7144}{7500} = .95$$

Suppose that a fifth category had been used in this example and that $n_5 = 0$; that is, there was an empty category. The computation of D will be the same except that h will be changed from 4 to 5. The result in this case is .89, indicating less variability.

As a further example, consider the grading practices of the two teachers whose grade distributions are given in Table 25.

TABLE 25

Distributions of Grades Assigned by Two Teachers

	TEACHER I	TEACHER II
A's	8%	10%
B's	13	20
C's	63	40
D's	10	20
F's	6	10
	100%	100%

The set of grades with the most variability is the set which best differentiates the various levels of excellence. Since only percentages are given, it may appear that D cannot be computed. It will be found, however, that the computation is possible. For teacher I suppose that n students have been graded. Then

$$D = \frac{5(n^2 - [(.08n)^2 + (.13n)^2 + (.63n)^2 + (.10n)^2 + (.06n)^2])}{4n^2}$$

$$= \frac{5(.5662n^2)}{4n^2}$$

$$= .71$$

Since n^2 cancels out of the calculation, the value of D depends on the proportions rather than on the actual numbers of data. For teacher II, the value D is .93; thus, the variability in the grades of teacher II is greater than the variability for teacher I.

Suggestions for Further Reading

GUILFORD, J., 1956. *Fundamental statistics in psychology and education.* (3rd ed.) New York: McGraw-Hill.
> Chapter 5.

WALLIS, W., and ROBERTS, H., 1956. *Statistics: a new approach.* Glencoe: Free Press.
> Chapter 8.

WALKER, H., and LEV, J. 1958. *Elementary statistical methods.* New York: Holt.
> Chapter 7.

PROBLEMS

1. Alter the set of numbers 3, 6, 9, 12, and 15 so that the range will be increased while the mean remains unchanged.
2. Repeat problem 1 with "increased" replaced by "decreased."
3. Alter the set of numbers 3, 6, 9, 12, and 15 so that the mean will be increased while the range is left fixed.
4. Repeat problem 3 with "increased" replaced by "decreased."
5. Make up a list of five numbers having a mean of 40 such that none of the five numbers is within ten units of the mean.
6. Make up a list of five numbers having a mean of 40 such that all are within two units of the mean.
7. Construct a pair of possible salary schedules from which the example involving a $10,000 mean and ranges of $5,000 and $92,000 could be taken.
8. What kind of statistical sleight-of-hand is accomplished in the pricing of an article at $3.98 or $1,495.00?
9. From a consideration of the definitions of the mean deviation and the standard deviation, give reasons why these quantities can never be negative. Under what circumstances could they be zero?
10. What conclusion could be drawn concerning a group of people for whom all the standard deviations of Table 19 are very close to zero—say, less than 1 in every case?
11. Find the sum of the deviations of the numbers 0, 1, 1, 2, 3, 5, 8, 13, 21, and 34 from their mean.
12. Find the mean deviation of the ten numbers in problem 11.
13. Find the mean deviation of the data in Table 14 (page 87). (Note that $\bar{X} = 56$ for these data.)
14. Use the classification of Table 16 (page 94) to find the mean deviation of the data of Table 14 by means of the grouped data technique. Explain the difference between the result of this problem and that of problem 13.
15. If every datum is doubled, what is the effect on the mean, the deviations from the mean, and the mean deviation?
16. Repeat problem 15 with "doubled" replaced by "multiplied by a constant k."
17. Use the definition of the standard deviation to find the standard deviation of the numbers in problem 11.
18. Find the standard deviation of the numbers 1, 2, . . . , 10.

19. Show that 1 and 2 have a standard deviation and a mean deviation both equal to $\frac{1}{2}$. Can you find another pair of numbers with the same property?

20. Analyze the formula for the mean deviation relating each component of the formula to some requirement of a measure of variability.

21. Repeat problem 20 for the standard deviation.

22. It is impossible to find a set of numbers between 66 and 83 and having a standard deviation of 9. Why is this? Make up a similar statement concerning all numbers between 80 and 100.

23. The formula

$$s^2 = \frac{1}{n} \sum_{i=1}^{n} X_i^2 - \bar{X}^2$$

is developed on page 123. Write out each step of this derivation in detail using $n = 3$, $X_1 = 2$, $X_2 = 3$, and $X_3 = 5$, thus verifying the result for a particular instance. The first line of your work will read

$$s^2 = \tfrac{1}{3}\{(\tfrac{10}{3} - 2)^2 + (\tfrac{10}{3} - 3)^2 + (\tfrac{10}{3} - 5)^2\}$$

and the last line should read

$$s^2 = \tfrac{1}{3}(2^2 + 3^2 + 5^2) - (\tfrac{10}{3})^2$$

24. Find and compare the numerical values of the first and last lines of your work on problem 23.

25. Use the formula given in problem 23 to find the standard deviation of the data in the first four columns of Table 14.

26. Use the formula $s = \frac{1}{n}\sqrt{n\sum X^2 - (\sum X)^2}$ to compute the standard deviation of the data in the first four columns of Table 14 after each of these data have been increased by 5.

27. How are the equal results of problems 25 and 26 to be explained in view of the fact that different formulas were used on different data? Is there a cancellation of differences here? That is, does changing the data offset the change in formulas?

28. Use Theorem 1 on the standard deviation to simplify the computation of the standard deviation of 51, 53, 57, and 59.

29. Use Theorem 2 on the standard deviation to simplify the computation of the standard deviation of the numbers 5, 15, 35, and 45.

30. Use Theorems 1 and 2 together to reduce to smaller numbers the computation of the standard deviation of 20, 28, 40, and 60.

31. Find the standard deviation of the numbers 11, 12, 13, . . . , 20 and compare with problem 18.

32. Find the standard deviation of the numbers 2, 4, 6, . . . , 20 and compare with problems 18 and 31.

33. Use both theorems on the standard deviation to compute the standard deviation of the data of Table 14 as classified in Tables 15 and 16.

34. Reclassify the data of Table 20 into seventeen class intervals of length 3, and compute the mean and standard deviation of the grouped data using the techniques illustrated in Tables 16 and 22.

35. Show that if each datum is multiplied by c and if $(1 - c)$ times the mean is added to each result, the new mean will be the same as the former one and the new standard deviation c times the former one.

36. The mean and standard deviation of the numbers 3, 9, 12, 21, and 30 are, respectively, 15 and 9.49. Make changes in the given numbers so that the mean is increased by 3 but the standard deviation remains unchanged.

37. Alter the numbers given in problem 36 so that the mean is halved and the standard deviation doubled.

38. Alter the numbers given in problem 36 so that the mean remains unchanged but standard deviation is increased by 3.

39. Alter the numbers given in problem 36 so that the mean is tripled and the standard deviation is halved.

40. What are the least and greatest possible values of the standard deviation if
    (a) $n = 200$ and the range is 50?
    (b) $n = 50$ and the range is 200?
    (c) n is the square of the range?

41. The expression $\dfrac{R}{4} \cdot \dfrac{\sqrt{2n+2}}{\sqrt{2n}}$ is said to be very close to $\dfrac{R}{4}$. How close are the two numbers if
    (a) $n = 10$?
    (b) $n = 100$?
    (c) $n = 1,000$?

42. Let a first set of data have $n = 100$, $R = 60$, and $s = 15$. Let a second set of data have $n = 80$, $R = 50$, and $s = 10$. Which set of data is highest in the range of variability for its size (n) and range (R)?

43. While the equation of the normal curve given on page 132 is rather complicated, it is possible to tell how high the curve rises by plotting one special point. If $X = \mu$, the exponent of e becomes zero; hence, $y = \dfrac{1}{\sigma\sqrt{2\pi}}$ in this case. Compute the length of the maximum ordinate for $\sigma = 1$, $\sigma = \frac{1}{10}$, and $\sigma = 10$.

44. The graph of the curve $y = 1/x$ is asymptotic to the x-axis and the y-axis. Find another curve which, like this one and the normal curve, is asymptotic to the x-axis.

45. For what value of z will the ordinates at $\mu \pm z\sigma$ to a normal curve enclose 10 per cent of the area under the curve? (Use Appendix Table A.)

46. Repeat problem 45 for 20 per cent, 30 per cent, . . . , 90 per cent, in place of 10 per cent. Make a sketch of these results and that of problem 45.

47. If the mean of a normal distribution is 15 and the standard deviation is 6, what will be the values of the points $\mu \pm z\sigma$ for z equal to the values computed in problems 45 and 46? Make a sketch.

48. If the data tabulated below are normally distributed, how many of the data should lie between $\bar{X} - .5s$ and $\bar{X} + .5s$. How many actually do lie there?

3	39	59	76	89	98	109	120	132	158
6	39	59	76	89	99	110	121	132	160
8	40	62	77	89	99	111	121	135	160
10	43	62	77	89	100	111	122	137	162
12	43	63	78	90	101	112	122	137	163
15	45	65	79	92	101	113	123	140	165
17	48	66	80	93	101	114	123	142	169
19	50	68	81	95	103	115	124	145	170
22	52	69	82	95	105	116	126	146	177
25	53	69	83	96	106	116	127	147	177
26	54	70	83	96	106	117	128	147	179
28	55	70	83	97	106	117	129	151	180
32	56	73	85	97	106	118	129	151	185
35	57	74	86	97	107	118	130	152	189
37	57	75	88	97	107	119	130	154	195

49. Repeat problem 48 for $\bar{X} - zs$ and $\bar{X} + zs$ for $z = .2, .4, .6, .8, 1, 1.2,$ 1.4, 1.6, and 1.9.

50. Suppose 100 people are polled in January and again in May on a question. If the results are as shown below, which poll reveals the most variability in the responses?

	PRO	CON	UNDECIDED
January	35	40	25
May	45	46	9

51. Repeat problem 50 using the following data:

	PRO	CON	UNDECIDED
January	35	40	25
May	60	38	2

What trend is to be expected in the index of dispersion as the Undecided category declines in numbers?

52. Find the indices of dispersion for each of the three classifications given below.

	1	2	3	4
A	10	20	30	40
B	20	20	30	30
C	20	20	60	0

I propose ... to range men according to their natural abilities.

SIR FRANCIS GALTON

CHAPTER

5

INDIVIDUAL PERFORMANCE

HAVING BEEN INTRODUCED to the methods for describing the variability of a frequency distribution, the student is now in a position to perceive how these methods make it possible to solve a further problem faced by the behavioral scientist. The problem, in general, is that of evaluating a single individual's performance. More specifically, it is that of *comparing an individual's performance with a standard*. How does this problem arise?

THE NEED FOR A STANDARD REFERENT

In attempting to measure an individual's height, we place him against a ruler or yardstick or scale in such a fashion that we compare his height with that of the mark on the scale which matches his height. If other individuals are similarly measured, it is obvious that the act of measurement in this case consists of *comparing* each individual's height with a standard. Once this is done, each individual's height can be compared with the others because all measurements were made against the same standard—the conventional measuring scale of length. What makes this so simple and obvious is the existence of an absolute zero—an easily determined origin from which all measurements start—and of equal intervals on the scale. In short, a ratio scale makes the matter of comparison simple.

If a ratio scale is not available, however, the matter of comparison becomes somewhat more complex. If an absolute zero has not been determined, some other reference point from which all measurements start must be found. Thus, for example, before an absolute zero was determined for the temperature scale, the freezing and boiling points of water were used as reference points for the measurement of temperature. Choice of these reference points made sense, both theoretically and practically. The man in the street was just as interested in these two points as the man in the laboratory, for when a liquid as commonly used as water changes its form to a solid, or to a gas, nearly everyone is in one way or another affected by the change.

Now consider the behavioral scientist's problem in connection with, say, the measurement of intelligence. An absolute zero of intelligence has not been determined. What shall the reference point be? If there were obvious definite points on the intelligence scale where it became apparent that intelligence changed its *form*, these critical points could be used as reference points. But there are no clear or obvious changes in behavior at any point along any scale ever devised (and this is true for the vast majority of psychological measuring scales).

Consider the following example. If a 100-item spelling test is administered to a number of students and student A answers sixty items correctly, his "raw score" on the test is 60. Reporting such a "raw score" is not very informative, however: by itself it tells us nothing about the student's ability as a speller, and, in general, it does not indicate whether the individual's rating is good or poor. More accurately, a raw score does not indicate an individual's position on a scale *relative to some standard*. Because no obvious *behavioral* referents have been discovered, it is necessary to construct *statistical* reference points. What are the requirements such contrived reference points must meet?

REQUIREMENTS

A standard reference point should be stable. It should also be as meaningful as possible to the layman.

If reference points are not stable, they cannot serve their purposes as standards, for stability is the very essence of a standard. Indeed, if a given standard is not as stable as desirable, scientists are apt to undertake special efforts to provide the necessary stability. Thus, for example, the universally agreed-upon standard referent for length is kept at a constant temperature in an institute accessible to all scientists. Contrived statistical reference points for human and animal behavior cannot, of course, possess such stability, for they are dependent upon the performances of individuals. But standard referents must always be chosen with regard to the amount of stability they possess.

Reference points should also make sense to the layman, if at all possible, for he is highly concerned with behavioral comparisons. He will want to know how not only his own performance but those of his children compare with the performances of others. No one knows better than a school teacher how important it is to have a standard referent that makes sense to the layman.

METHODS FOR COMPARING PERFORMANCE

Two methods for evaluating the test performance of individuals will be discussed: One—the percentile-score method—is applicable to ordinal scales, and the other—the standard-score method—is applicable to interval scales. (Nominal scales need not be discussed, because these scales do not *order* individuals. Ratio scales are not discussed, because such scales, having an absolute origin, automatically provide a standard reference point.)

Reference points for ordinal scales—percentile scores

The most obvious and stablest point on an ordinal scale is the point of central tendency—the median. And the median, as a *center point*, is a referent the layman can easily grasp (particularly if the word "average" is used for "median"). Thus, for example, a mother can readily understand that her child is near the center of the group, well above the center, or well below. People have become so accustomed to the idea that psychological tests provide *relative* comparisons that such an explanation is quickly accepted. But the behavioral scientist needs a more refined reference system. The mere fact of an individual being above or below the median is too crude an indication of his performance relative to that of others. For this reason, the distribution is divided into finer groupings. Thus, not only is the center point—the point above and below which 50 per cent of the cases lie—located, but also each of the other percentage points. Thus, the point, or score, on the distribution which divides the distribution at 1 per cent and 99 per cent is located, as well as 2 per cent and 98 per cent, 3 per cent and 97 per cent, 4 per cent and 96 per cent, and so on. As a result, once an individual's score on the test is known, it is possible to report whether his score exceeds that of 1 per cent of the others who took the test, or 2 per cent, 3 per cent, 95 per cent, or any other percentage. Indeed, it is customary for publishers of commercial tests to set up tables which list the *percentile equivalents* of each raw score. (Each percentile point is calculated by exactly the same principle as that used for the median; the procedure is illustrated in detail in the mathematical section of this chapter.)

Such a table is presented in Table 26. Given a table of this type, it is

TABLE 26

A Set of Raw Scores and Their Percentile Equivalents on a Sub-test of the Differential Aptitudes Test (Bennett, G., Seashore, H., and Wesman, G. Published by the Psychological Corporation, N.Y., 1959).

SPACE RELATIONS

RAW SCORE	PERCENTILE
87+	99
80–86	97
74–79	95
69–73	90
64–68	85
61–63	80
57–60	75
54–56	70
51–53	65
47–50	60
44–46	55
40–43	50
37–39	45
33–36	40
30–32	35
26–29	30
22–25	25
19–21	20
15–18	15
10–14	10
6–9	5
2–5	3
0–1	1

possible for a schoolteacher to locate any student's performance relative to all others taking the test, whether the others happen to be those in his own classroom or those taking the test throughout the state or nation. Thus, the teacher can ascertain the fact that a student's performance exceeded that of 75 per cent or of only 15 per cent of those in the reference group. Clearly, information of this sort is highly valuable in interpreting test performance.

BOX 17

Self-portraiture in Profile

A frequently used form for conveying to parents the relative progress of their children in school is the one shown. The tests used are the Iowa Tests of Educational Development. Note that the graph makes it possible to compare the performance of the student (heavy solid line in figure) with students in his own school (dashed line in figure) as well as with the national average (heavy line in figure). Note also how clearly the graph illustrates the fact that "average" performance in the school from which these data were taken is far above the national "average." The remarks below are those provided by the test publisher in order to interpret the meaning of the scores for the student.

"INTERPRETING YOUR PROFILE
OF SCORES
"The numbers you have plotted are called percentiles. A percentile score tells what percentage of students at your grade level had lower scores than the one corresponding to that position on the chart. For example, a percentile score of 80 means that 80 per cent of a very large and typical group

of high school students at your grade level received lower scores. The 50th percentile line is printed in bold type to indicate the point—called the *national average*—that separates the upper 50 per cent of this group from the lower 50 per cent.
"Your teacher may also want you to know how your scores compare with those of the other students of your school in your grade. This will require drawing a *dotted line* profile that is based on ten numbers that your teacher will put on the board. Label this profile 'school average.'
"As you look at your profile, it probably does not go straight across the chart. Instead, it has peaks and valleys. It is by noting these high and low positions that you can learn of your strengths and weaknesses in the light of (1) your other scores, (2) the national average, and (3) the school average."

Reprinted by permission of Science Research Associates, Inc., from *Your scores on the Iowa tests of educational development and what they mean.* Copyright 1949, 1958 by State University of Iowa.

STUDENT PROFILE

NAME_____ GRADE____

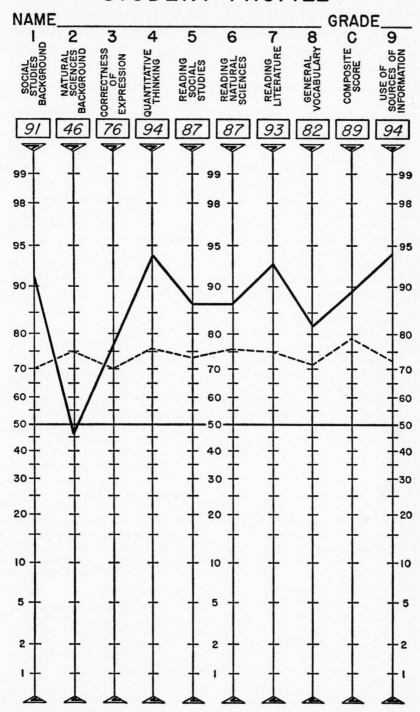

1	2	3	4	5	6	7	8	C	9
SOCIAL STUDIES BACKGROUND	NATURAL SCIENCES BACKGROUND	CORRECTNESS OF EXPRESSION	QUANTITATIVE THINKING	READING SOCIAL STUDIES	READING NATURAL SCIENCES	READING LITERATURE	GENERAL VOCABULARY	COMPOSITE SCORE	USE OF SOURCES OF INFORMATION
91	46	76	94	87	87	93	82	89	94

It should be pointed out that this method makes it possible to compare not only the performances of two individuals on one test, but also the performances of one individual on two different tests. Thus, for example, if student A receives a percentile score of 80 on an arithmetic test and a percentile score of 15 on a spelling test, it is clear that his knowledge of arithmetic far exceeds his ability in spelling—*relative to the others taking the tests*. Indeed, a profile of the student's performance (relative to a reference group) for several different tasks may be drawn, and such profiles are widely used in evaluating a student's performance. An example of a typical profile sheet is presented in Box 17.

As may be seen, then, the percentile score method meets the needs and requirements for a reference system for ordinal scales rather well. Note, however, that the teacher can not ascertain *how much* student A's ability exceeds that of student B. All that can be learned from the percentile method is that student A's performance exceeded that of, say, 70 per cent of the reference group, while student B's performance exceeded that of only 20 per cent of the reference group, and thus that the performances of 50 per cent of the students taking the test stood between those of students A and B.

Of course, the reason that the percentile method offers valuable but limited information is that the data are merely ordered. The distance between scores is not specified. We now turn to procedures for setting up reference points for interval scales, in which distance between scores is specified.

Reference points for interval scales

Z-scores

If a psychological test provides interval-scale scores, then it becomes possible to develop a somewhat more refined system—*the standard score method* (see page 158). Though this method is better suited to the needs of the behavioral scientist, it involves the standard deviation concept and is therefore less useful to the layman. For this reason, the percentile method is often employed when test performance is to be explained to laymen, even though the standard score method could be employed.

The standard score method is based on the replacement of each raw score X by a z-score of the form

$$z = \frac{X - \bar{X}}{s}$$

where $\bar{X}$ and s are, respectively, the mean and standard deviation of the set of raw scores. If the deviation $X - \bar{X}$ of the score X from the mean $\bar{X}$ is de-denoted by x, the z-score corresponding to X may be expressed as x/s. This conversion of X into z is a means whereby the number of standard deviations separating $\bar{X}$ and X can be stated. The division of the deviation from the mean by s gives precisely this number of standard deviations. A raw score of seventy-six correct test items may thus be converted into a score of, say, 1.36 standard deviations above the mean. Or if $z = -.38$ instead of 1.36, the z-score would be .38 standard deviations below the mean.

The z-score corresponding to the raw score which is equal to the mean is 0. Raw scores which are below the mean transform into negative z-scores, and raw scores above the mean transform into positive z-scores. Whereas each raw score differs from the mean by *some number of test items*, each z-score differs from zero by *some number of standard deviations*. Thus, not only is the reference point changed, but so also are the units in which scores are stated. The units for z-scores are standard deviations, and, hence, each score is expressed in terms of the variability of the population as well as in terms of comparative size.

Suppose, for example, a group of students takes an arithmetic test. If the mean of the distribution of scores is 80 and the standard deviation is 10, a raw score of 90 would be equal to a z-score of $+1.00$, because

$$\frac{X - \bar{X}}{s} = \frac{90 - 80}{10} = \frac{10}{10} = 1.00$$

The meaning of this z-score is clear and unequivocal—it indicates that a raw score of 90 is exactly one standard deviation above the mean. If the distribution is normal in form, this fact in turn indicates that 84 per cent of the scores on the test lie below a raw score of 90 and that 16 per cent lie above 90. That important and useful information is not provided unless the difference between a score and the mean is expressed in terms of the standard deviation. Figure 14 illustrates this point.

Thus, because z-scores express the distance of each score from the mean, $X - \bar{X}$, in terms of the variability, s, of the distribution, behavioral scientists are provided with a score which conveys far more information than a raw score. Indeed, z-scores convey sufficient information to make comparisons among individuals possible.

Consider the following examples of how the z-score technique facilitates comparison of individual performance. John, George, and Mary take a test which will determine whether they will be permitted to enter the University, and their raw scores are as follows: John, 445; George, 505; and Mary, 610. All we can learn from these facts is that Mary scored higher than George, who, in turn, had a higher score than John. They do not tell us very much more than that. However, if each of the above raw scores is translated into z-scores, we learn that John's z-score is $-.55$ (indicating that he stands slightly more than one half of a standard-deviation unit below the mean), George's z-score is $+.05$ (indicating that he stands almost at

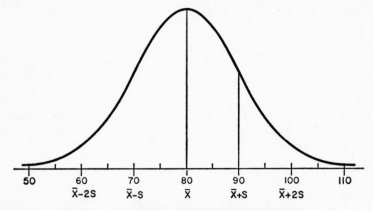

50	60	70	80	90	100	110
	$\bar{X}-2S$	$\bar{X}-S$	$\bar{X}$	$\bar{X}+S$	$\bar{X}+2S$	

Fig. 14. A normal distribution curve with a mean of 80 and a standard deviation of 10.

the mean), and Mary's z-score is $+1.10$ (indicating that she stands slightly higher than one standard deviation above the mean). If it is desirable to know where each of the three students stands with respect to the percentage of students having lower scores than he does, and *if the scores are normally distributed*, all that is necessary is to look at Table A in the appendix; thus it may be ascertained that approximately 21 per cent of the students taking the test stand between John and the mean. Of course, since 50 per cent of the students are above the mean, 71 per cent (50 + 21 per cent) of the students have scores higher than John, and 29 per cent, therefore, have scores lower than he. Because George's score is so close to the mean, approximately half (50 per cent) of the group have scores higher and half have scores lower than he does. Mary's score of $+1.10$ places her higher than 86 per cent of the group. (All this, of course, assumes that this distribution of scores is in the form of a normal probability distribution.) The standard-score technique, it is clear, facilitates comparison of the performances of different individuals on the same test. (See Box 18.)

BOX 1 8

A Behavioral Scientist Does It Himself

It should be called to the student's attention that it is not a perfectly obvious idea that a subject's performance should be measured in terms of the variability of the distribution. In order to appreciate the importance of this idea, let the student imagine himself dealing with the problem Galton faced in about 1875. He was deeply involved and concerned with the problem of trying to discover the general laws of inheritance. The specific issue he was attempting to cope with was whether it was indeed true, as some of his contemporaries were asserting, that bodily measurements such as arm length, foot length, weight, etc., are independent of one another. The prime difficulty in settling this matter was that any measure yet devised of the relation between two variables was affected by the units in which the variables themselves were measured. According to Galton's student, Karl Pearson, an eminent scientist in his own right, "It was not till more than 13 years after his first attack on the subject that Galton realized . . . (that each character) should be measured in its own variability as a unit."

We can see how much the discovery of this important concept meant to Galton, for he later described the moment of insight. In his own words: "As these lines are being written, the circumstances under which I first clearly grasped the important generalization that the laws of heredity were solely concerned with deviations expressed in statistical units, are vividly recalled to my memory. It was in the grounds of Naworth Castle, where an invitation had been given to ramble freely. A temporary shower drove me to seek refuge in a reddish recess in the rock by the side of the pathway. There the idea flashed across me, and I forgot everything else for a moment in my great delight." Galton had hit upon a way to make measurements that were independent of the original units in which the measures were taken.

Note further that Galton's solution to his problem provides one of the first examples of a behavioral scientist clearly recognizing the need for a statistical concept and then inventing it. In the next chapter we shall see how Galton went on from this point to invent the concept of "correlation," which depends almost entirely upon grasping the idea of making measurements in terms of "deviations (from the mean) expressed in statistical units."

Pearson, K. 1930. *The life, letters and labours of Francis Galton.* V. III A. Cambridge: Cambridge University Press.
Galton, F. 1908. *Memories of my life.* London: Methuen.

The standard-score technique also makes it possible to compare the performance of the same individual on different tests (as does the percentile-score method). If John reports that he has scores of 82 on a spelling test, 35 on an arithmetic test, and 47 on a geography test, it is impossible for us to evaluate his performance. If, however, he reports z-scores of -1.00 on the spelling test, $+.75$ on the arithmetic test, and $+1.96$ on the geography test, his performance on the three tests becomes obvious —spelling certainly needs more attention than does geography.

It is apparent that although the z-scores convey their meanings quite clearly, the fact that they provide a set of scores that runs from a negative number through zero to a positive number is a disadvantage. One has to deal with a set of numbers half of which will be negative and half positive. Moreover, a large portion of the numbers will be decimals between $+1.00$ and -1.00; such numbers are somewhat awkward to deal with, and laymen are likely to be dubious of the worth of a score of 0, no matter how often they are told that it was the average score on the test. For these reasons, z-scores are often transformed into "standard scores."

Standard scores

Standard scores are derived from z-scores in the following way. First a convenient mean, say, $\bar{Y} = 50$, and a convenient standard deviation, say $s_Y = 10$, are chosen. The scores are then transformed by the equation

$$\frac{X - \bar{X}}{s_X} = \frac{Y - \bar{Y}}{s_Y}$$

in which the original data are indicated by X and the new standard scores by Y. Thus, if the original mean was $\bar{X} = 25$, and the original standard deviation was $s_X = 5$, we would have

$$\frac{X - \bar{X}}{s_X} = \frac{Y - \bar{Y}}{s_Y}$$
$$\frac{X - 25}{5} = \frac{Y - 50}{10}$$

Then, for any given score in X we solve for its corresponding value in the new standard-score scale, Y. In the above case, a raw score of 35 would be transformed as follows:

$$\frac{X - \bar{X}}{s_X} = \frac{Y - \bar{Y}}{s_Y}$$

$$\frac{35 - 25}{5} = \frac{Y - 50}{10}$$

$$\frac{10}{5} = \frac{Y - 50}{10}$$

$$2 = \frac{Y - 50}{10}$$

$$20 + 50 = Y$$

$$Y = 70$$

Note very carefully the fact that the original score (35) in X was exactly two standard deviations above the mean of the X scores, and that the corresponding score (70) in Y is also exactly two standard deviations above the mean of the Y scores. In short, this transformation *maintains the same relative position of every score in the distribution*. Thus, standard scores have the virtue of maintaining the properties of the original distribution, while transforming the original numbers into more convenient forms. Many test manuals provide a table of original scores transformed into standard scores as a result of the test being administered to certain groups.

By way of caution

In our discussion of requirements (page 149) we noted that standard reference points should be stable as well as meaningful to the layman. And, although we have discussed the problem of meaningfulness, we have deferred the discussion of stability to this point so that the student could understand the problem of stability in light of the methods employed to construct standard reference points. It will now be apparent, for example, that the reference points (such as percentile scores, z-scores, and so on) employed in connection with psychological tests are always expressed *in relation to some distribution of test scores*. Now, since these test scores must, of course, be produced by the subjects taking the tests, any set of reference points will always be relative to a specific group of subjects. As a result, the specific reference system (such as the set of raw scores equivalent to a set of percentile scores) may change if the *reference group* changes.

Consider the following example. Suppose an intelligence test is administered on a nation-wide basis, and that the mean raw score on the test is 213. Suppose further that this mean score is set equivalent to a standard score of 100. Now imagine that the same test is given 10 years later, and the mean score is now 221: even though the new mean is also set at a standard score of 100, the reference system is now relative to a new group. A test score made by any individual now taking the test must be expressed relative to one reference group or the other, and it must be made perfectly clear which reference group is being used.

The above example is perfectly clear and easy, because only two reference groups are involved. Unhappily, the actual situation is far from being so simple, for there are *many* intelligence tests, and many other psychological tests as well. There are hundreds of reference groups being used every day. "To range men according to their natural abilities" has become commonplace. Therefore, the student must be aware of the fact that, although the *methods* for constructing standard reference points are uniform, the actual reference points used to compare the performance of persons taking tests are so varied that the essence of standardization—stability of referent—so nicely illustrated by the standard referent for length (a bar in a glass case at a specified temperature) is virtually nonexistent in the measurements of the behavioral sciences.

⟨ Mathematically . . .

INDIVIDUAL PERFORMANCE AS MEASURED BY PERCENTILES

The mathematical model by which percentile scores are defined and computed is a scale or grid against which an individual performance may be viewed in comparison with others. This scale or grid consists of 100 intervals of equal length, and these are numbered from 0 to 99, inclusive. If a given datum exceeds 27 per cent of all the data, then the percentile score for that datum is 27, and it is said to be at the twenty-seventh percentile. A datum which exceeds 89 per cent of all the data is said to be at the eighty-ninth percentile. It is clear that every datum will exceed some percentage (from 0 to 99 per cent, inclusive) of the whole set of data of which it is a part. Whatever percentage this is, the percentile score is obtained by simply dropping the percentage sign and rounding off the result to the next smaller whole number.

The following example is based on a test given to 340 high school seniors. The test consists of 120 questions, some of which are quite easy and some of which are extremely difficult. The lowest score obtained by any of the 340 students is 27, and the highest is 103. What will be the percentile score (or rank) of a student who has 85 correct answers and who has thereby equaled or excelled 263 of his classmates? The answer is obtained by dividing 263 by 340, the result of .774 indicating that 263 is 77.4 per cent of 340. The student with 85 correct answers is then said to be *at the seventy-seventh percentile.*

Note that the fraction .4 is dropped in the process of rounding 77.4 off to the next smaller whole number. All percentages above 77.0 per cent and not more than 78.0 per cent correspond to the seventy-seventh percentile. This rule occasionally requires that a whole unit be rounded off. For example, a student who exceeds eighty-five students in the above example exceeds exactly 25.0 per cent of his classmates; it is necessary to round this percentage off to 24 to obtain the percentile rank of the student.

The preceding example contains a variety of information which is not used in computing the percentile scores for given students. Note, for example, that the high score and the low score played no part in the computation. Neither did the number of questions asked or the number answered appear in the calculations. It was necessary to know only two things to accomplish a given calculation: How many students took the test and how many had scores no larger than the one for which the computation was being made.

The seventy-seventh-percentile score computed for the student above measures his performance by dividing the class of 340 into two parts, the lower of which he leads; that is, the whole group is divided into the lower 77 per cent and the upper 23 per cent. The value assigned to the performance is the size of the lower group measured in percentage points.

Since 1 per cent of 340 is 3.4, the three lowest scores will be assigned to the zeroth percentile even though their scores (27 and higher) were not 0. This is because the new units are "per cent of actual participants excelled in the test." Even though the class leader scored only 103 out of 120 (86 per cent), the score 103 is assigned to the ninty-ninth percentile. Note that no score can be assigned to the one-hundredth percentile, since no member of any group may exceed everyone (including himself) in the group.

The scale of percentiles has a fixed minimum (0) and a fixed maximum (99). The scale advances in units of 1 and thus divides the scale into 100 apparently equal parts. Since all measurements are rounded off by dropping to the largest whole per cent below the actual calculation, there are exactly 100 points on which a measurement, or score, may fall. These are only *apparently* equal subdivisions, however, because it may be much harder to move from the eighty-fifth to the eighty-sixth percentile than it is to move from the twenty-first to the twenty-second. The fiftieth percentile is not to be thought of as representing a performance that is twice as good as that ranked at the twenty-fifth percentile; one may exceed hundreds of scores by a small margin and thus gain a high percentile rank with only a small superiority of performance.

In many practical applications it is desired to have a list of numbers to which test scores may be directly compared in order to obtain the percentile rank for a given score. To see how this may be done, suppose that the number of data being studied is n and that these n data are X_1, X_2, . . . , X_n. Let it be assumed that the X's are arranged in order from small to large, X_1 being the smallest and X_n the largest.

Before going further, it is convenient to give meaning to a fractional subscript. The number $X_{14.6}$ is understood to be the number which lies 6 tenths of the way from X_{14} to X_{15}. In general, X_{m+f}, where m is the whole part and f is the fractional part, denotes a number between X_m and X_{m+1}. The fractional part, f, gives the fractional part of $X_{m+1} - X_m$ (the distance from X_m to X_{m+1}) which must be added to X_m to obtain X_{m+f}.

With the above meaning attached to fractional subscripts, the number which separates the X's in the kth percentile from those at the $(k-1)$th percentile is

$$(1) \qquad p_k = X_{\frac{k}{100}n + \frac{1}{2}}$$

The division by 100 is to convert k to a proportion. Thus $\frac{k}{100}n$ represents a proportion of n. The $\frac{1}{2}$ is added on so that the subscript will lie midway between k per cent and $k+1$ per cent of n. The quantity $\frac{k}{100}n + \frac{1}{2}$ will have a whole part and a fractional part—say, m and f, respectively. Then (1) becomes

$$(2) \qquad \begin{aligned} p_k &= X_{m+f} \\ &= X_m + f(X_{m+1} - X_m) \\ &= (1-f)X_m + fX_{m+1} \end{aligned}$$

which is the formula sought.

It will be noticed that if $k = 50$, formula (2) produces the median which is another name for the fiftieth percentile point. If k is 25, the result, p_{25}, is called the "first quartile," the median is the "second quartile," and p_{75} is the "third quartile." If k is a multiple of 10, p_k is said to be a "decile point"; thus, p_{70} is the "seventh decile point."

As an illustration of formula (2) suppose that n is 86 and that p_{34} is required. Formula (1) gives

$$p_{34} = X_{\frac{34}{100}(86) + .5}$$

$$= X_{29.74}$$

$$= .26X_{29} + .74X_{30}$$

If $X_{30} = 75$ and $X_{29} = 71$, then

$$p_{34} = .26(71) + .74(75)$$

$$= 18.46 + 55.50$$

$$= 73.96.$$

As an extended example of computing percentiles, all percentile points for the data of Table 27 are given in Table 29 (number of data, $n = 144$), while Table 28 gives the details of computation for selected values of k between 1 and 99 inclusive.

TABLE 27

144 Test Scores Arranged from Small to Large

38	52	60	65	70	75	79	85	92
38	52	60	66	71	75	79	85	93
40	52	61	66	71	75	79	85	93
42	53	61	66	71	75	80	85	94
42	53	61	66	71	75	81	86	95
45	53	61	66	71	75	81	86	96
46	53	61	66	71	76	81	86	96
47	56	62	67	72	76	82	87	99
47	57	62	67	72	76	82	88	99
48	58	62	68	72	77	82	89	100
49	58	63	68	73	77	82	89	101
49	58	63	68	73	77	83	89	101
49	58	64	70	73	78	83	89	105
51	59	65	70	74	78	83	89	106
51	59	65	70	74	78	84	91	106
51	59	65	70	75	78	84	92	110

TABLE 28

Calculations for Selected Percentiles for the Data of Table 27

k	$\frac{k}{100}(144) + \frac{1}{2}$	m	f	X_m	X_{m+1}	$p_k = (1 - f)X_m + fX_{m+1}$
2	3.38	3	.38	40	42	40.76
5	7.70	7	.70	46	47	46.70
36	52.34	52	.34	66	66	66.00
97	140.18	140	.18	101	105	101.72
99	143.06	143	.06	106	110	106.24

TABLE 29

First to Ninety-ninth Percentile Points for the Data of Table 27

	0	1	2	3	4	5	6	7	8	9
0		38.00	40.76	42.00	45.26	46.70	47.14	48.58	49.00	49.92
10	51.00	51.34	52.00	52.22	53.00	53.00	54.62	56.98	58.00	58.00
20	58.30	59.00	59.18	60.00	61.00	61.00	61.00	61.38	62.00	62.26
30	63.00	64.14	65.00	65.00	65.46	66.00	66.00	66.00	67.00	67.00
40	68.00	68.00	69.96	70.00	70.00	70.30	71.00	71.00	71.00	71.06
50	72.00	72.00	73.00	73.00	74.00	74.70	75.00	75.00	75.00	75.00
60	75.90	76.00	76.78	77.00	77.66	78.00	78.00	78.98	79.00	79.86
70	81.00	81.00	82.00	82.00	82.06	83.00	83.00	84.00	84.82	85.00
80	85.00	86.00	86.00	87.02	88.46	89.00	89.00	89.00	91.22	92.00
90	93.00	93.54	94.98	96.00	98.58	99.30	100.74	101.72	105.62	106.24

INDIVIDUAL PERFORMANCE AS MEASURED BY z-SCORES

Just as the set of percentile points from zero[th] to ninety-ninth form a grid or scale against which individual performance may be gauged, so also can a measuring scale be devised based on the mean and standard deviation of a distribution of data. The mean provides a reference point, and the standard deviation, being a measure of variability, provides the unit whereby variation between individual data can be measured.

The z-score corresponding to a given datum (often called a "raw score") is the deviation of that datum from the mean expressed in terms of the standard deviation. In symbols, the score z_i corresponding to the datum X_i is given by

$$z_i = \frac{X_i - \bar{X}}{s}$$

To illustrate this formula, suppose that $X = 6$ is a datum in a set of data whose mean is $\bar{X} = 10$ and whose standard deviation is $s = 2$.

Then

$$z = \frac{6 - 10}{2} = -2.$$

This means that 6 lies two standard deviations to the left of (less than) the mean. If the data happen to be normally distributed, the score $z = -2$ also conveys the information that approximately 97.5 per cent of the data exceed the datum 6.

Even if the data are not normally distributed, the z-scores provide a basis for comparison, because they are based on a fixed reference point and a fixed unit. The z-score corresponding to the mean is

$$z = \frac{\bar{X} - \bar{X}}{s} = 0$$

Data less than the mean have negative z-scores, and those greater than the mean have positive z-scores.

TABLE 30

Computation of z-scores for Selected Data from Table 27

X	$X - 71.99$	$z = \dfrac{X - 71.99}{15.72}$
38	−33.99	−2.16
40	−31.99	−2.03
42	−29.99	−1.91
71	−.99	−.06
72	.01	0
73	1.01	.06
99	27.01	1.72
100	28.01	1.78
110	38.01	2.42

TABLE 31

All z-scores for the Data of Table 27

−2.16	−1.27	−.76	−.44	−.13	.19	.45	.83	1.27
−2.16	−1.27	−.76	−.38	−.06	.19	.45	.83	1.34
−2.03	−1.27	−.70	−.38	−.06	.19	.45	.83	1.34
−1.91	−1.21	−.70	−.38	−.06	.19	.51	.83	1.40
−1.91	−1.21	−.70	−.38	−.06	.19	.57	.89	1.46
−1.72	−1.21	−.70	−.38	−.06	.19	.57	.89	1.53
−1.65	−1.21	−.70	−.32	−.06	.26	.57	.89	1.53
−1.59	−1.02	−.64	−.32	0	.26	.64	.95	1.72
−1.59	−.95	−.64	−.32	0	.26	.64	1.02	1.72
−1.53	−.89	−.64	−.25	0	.32	.64	1.08	1.78
−1.46	−.89	−.57	−.25	.06	.32	.64	1.08	1.85
−1.46	−.89	−.57	−.25	.06	.32	.70	1.08	1.85
−1.46	−.89	−.51	−.13	.06	.38	.70	1.08	2.10
−1.34	−.83	−.44	−.13	.13	.38	.70	1.08	2.16
−1.34	−.83	−.44	−.13	.13	.38	.76	1.21	2.16
−1.34	−.83	−.44	−.13	.19	.38	.76	1.27	2.42

Comparison of disparate data can be easily made using z-scores. Suppose that a student scores 86 in arithmetic ($\bar{X} = 75$, $s = 7.5$) and 62 in English ($\bar{X} = 55$, $s = 4$). His z-scores are

$$z_m = \frac{86 - 75}{7.5} = 1.47$$

$$z_e = \frac{62 - 55}{4} = 1.75$$

It is clear that the student is better in English than in mathematics, because he varies more from the mean in standardized units in English than he does in mathematics. The change in performance by a student taking different tests at different times in the same subject may be compared in the same way.

To illustrate on a larger scale the computation of z-scores, the data of Table 27 will be used. Table 30 shows the detailed computation for selected data, and Table 31 gives the results for all the data. The mean is 71.99 and s is 15.72 for the data of Table 27.

An inspection of Table 31 shows that equal data in Table 27 have equal z-scores. The scores in this case range from -2.16 to $+2.42$. Each of these scores shows how many standard deviations separate the corresponding datum from the mean of the distribution. The scores of 72 are so close to the mean 71.99 that the corresponding z-scores are, to two decimal places, equal to 0.

The conversion of X-scores into z-scores consists of subtracting $\bar{X}$ from each X and of dividing the result of this subtraction by s. The result is that the mean of the z's is $\bar{X}$ less than that of the X's, and the standard deviation of the z's is $1/s$ times that of the X's; that is, the z-scores have a mean of 0 and their standard deviation is 1.

STANDARD SCORES OF INDIVIDUAL PERFORMANCE

Standard scores have a chosen mean of $\bar{Y}$ and a chosen standard deviation of s_Y. If a set of standard scores is desired instead of z-scores, the basic formula for the transformation is

$$\frac{X - \bar{X}}{s_X} = \frac{Y - \bar{Y}}{s_Y}$$

If both sides of this formula are multiplied by s_Y, the result is

$$\frac{s_Y}{s_X}(X - \bar{X}) = Y - \bar{Y}$$

Now when $\bar{Y}$ is added to both sides of this result, a convenient formula for computing standard scores emerges:

$$Y = \frac{s_Y}{s_X}(X - \bar{X}) + \bar{Y}$$

The numbers $\bar{Y}$ and s_Y can be any numbers one cares to use (except, of course, that s_Y must be positive). This formula produces for each raw score X a new score Y. These new scores will have exactly the mean $\bar{Y}$ and standard deviation s_Y chosen for them in advance. To see that this is the case, it is necessary to recall some of the properties previously proved for the mean and the standard deviation. These are repeated here for ready reference in the analysis of the formula:

(1) Multiplying each datum by a constant multiplies the mean by the same constant.

(2) Adding a constant to each datum adds the same constant to the mean.

(3) Multiplying each datum by a constant multiplies the standard deviation by the same constant.

(4) Adding a constant to each datum leaves the standard deviation unchanged.

The mean of the X's is $\bar{X}$. By (2), the numbers $(X - \bar{X})$ have 0 as their mean. The numbers $\frac{s_Y}{s_X}(X - \bar{X})$ have 0 as their mean by (1) and the fact that $\frac{s_Y}{s_X}$ is a constant. Adding $\bar{Y}$ to each of these numbers gives $\frac{s_Y}{s_X}(X - \bar{X}) + Y$, which, by (2), have $0 + \bar{Y} = \bar{Y}$ as their mean. But this manipulation of X has produced exactly the standard score, Y. To see that the Y's have s_Y as their standard deviation, note that by (4) the numbers $(X - \bar{X})$ have the same standard deviation, s_X, as do the X's. By (3), the factor $\frac{s_Y}{s_X}$ multiplies the standard deviation s_X by $\frac{s_Y}{s_X}$, giving s_Y as the standard deviation of the numbers $\frac{s_Y}{s_X}(X - \bar{X})$. Adding $\bar{Y}$ to these numbers completes the transformation of X into Y but has no effect in the standard deviation according to (4); hence, it remains s_Y. This concludes the demonstration that the X-scores with mean $\bar{X}$ and standard deviation s_X have been transformed into a set of standard scores, Y, with mean $\bar{Y}$ and standard deviation s_Y. (Standard scores are usually expressed in terms of letters appropriate to a given technique—T-scores, and the like. We shall use upper-case Y.)

If X is a raw score and Y is the corresponding standard score, then the z-score corresponding to X is

$$z_1 = \frac{X - \bar{X}}{s_X}$$

and the z-score corresponding to Y is

$$z_2 = \frac{Y - \bar{Y}}{s_Y}$$

Substituting for Y in terms of X as given in the formula for standard scores, the result is

$$z_2 = \frac{\dfrac{s_Y}{s_X}(X - \bar{X}) + \bar{Y} - \bar{Y}}{s_Y}$$

$$= \frac{X - \bar{X}}{s_X}$$

$$= z_1$$

These calculations show that the z-scores of the raw scores and the z-scores of the standard scores are identical. It is therefore possible to use the formula

$$Y = s_Y z + \bar{Y}$$

to compute standard scores from z-scores. This formula is obtained by solving $z = \dfrac{Y - \bar{Y}}{s_Y}$ for Y.

To illustrate

To convert the raw scores of Table 27 to standard scores, it is first necessary to choose a mean and standard deviation. Let $\bar{Y} = 50$ and $s_Y = 10$. Then, since $\bar{X} = 71.99$ and $s_X = 15.72$, the conversion formula is

$$Y = \frac{10}{15.72}(X - 71.99) + 50$$

Applying this formula to $X = 85$ gives

$$Y = \frac{10}{15.72}(85 - 71.99) + 50$$
$$= 58.28$$

If the z-score for this standard score is computed by the formula

$$z = \frac{Y - \bar{Y}}{s_Y}$$

the result is

$$z = \frac{58.28 - 50}{10}$$
$$= .83$$

This is also the z-score corresponding to the raw score $X = 85$. What is illustrated here is the fact that

$$\frac{X - \bar{X}}{s_X} = \frac{Y - \bar{Y}}{s_Y}$$

for all X and all Y. In fact, the formula for computing standard scores is obtained by multiplying both members above by s_Y and then adding $\bar{Y}$ to both members. This leaves Y isolated on the right and the proper expression for Y in terms of X on the left.

The computations for changing the data of Table 27 into standard scores having a mean of 75 and a standard deviation of 8 are illustrated in Table 32. The fact that the mean and standard deviation for the standard

TABLE 32

The Conversion of Selected Data from Table 27 into
Standard Scores Having $\bar{Y} = 75$ and $s_Y = 8$

X	$(X - 71.99)$	$\frac{8}{15.72}(X - 71.99)$	$Y = \frac{8}{15.72}(X - 71.99) + 75$
38	−33.99	−17.30	57.70
50	−21.99	−11.19	63.81
70	−1.99	−1.01	73.99
75	3.01	1.53	76.53
100	28.01	14.25	89.25
110	38.01	19.34	94.34

scores can be chosen at will makes it possible to choose the range over which the Y scores are to run. Suppose, for example, that one wishes to transform the lowest score of Table 27 into 0 and the highest into 100, the other scores assuming appropriate values between 0 and 100. This means that one must have

$$0 = \frac{s_Y}{15.72}(38 - 71.99) + \bar{Y}$$

and

$$100 = \frac{s_Y}{15.72}(110 - 71.99) + \bar{Y}$$

since the lowest and highest X-scores are 38 and 110, respectively. Simplifying these equations by multiplying both sides by 15.72 and performing the indicated subtractions gives

$$0 = -33.99s_Y + 15.72\bar{Y}$$
$$1{,}572 = 38.01s_Y + 15.72\bar{Y}$$

Subtracting corresponding members of the first equation from those of the second gives

$$1{,}572 = 72s_Y$$

and

$$s_Y = \frac{1{,}572}{72} = 21.83$$

Substituting this value into the first equation above gives

$$0 = -33.99(21.83) + 15.72\bar{Y}$$

from which it is apparent that

$$\bar{Y} = \frac{(33.99)(21.83)}{15.72} = 47.06$$

Hence, if standard scores for the data of Table 27 are computed using $s_Y = 21.83$ and $\bar{Y} = 47.06$, then these standard scores will range from 0 to 100 exactly.

Suggestions for Further Reading

ANASTASI, A. 1961. *Psychological testing*, (2nd ed.). New York: Macmillan.

CRONBACH, L. 1960. *Essentials of psychological testing*, (2nd ed.). New York: Harper.

NUNNALLY, J. 1959. *Tests and measurements*. New York: McGraw-Hill.
    All three of the above are general texts concerning problems of psychological testing. And all three carry discussions of percentiles and standard scores.

PROBLEMS

1. The keeping of time records for various racing events is a fairly recent development in sporting history. Write a short paragraph explaining the connection between such records and the problem of relative and absolute standards. Have such records had an effect on athletic performance?

2. Which, if any, of the following are measured against a standard having an absolute zero? (a) altitude (on the earth), (b) velocity, (c) humidity, (d) half life (of radioactive substances), (e) excellence (academically).

3. In a group of 300 students the highest test score was 186 and the second highest 152. In converting these scores to percentile scores, it is found that both are in the ninety-ninth percentile. What property of the percentile scoring scale causes these quite different scores to be given the same percentile score?

4. Which of the statements below is true and which is false? Explain your choice in a few sentences.
    (a) If percentile scores can be computed, then so also can z-scores.
    (b) If z-scores can be computed, then so also can percentile scores.

5. (a) Is it possible that a test score can be in the sixtieth percentile and yet be less than the mean test score? Explain your answer.
    (b) Repeat (a) with "mean" replaced by "median."
    (c) Repeat (a) with "less than" replaced by "greater than."
    (d) Repeat (b) with "less than" replaced by "more than."

6. (a) Devise a set of fifty scores which will exemplify the property stated in problem 5(a).

   (b) Repeat (a) for the property stated in problem 5(c).

7. If a grade of 56 per cent on a test is found to be in the eighty-third percentile, what conclusion concerning the test may reasonably be drawn? What if, instead, a grade of 86 per cent is found to be in the twentieth percentile?

8. Under what circumstances would you expect to get a grade of C for a zero score?

9. The use of percentiles and standard scores to compare individual performances rests to a large extent on the stability of the reference points in these scales. What means are used to obtain adequate stability of these reference points?

10. Suppose it is known that the scores for a certain test are normally distributed with mean 60 and standard deviation 8.

    (a) If your z-score is .72, what is your percentile rank?

    (b) What information given above is not required for the solution of (a)?

11. The z-score is a special case of the standard score. What values chosen for $\bar{Y}$ amd s_Y will produce standard scores identical with the z-scores?

12. If $X_{21} = 39$ and $X_{22} = 42$, what is the value of each of the following? (a) $X_{21.42+.5}$, (b) $X_{21.42}$, (c) $X_{43/2}$.

13. What is the percentile rank of the following scores in Table 20 (page 116)? (a) 75, (b) 81, (c) 98, (d) 103.

14. Use the data of Table 20 to make a table of decile points like that in the first column of Table 29.

15. Compute z-scores for the scores in the first row of Table 27. Use the mean and standard deviation as given in the text for these data.

16. Achievement tests in English, mathematics, and social studies were given to a large class of high school seniors, with the following results.

	ENGLISH	MATHEMATICS	SOCIAL STUDIES
$\bar{X}$	82.35	77.84	86.72
s	6.57	8.78	5.69

(a) In what subjects does a student do best if he receives grades of 82 in English, 74 in mathematics, and 83 in social studies?

(b) What are the z-scores of a student who scores 84 on all three tests?

17. If the data of Table 27 are converted to standard scores having mean 50 and standard deviation 25, what will be the standard scores corresponding to the data in the last row of the table?

18. Using as data only the first three columns of Table 27, convert these scores into standard scores having mean 70 and standard deviation 10.

19. Suppose that the scores in the first two columns of Table 27 represent the raw scores of a certain test. It is desired to convert these scores into standard scores the lowest of which is to be 50 and the highest of which is to be 99. What mean and what standard deviation should be chosen to achieve this range in the standard score distribution?

20. Repeat problem 19 using 0 for the lowest standard score and 49 for the highest standard score.

Consistence, thou art a jewel.

ANON.

C H A P T E R

6

CORRELATION

DESCRIBING the relation between two variables has always been one of the fundamental tasks of the scientist. The scientific stature of the physical sciences rests on the fact that interrelations among a large number of variables have been described with an impressive degree of exactness, and the main task which challenges the behavioral scientist is that of describing the interrelations among the significant features of the behavior of animals and men. The invention of the *correlation coefficient* has played a highly important role in the search for these interrelations. The correlation coefficient is a statistical measure which describes the *degree* of relation between two (or more) variables. Until the correlation coefficient became available, scientists had no convenient way of describing the amount of relation between two variables. (See Box 19.)

THE NEED FOR A MEASURE OF RELATION

For centuries there has been no difficulty in describing the relation between two variables, provided the relation is exact; a mathematical formula or equation may be devised to represent relations among variables (for example, $A = \pi r^2$ representing the relation between area and radius). Such a formula will permit the values in one variable to be calculated from given values of the other variable. The precise formulas of physics furnish the prime scientific examples of the use of such equations (one of which is provided in Figure 15. Note that each point represents two values.)

However, the variability encountered in most studies by biological and behavioral scientists makes such *perfect* relations extremely rare. The

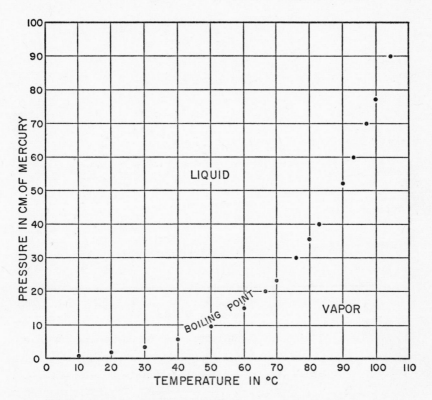

FIG. 15. A graph of the boiling point for water. Adapted from *Elements of physics: for students of science and engineering,* 1st Edition, by George Shortly & Dudley Williams. Copyright 1953 by Prentice-Hall, Inc., Englewood Cliffs, N.J.

consistence provided by such perfect relations is "a jewel" seldom found. And therein lies the need for a quantitative measure of the *degree* of relation between two variables.

The data in Figure 16 provide an example from the biological sciences of a relation between two variables which is far from exact. It is quite clear, for example, that the points in the graph in Figure 16 do not lie along a single line, as do the points in Figure 15, where individual points deviate from the line only because of lack of precision in taking the measurements. The data in Figure 16, on the other hand, deviate from the line which could possibly be drawn through them because of natural variability among living organisms. Achieving greater precision of measure-

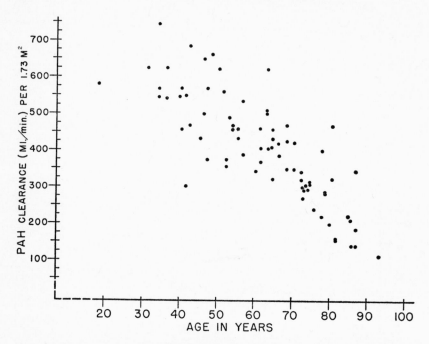

Fig. 16. This graph shows the relation between age and renal plasma flow (flow of blood through the kidney). Reprinted from *Physiological basis of medical practice,* 7th Edition, by Charles H. Best and Norman B. Taylor. Copyright 1961 by The Williams & Wilkins Company and reprinted with their permission.

ment will not result in all of the plotted points in Figure 16 falling exactly on any one line. A technique is needed, therefore, to describe such imperfect relations between variables as that represented in Figure 16.

Of course, variability makes itself felt in the relation between behavioral as well as biological variables. Note, for example, the variability present in the graph in Figure 17.

Assume for the moment that no procedure exists for measuring the degree of relation between two variables, and compare Figures 16 and 17. In which graph is there a greater amount of relation between the variables? Clearly a technique which would permit the precise quantification of the degree of relation in each set of data is necessary in order to compare them with confidence. In short, not only does a measure of the degree of relation between two variables quantify what otherwise must be left to subjective appraisal, but such quantification permits the *comparison* of the strength of one relation with that of another. Are the abilities of children more

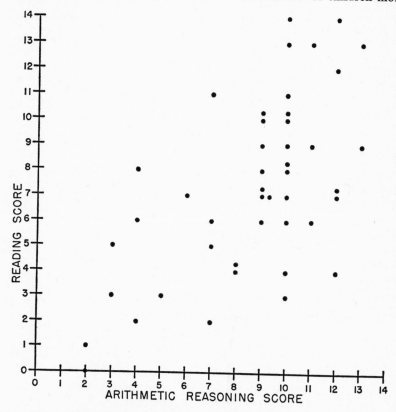

FIG. 17. This graph shows a relation between two sets of test scores.

closely related to the abilities of their mothers or those of their fathers? Is ability more closely related to heredity or to environment? Are political attitudes more highly related to income than they are to amount of education? Questions such as these touch only a tiny fraction of the widespread areas which have need for a quantitative measure of the degree of association, but they illustrate how such a measure helps increase our understanding of behavior.

One further point. As indicated earlier, mathematical formulas or equations make it possible to calculate the values in one variable from given values in the other: thus, the area of a circle may be calculated from a knowledge of its radius, or—in the case of the example in Figure 15—the pressure of boiling water can be calculated from a knowledge of its temperature. Another way of putting this is to say that the pressure of boiling water can be *predicted* from its temperature. The important point

---

BOX 19
The Invention of the Correlation Coefficient

There are two reasons for calling the student's attention to Sir Francis Galton's invention of the correlation coefficient. First, this invention (about 1875) opened up vast new possibilities for research in biology, psychology, anthropology, sociology and education. Second, the story of the invention provides a nice illustration of a scientist perceiving the needs and requirements for a statistical technique, taking the first steps toward developing it, and then having the logic of his idea checked by mathematicians.

It is difficult to imagine what modern behavioral science would be like without the correlation coefficient. The possibility of expressing a degree of relationship among variables profoundly changed not only our conception of what could be studied, but even our ideas of causality—or at least so argues

Karl Pearson. He says that Galton reasoned as follows: "A is not the sole cause of B, but it contributes to the production of B; there may be other, many or few, causes at work, some of which we do not know and may never know. Are we then to exclude from mathematical analysis all such cases of incomplete causation?" Galton's answer was: "No, we must endeavor to find a quantitative measure of this degree of partial causation . . ." Pearson makes the further astute observation that the physicist was "clearly picking out a few of the more important causes . . . and wisely concentrating on these . . . ;" but "the physicist's method of describing phenomena was seen to be fitting only when a high degree of correlation existed." Once the notion of partial causation was accepted, and a quantitative measure of it was developed,

---

here is that behavioral scientists need to make predictions of this sort also. For example, the ability to predict the performance of individuals in school and in various occupations is so important as to obviate discussion. Equally important is the ability to predict the results of laboratory experiments which relate one variable to another, for one of the essential ways to test a scientific theory is to check the accuracy of the predictions made from it. And we shall see that predictions like those indicated above (wherein the values of one variable may be calculated from given values of the other variable) may be made from a quantitative measure of their relationship. In short, such a measure is highly important in the scientific task of prediction.

---

then "Biological phenomena in their numerous phases, economic and social, were seen to be only differentiated from the physical by the intensity of their correlations. The idea Galton placed before himself was to represent by a single numerical quantity the degree of relationships, or of partial causality between the different variables of our ever-changing universe." Thus does Karl Pearson, Galton's student, describe Galton's perception of the needs and requirements for a measure of the degree of relationship between variables.

Once Galton had clearly grasped the nature of his problem and taken some steps toward the solution of it, the mathematical reformulation of his problem and its solution (both provided by the mathematician Dickson) was straightforward. And, once the correlation coefficient was developed in good mathematical form, many interesting and rewarding derivations and elaborations were made from it—which in turn led to the investigations of new problems.

Before leaving this point, the student should have a glimpse of the awe with which Galton greets the work of his friend Dickson whom he asked to verify his hunch about the solution of his problem: "The problem may not be difficult to an accomplished mathematician, but I certainly never felt such a glow of loyalty and respect towards the sovereignty and wide sway of mathematical analysis as when his answer arrived, confirming, by purely mathematical reasoning, my various and laborious statistical conclusions with far more minuteness than I had dared to hope, because the data ran somewhat roughly, and I had to smooth them with tender caution."

Pearson, Karl. 1940. *The life, letters, and labours of Francis Galton.* V. IIIA. Cambridge: Cambridge University Press.
Galton, F. 1894. *Natural inheritance.* New York: Macmillan.

THE REQUIREMENTS

A good measure of the degree of association should meet the following general requirements, each of which will be discussed in detail below.

1. It should be independent of the specific units of measurement employed to measure the variables being related; it should be a *general* measure.

2. It should not be restricted to a single type of measurement but should have a wide applicability encompassing as many kinds of measurement as possible.
3. It should have fixed reference points; that is, it should have upper and lower bounds indicating the extremes of little or strong association between the variables.
4. It should be independent of the size of the sample studied so that its value will not change merely by changing the size of the sample.
5. It should be convenient for making predictions.
6. It should have a mathematical form which lends itself well to further elaboration and analysis aimed at making its interpretation precise and uniformly understood by a large variety of users.
7. Its size should depend solely on the extent to which two sets of data are related.

Independence of specific units of measurement

The first of the above requirements can best be justified by considering measures that fail to meet the requirement. If a measure of association had to be expressed in terms in which the original measurements were taken, it would have to be stated whether length measurements were taken in inches, feet, meters, or some other unit, since the result would be in terms of some specific unit. Separate formulas would be required for different combinations of measurements such as weight and density, reading speed and I.Q., and countless others. All these disparities of measurement methods and units can be resolved by the use of a measure having no units of *any* kind associated with it.

Application to various types of measurement

This requirement needs no elaboration at this point, for all statistical procedures should be widely applicable. We shall have more to say about various methods of measuring degrees of association and their relation to types of measuring scales—nominal, ordinal, and so on—when we discuss specific methods.

Fixed reference points

Because it is plain that two factors, or variables, can be either *completely, perfectly* associated (as illustrated in the example of pressure and temperature in Figure 15) or may have *no relationship* whatever, these two conditions suggest themselves as fixed reference points. The situation is similar to that of percentages, which are easily interpreted and compared because 0 and 100 mark off the extremes of none or all. Just as a percentage between 0 and 100 may be interpreted according to its distance from these extremes, so also should our measure of association have such reference points for easy interpretation. Put more exactly, because the upper and lower limits of association can be precisely described and defined, inter-pretation of a measure of association will be simplified if fixed values are assigned to these limiting conditions.

Independence of sample size

This requirement also is necessary for ease of interpretation. If sample size affects the measurement value, then different sizes of samples could produce differing values for a given degree of association and the problem of comparing the results of two experiments would then be greatly com-plicated. Samples of equal size are often difficult and sometimes impossible to obtain, but by minimizing the effect of sample size the measure will depend more on the degree of relation that exists and less on unavoidable inequalities. Any statistic whose value can be manipulated up or down by varying the sample size becomes more an index of the availability of sub-jects than a measure of the phenomenon being studied.

Convenience in making predictions

This requirement arises from the fact that a knowledge of the be-havior of one variable, together with knowledge of how it is related to a second variable, makes it possible to predict, at least to some extent, how the second variable will behave. For example, since there is a fairly strong association between changes in barometric pressure and rainfall, by study-ing the changing pressure it is possible to predict with considerable con-fidence the outlook for rain; this is one of the important uses of such measures. The measure to be developed should thus be purely quantitative, so that it may become a part of a prediction equation.

Mathematical form

Every statistical formula of fundamental importance becomes itself an object of study. The degree of confidence that can be placed in it under various circumstances must be discovered, and relationships between one statistical formula and others must be investigated. If a measure of asso-ciation is to be maximally useful, it must have a mathematical form which lends itself easily to algebraic manipulation and elaboration. (It will be recalled that the same considerations led to the use of the squares of the deviations from the mean rather than the absolute values of deviations in the development of a measure of variability.)

Dependence on the relation between two variables

This requirement is the most important of all, since it describes the fundamental objective of the measure we seek: a means by which concomitant variation, the covariation of two variables, can be measured.

If two variables are so related that certain values of one variable are always or nearly always associated with corresponding values of the other, then the two variables are said to "vary concomitantly." It may be that the highest values of one variable correspond to the lowest values of the other, or that all the values of one variable are greater by some constant than the corresponding values of the other; both of these as well as many other situations would be cases of concomitant variation. A measure of the degree to which this concomitance or jointness of variation exists is the basic object of the present inquiry.

METHODS FOR MEASURING DEGREE OF RELATION

There are several measures called *correlation coefficients*. Some of these meet all, and most of them meet nearly all, of the seven requirements discussed above. Some correlation coefficients are particularly appropriate for interval data; others are designed for data scaled in other ways. Our discussion will be limited to two of the several coefficients of correlation: the *rank-order correlation coefficient and the Pearson product-moment correlation coefficient*. These two illustrate well the general principles of correlation measurement, and an understanding of them will illuminate the logic underlying more specialized correlation coefficients. (See references at the end of the chapter.) The rank-order correlation coefficient is appropriate for ordinally scaled data as well as for data taken from interval and ratio scales, while the Pearson product-moment correlation coefficient is appropriate for data taken either from an interval or a ratio scale. These are the most commonly used of all correlation coefficients, and each will be fully discussed here.

The letter r is generally used to denote a correlation coefficient. If it is necessary to distinguish between different coefficients, subscripts are used. The rank-order correlation coefficient, often referred to as "rank order r" may thus be denoted by r_r. The Pearson product-moment correlation coefficient is frequently called "Pearson r" and is denoted here by r_p if the context makes a subscript necessary.

Rank-order correlation

To see how the rank-order correlation coefficient meets the general requirements set forth above, consider the following typical example. The problem is to measure the degree of association between two variables— say, verbal reasoning (VR) and creativity (Cr). Fictitious data are presented in Table 33 below.

TABLE 33

The Organization of Rank-Order Data

(1)	(2)	(3)	(4)	(5)
			DIFFERENCES BETWEEN	
	RANK ON	RANK ON	RANKS	DIFFERENCES SQUARED
SUBJECT	VR TEST	CR TEST	d	d^2
A	5	6	+1	1
B	8	9	+1	1
C	2	1	−1	1
D	3	7	+4	16
E	7	5	−2	4
F	9	8	−1	1
G	1	2	+1	1
H	4	4	0	0
I	6	3	−3	9
				$\Sigma d^2 = \overline{34}$

In Table 33 the subject is identified in column (1), and his rank on each test is listed in columns (2) and (3). A subject's rank is assigned according to his performance on the test. The subject with the highest score is given rank 1, the subject with the second highest score is given rank 2, and so on. The difference between a subject's rank in the VR test and his rank in the Cr test is noted in column (4), and the square of each difference is in column (5).

The rank order-correlation coefficient is computed using the data in column (5) in relation to n. The formula is

(1) $$r_r = 1 - \frac{6\sum d^2}{n(n^2 - 1)}$$

The structure of the formula will be explained below, as it is tested against the seven requirements listed previously.

By substituting ranks for test scores, Requirement 1 (independence of specific units of measurement) is met. Note that when expressed in terms of ranks the relative standings of the nine subjects become independent of any system of units. The original units of measurement could have been pounds, inches, or any other ordered units.

Requirement 2 (application to various types of measurement) is quite adequately met by the above formula, since all except nominally scaled data may be transformed into ranks and thus made subject to the method.

The reason for the form of the formula, and the reason for the inclusion of the numbers 1 and 6, as well as *n*, is to satisfy Requirements 3 and 4 (fixed reference points and independence of sample size). In order to understand how the formula does satisfy these requirements, it is important to consider carefully columns (4) and (5) of Table 33. Columns (4) and (5) are of crucial importance, because they indicate the degree to which a subject's relative standing (rank) on one variable is matched with his relative standing (rank) on another. If, for example, each subject's rank on one variable were identical with his rank in the other, the relation would be termed a *perfect positive correlation*. In such a situation the difference column, (4), and the squared differences column, (5), would contain only zeros. Table 34 illustrates a situation in which two variables are perfectly, positively correlated. (Note the zeros in columns (4) and (5).)

TABLE 34

Perfect Positive Correlation

(1) SUBJECT	(2) RANK$_1$	(3) RANK$_2$	(4) d	(5) d^2
A	1	1	0	0
B	2	2	0	0
C	3	3	0	0
D	4	4	0	0
E	5	5	0	0
				$\Sigma d^2 = \overline{0}$

When a subject's relative performance on one test differs from that on the other, there will be a difference between his ranks on the two tests. As the discrepancy between the ranks of subjects *increases*, the correlation between the two variables is, of course, *decreased*. Table 35 illustrates a situation in which the correlation is less than perfect (in contrast to Table 34). Be certain to note in Table 35 how the differences, *d*, between ranks in column (4) lead to an increase in the sum of the squared differences between ranks in column (5) (in contrast to the zeros in column (5) of Table 34).

TABLE 35

Some (Almost) Uncorrelated Data

(1) SUBJECT	(2) RANK$_1$	(3) RANK$_2$	(4) d	(5) d^2
A	1	6	5	25
B	2	1	−1	1
C	3	2	−1	1
D	4	5	1	1
E	5	3	−2	4
F	6	4	−2	4
				$\Sigma d^2 = \overline{36}$

Table 34 illustrates how perfect positive correlation results in the sum of the squared differences being equal to zero, and Table 35 illustrates a situation in which two variables are uncorrelated—in fact, almost completely independent of one another—with a definite increase in the size of Σd^2.

We now turn to situations in which the ranks are *exactly* reversed. In such cases the relation between the two variables is termed a *perfect negative correlation*. Two variables may, of course, be negatively, or inversely, related. Time spent in extracurricular activities, for example, might be found to be negatively related to grade average; that is, the more time spent on extracurricular activities, the lower the grade average. Negative relationships occur fairly often in the biological and social sciences.

Table 36 below illustrates a perfect negative correlation between two variables. Note how the ranks are exactly reversed.

TABLE 36

Perfect Negative Correlation

(1) SUBJECT	(2) RANK$_1$	(3) RANK$_2$	(4) d	(5) d^2
A	1	6	5	25
B	2	5	3	9
C	3	4	1	1
D	4	3	−1	1
E	5	2	−3	9
F	6	1	−5	25
				$\Sigma d^2 = \overline{70}$

The three situations illustrated above show that the sum of the squared differences in ranks is a direct clue to the correlation between ranks. When the correlation is perfectly positive, $\sum d^2$ will equal zero; and when the correlation is perfectly negative, the sum of the squared differences is at a maximum (no other arrangement will produce a larger $\sum d^2$).

The constants 1, 6, and n in formula (1),

$$r_r = 1 - \frac{6\sum d^2}{n(n^2 - 1)}$$

are so chosen that when $\sum d^2$ is minimum r_r will be $+1$ and when $\sum d^2$ is maximum r_r will be -1. These limits, $+1$ and -1, are operative no matter how large the sample may be. They constitute the fixed reference points of Requirement 3. The value of $\sum d^2$ when there is neither a tendency to negative or positive correlation is such that the second term of the above formula, $\frac{6\sum d^2}{n(n^2 - 1)}$ is 1 so that $r_r = 0$ in this case. All of these limiting and special values of $\sum d^2$ will be fully discussed in the mathematical section of this chapter.

As pointed out in the discussion of Requirement 3, a good measure of association should have definite reference points which always convey the same meaning. The rank-order correlation coefficient does provide such referents, and we can see how they can be obtained if two facts about the sum of the differences are kept in mind—namely, when the correlation is perfectly positive, the sum of the squared differences is *zero*, and when the correlation is perfectly negative, the sum of the squared differences is at its *maximum*. These two mathematical facts have served as anchors, so to speak, and made it possible to fix *+1.00 as the reference point for perfect positive correlations,* *−1.00 the reference point for perfect negative correlations, and .00 as the reference point for the absence of any relation between the variables.*

Returning to Requirement 4 (independence of sample size), it will be noted that the formula for measuring the degree of relation between ranks includes n, the number of subjects, in the denominator. This makes sense, for, although the total sum of the squared differences between ranks is a direct clue to the extent of the relationship between two variables, it is not a completely satisfactory measure in itself, because the sum of the squared differences is partly determined by the number of cases. Certainly if study A contained 100 cases and study B contained only 10, it would be expected that more differences in rank would occur in study A, simply because there would be more opportunities for differences to occur among 100 cases than among 10. Therefore, the sum of the squared differences should be, and is, expressed in relation to the number of cases included, thereby eliminating the effect of sample size.

Requirements 5 and 6 (ease of prediction and mathematical form) raise problems for the procedure indicated for measuring the relation between ranks, but these problems are beyond the present scope of inquiry. Suffice it to say that the equation presented above for rank order r does not readily lend itself to prediction studies, but the mathematical form of this equation is satisfactory for our purposes. The student who wishes to pursue these points will find them discussed in references listed at the end of this chapter.

Requirement 7 (sole dependence on the extent to which two variables are related) is excellently covered by the use of $\sum d^2$ in the equation. The squared differences between ranks are closely connected to the amount of association between the variables studied.

If formula (1) is evaluated for the VR and Cr data of Table 33, the result is

$$r_r = 1 - \frac{6\sum d^2}{n(n^2 - 1)}$$
$$= 1 - \frac{6(34)}{9(80)}$$
$$= .72$$

It may be concluded that high VR performances are found quite frequently, but not always, to be paired with high Cr performances, and similarly for low performances. In other words, there is a fairly high amount of correlation between VR and Cr.

When the data from Table 34 are inserted in formula (1), the result is

$$r_r = 1 - \frac{6(0)}{5(24)}$$
$$= 1 - 0$$
$$= 1$$

The correlation between ranks in Table 34 being perfect, r_r, of course, equals $+1.00$.

When the data from Table 35 are inserted in formula (1), the result is

$$r_r = 1 - \frac{6(36)}{6(35)}$$
$$= 1 - 1.03$$
$$= -.03$$

The correlation coefficient $-.03$ indicates that there is practically no relation between the ranks. Variables 1 and 2 of Table 34 are unrelated.

Inserting the data of Table 36 in formula (1), the computation becomes

$$r_r = 1 - \frac{6(70)}{6(35)}$$
$$= 1 - 2$$
$$= -1$$

In this case, where the ranks are exactly reversed, we find r_r to be equal to -1.00, indicating a perfect inverse correlation between variables 1 and 2 of Table 36.

Finally, it should be noted that *ties* in rank may occur and that some provision should be made for such events. But this is very simply done. For example, if two subjects are tied for fifth rank, each would be assigned the rank $\frac{5 + 6}{2} = 5.5$. If five subjects were tied for ninth rank, each would be assigned a rank of $\frac{9 + 10 + 11 + 12 + 13}{5} = 11$.

Pearson product-moment correlation coefficient

It will be clear from the above discussion that the rank-order correlation method meets the needs of the behavioral scientist working with data which consist of rankings of relative performance. Note that the rank-order method does not deal with measurements, or scores, themselves; it deals with a different kind of information—relative position, or rank order. However, in the case where the scores are available in interval-scale form, a measure of association is needed that can deal directly with the scores themselves. Since the interval scale provides a measure of distance as well as direction, and thus presents more information than an ordinal scale, it is appropriate that a measure of association be employed that will take into consideration the additional information. As long as more information is available, it should, of course, be used. And the Pearson product-moment correlation coefficient does just that.

The Pearson correlation method should, of course, meet the seven requirements for a measure of association set forth above. The purpose of the following discussion is to show to what extent the method does meet these requirements and the logic behind the structure of the mathematical formula. The mathematical section of this chapter presents the derivation of formulas for Pearson *r;* here we present only the rationale of Pearson *r* in relation to the requirements for a measure of association.

There are many ways to compute Pearson *r*. The formula to be discussed here is one of these, but it is not one which is of much use in computational work, being too cumbersome and unwieldy. However, the formula presented below is simple in visual and logical form, and it is well suited for illustrating how Pearson *r* meets the needs and requirements of the behavioral scientist.

Pearson *r* may be defined in mathematical terms as the mean product of the *z*-scores of two variables; that is,

$$r_p = \frac{\sum z_X z_Y}{n}$$

The fact that r_p may be described as a mean is clear from the formula. Note that r_p is equal to a *sum* $(\sum z_X z_Y)$ divided by the number of terms (n) included in the sum. The numerator of the formula requires clarification, since it involves a new concept—the sum of a product $(\sum z_X z_Y)$. This product is best explained through the use of an example. Suppose the task is to discover the correlation between fathers' intelligence and the intelligence of their sons. Fictitious data which will illustrate the nature of the products $z_X z_Y$ are set forth in Table 37.

Note that each raw score is changed to a *z*-score by subtracting each raw score from the mean and dividing by the standard deviation of the distribution (see columns (3) and (6)). As the student will recall from Chapter 5 (page 154), this step is taken because transforming raw scores to *z*-scores provides a number descriptive of magnitude but independent of its original units (such as pounds, inches, wave lengths) so that individual scores on different measures may be compared. Note also that each z_Y score is multiplied by each corresponding z_X score. This product appears in column (7). The sum of these products appears at the bottom of column (7), and this is the figure which appears in the numerator of the formula

$$r_p = \frac{\sum z_X z_Y}{n}$$

The denominator needs no explanation, since n, as usual, merely denotes the number of terms summed.

Obviously, the mechanics of calculating a Pearson correlation co-efficient are simple enough. As in the case of r_r, we shall not derive r_p here but simply indicate how the degree of association between the two variables is reflected in the size of r_p. Let us consider four cases: Case I represents a

TABLE 37

The Product Moment Correlation Coefficient in Terms of z-scores

(1) FATHER'S I.Q. X	(2) $X - \bar{X}$	(3) $\frac{X - \bar{X}}{s_X} = z_X$	(4) SON'S I.Q. Y	(5) $Y - \bar{Y}$	(6) $\frac{Y - \bar{Y}}{s_Y} = z_Y$	(7) $z_X z_Y$
120	17.7	2.03	121	16.7	1.80	3.65
110	7.7	.89	101	−3.3	−.35	−.31
107	4.7	.54	103	−1.3	−.14	−.08
105	2.7	.31	95	−9.3	−1.00	−.31
103	0.7	.08	112	7.7	.83	.07
100	−2.3	−.26	100	−4.3	−.46	.12
100	−2.3	−.26	118	13.7	1.47	.38
99	−3.3	−.38	91	−13.3	−1.43	.54
92	−10.3	−1.18	104	−0.3	−.03	.04
87	−15.3	−1.76	98	−6.3	−.68	1.20
						$\Sigma z_X z_Y = 5.30$

$$\bar{X} = 102.3 \qquad \bar{Y} = 104.3$$
$$s_X = 8.7 \qquad s_Y = 9.3$$
$$r_p = \frac{\Sigma z_X z_Y}{n}$$
$$= \frac{5.30}{10}$$
$$= .53$$

situation in which there is a perfect positive relation between two variables; Case II represents a situation in which there is a positive relation between two variables, but a weak, imperfect relation rather than a perfect one; Case III represents a situation in which there is no relation at all between two variables; and Case IV represents a situation in which there is a perfect negative relation between two variables.

Case I—Perfect Positive Relation

Suppose that there were a perfect positive relation between scores on a spelling test and scores on an arithmetic test. The data would look like those presented in Table 38. Note that when the relationship between the variables is perfect, each variation in the spelling test score is matched by the variation in the arithmetic test scores; compare columns (3) and (6). Note also that the algebraic sum of the product, $z_X z_Y$, is exactly equal to the number of events, n. Thus, when the relation is perfect (and positive) the numerator and denominator are equal, and, therefore, $r_p =$

TABLE 38

Perfect Positive Correlation in Terms of z-scores

(1) SPELLING X	(2) $X - \bar{X}$	(3) $\dfrac{X - \bar{X}}{s_X} = z_X$	(4) ARITHMETIC Y	(5) $Y - \bar{Y}$	(6) $\dfrac{Y - \bar{Y}}{s_Y} = z_Y$	(7) $z_X z_Y$
30	−17.5	−1.52	105	−15	−1.49	2.26
35	−12.5	−1.09	109	−11	−1.09	1.19
40	−7.5	−.65	113	−7	−.69	.45
45	−2.5	−.22	118	−2	−.20	.04
50	2.5	.22	122	2	.20	.04
55	7.5	.65	126	6	.59	.38
60	12.5	1.09	131	11	1.09	1.19
65	17.5	1.52	136	16	1.58	2.40
						$\Sigma z_X z_Y = \overline{7.95}$

$$\bar{X} = 47.5 \qquad \bar{Y} = 120$$
$$s_X = 11.5 \qquad s_Y = 10.1$$
$$r_p = \frac{\Sigma z_X z_Y}{n}$$
$$= \frac{7.95}{8}$$
$$= .99$$

+1.00. (The numerator in the equation for the data of Table 38 is slightly smaller than 8.00 because of rounding off of decimal places.)

The data of Table 38 are presented in Figure 18.

Case II—Imperfect Positive Relation Between Two Variables

The data in Table 39 show a less than perfect positive relation between spelling test scores and arithmetic test scores. In this case it will be observed that the negative products of $z_X z_Y$ reduce the numerical value of the numerator, which results in r having a value of +.72; this, of course, is less than +1.00. This situation is presented in Figure 19, in which the imperfection of the relation between the two variables becomes obvious. Note, for example, that each variation in spelling test scores is *not* matched

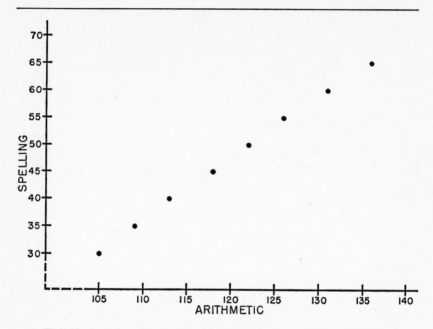

FIG. 18. A scatter diagram for the case of perfect positive correlation.

TABLE 39

Imperfect Positive Correlation

(1) SPELLING X	(2) $X - \bar{X}$	(3) $\dfrac{X - \bar{X}}{s_X} = z_X$	(4) ARITHMETIC Y	(5) $Y - \bar{Y}$	(6) $\dfrac{Y - \bar{Y}}{s_Y} = z_Y$	(7) $z_X z_Y$
80	17.7	1.69	20	4	1.55	2.62
72	9.7	.92	17	1	.39	.36
70	7.7	.73	16	0	.00	.00
68	5.7	.54	15	−1	−.39	−.21
60	−2.3	−.22	18	2	.78	−.17
60	−2.3	−.22	19	3	1.16	−.26
55	−7.3	−.70	14	−2	−.78	.55
50	−12.3	−1.17	12	−4	−1.55	1.81
46	−16.3	−1.55	13	−3	−1.16	1.80
						$\Sigma z_X z_Y = \overline{6.50}$

$$\bar{X} = 62.33 \qquad \bar{Y} = 16.00$$
$$s_X = 10.5 \qquad s_Y = 2.58$$
$$r_p = \frac{\Sigma z_Y z_Y}{n}$$
$$= \frac{6.50}{9}$$
$$= .72$$

by exactly the same variation in arithmetic test scores. Some individuals whose scores are plotted in Figure 19 have rather high spelling test scores but only average arithmetic test scores. And some individuals whose arithmetic test scores are quite low have spelling test scores which are somewhat above average. Thus, although Figure 19 indicates that, in the main, the better spellers are those students who are also better in arithmetic, the relation is less than perfect. The correlation coefficient r_p provides an exact quantitative measure of the degree of relation, or association, between the two sets of test scores—and therein lies its importance.

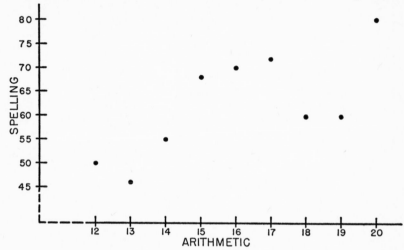

FIG. 19. A scatter diagram for the case of imperfect positive correlation.

Case III—No Relation Between Two Variables

The data in Table 40 represent a situation in which there is exactly no relation between spelling test scores and arithmetic test scores. In this case every positive $z_X z_Y$ product is cancelled by a negative $z_X z_Y$ product. Thus, the numerator of $\dfrac{\Sigma z_X z_Y}{n}$ becomes 0, and, of course, $r_p = 0$. The case of exactly no correlation occurs when there is no tendency in the data toward either positive or negative correlation.

Figure 20 illustrates the data of Table 40. It is apparent from Figure 20 that there is no relation at all between the test scores, for an individual who has a high spelling score may have a low arithmetic test score or a high arithmetic test score. The same is true for an individual with a low spelling-test score. And, of course, the same analysis can be made with respect to arithmetic test scores as they relate to spelling-test scores.

TABLE 40

An Example of Uncorrelated Data

(1) SPELLING X	(2) $X - \bar{X}$	(3) $\dfrac{X - \bar{X}}{s_X} = z_X$	(4) ARITHMETIC Y	(5) $Y - \bar{Y}$	(6) $\dfrac{Y - \bar{Y}}{s_Y} = z_Y$	(7) $z_X z_Y$
41	−31.22	−1.76	24	1	.15	−.26
53	−19.22	−1.09	30	7	1.09	−1.19
56	−16.22	−.92	20	−3	−.47	.43
73	.78	.04	15	−8	−1.24	−.05
74	1.78	.10	15	−8	−1.24	−.12
78	5.78	.33	23	0	0	.00
87	14.78	.83	35	12	1.87	1.55
92	19.78	1.12	27	4	.62	.69
96	23.78	1.34	18	−5	−.78	−1.05

$$\Sigma z_X z_Y = 0$$

$$\bar{X} = 72.22 \qquad \bar{Y} = 23.00$$
$$s_X = 17.71 \qquad s_Y = 6.43$$

$$r_p = \frac{\Sigma z_X z_Y}{n}$$
$$= \frac{0}{9}$$
$$= .00$$

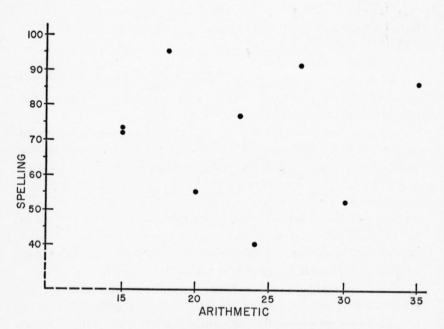

FIG. 20. A scatter diagram for the case of uncorrelated data.

It is now apparent that the Pearson correlation coefficient maintains the two important definite reference points mentioned earlier. When the relation between two variables is a *perfect positive* one, $r_p = +1.00$. When there is *no relation* whatever between the two variables, $r_p = .00$. As the value of r_p increases from one reference point (.00) to the other ($+1.00$), it provides a quantitative measure of the degree of association between the two variables. Thus, when $r_p = +.20$, it indicates a weak positive relation; when $r_p = +.40$, it indicates a stronger positive relation, and when $r_p = +.80$, it indicates a close positive relation between two variables. In short, the correlation coefficient varies in value from .00 to $+1.00$, and between these limits its value is a measure of the degree of association between two variables.

Case IV—Perfect Negative Relation Between Two Variables

Negative correlations will be reflected in a negative sum of the products $z_X z_Y$ in the numerator of $r_p = \dfrac{\sum z_X z_Y}{n}$. The fictitious data in Table 41 illustrate how a negative sum may occur.

Note that each positive z-score in one variable, column (3), is matched by a negative z-score in the other variable, column (6). Since a positive value multiplied by a negative value produces a negative value, the sum of the products $z_X z_Y$ is negative, and thus r_p is negative. These data are illustrated in Figure 21.

It may be seen from Figure 21 that the data are scattered in a manner exactly opposite to that in Figure 19. Of course, the correlation coefficient may take negative values from .00 to -1.00, thus indicating the *degree* of inverse relation between two variables.

It will be worthwhile for the student to note the value of the scatter diagram in making clear the character of the relation between the two variables in the hypothetical examples presented above. The careful investigator will make a scatter diagram, not as part of his computational procedure, but simply because he wants to know what the data look like. Inspection of the data is valuable for several reasons to be discussed below; here we need only point out that it is a good check on calculations, for even an inspection will make obvious any gross errors in calculations— as, for example, reversal of sign.

By way of caution

Pearson r will be found to be a good measure of association; it meets almost all the requirements set forth on pages 179–182. At the same time,

T A B L E   4 1

Perfect Negative Correlation

(1) SPELLING X	(2) $X - \bar{X}$	(3) $\dfrac{X - \bar{X}}{s_X} = z_X$	(4) ARITHMETIC Y	(5) $Y - \bar{Y}$	(6) $\dfrac{Y - \bar{Y}}{s_Y} = z_Y$	(7) $z_X z_Y$
30	−17.5	−1.53	135	15.12	1.53	−2.34
35	−12.5	−1.09	131	11.12	1.12	−1.22
40	−7.5	−.65	126	6.12	.62	−.40
45	−2.5	−.22	122	2.12	.21	−.05
50	2.5	.22	118	−1.88	−.19	−.04
55	7.5	.65	113	−6.88	−.70	−.46
60	12.5	1.09	109	−10.88	−1.10	−1.20
65	17.5	1.53	105	−14.88	−1.50	−2.30

$$\Sigma z_X z_Y = -8.01$$

$$\bar{X} = 47.50 \qquad \bar{Y} = 119.88$$
$$s_X = 11.46 \qquad s_Y = 9.89$$

$$r_p = \frac{\Sigma z_X z_Y}{n}$$
$$= \frac{-8.01}{8}$$
$$= -1.00$$

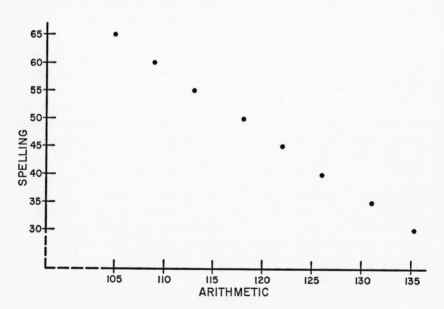

Fig. 21. A scatter diagram for the case of perfect negative correlation.

however, it is a measure which must be used with caution and thoughtful-ness, for it can easily mislead one. The reasons for this will be seen as we proceed. It will become apparent that r_p involves the same ambiguities as the mean. This should not be surprising because, as we have shown, the

product-moment r *is* a mean $\left(r_p = \dfrac{\sum z_X z_Y}{n}\right)$.

Pearson r meets Requirement 1 (independence of the specific units employed to measure the original variables) very well. As we saw above, all scores, or measurements, are transformed into standard scores $\dfrac{(X - \bar{X})}{s_X}$; thus, the units for each of the variables being related are ex-pressed in common units, independently of whether the original units were pounds, inches, spelling-test scores, or arithmetic-test scores. Transforma-tion of original "raw" scores into standard scores achieves a common unit because each measurement is expressed in terms of a relative score—dis-tance from the mean, $(X - \bar{X})$, per standard deviation unit, $\dfrac{(X - \bar{X})}{s_X}$. The original units, then, are dispensed with. The distribution of standard scores will have exactly the same shape, however, as the original scores.

Strictly speaking, the product moment r does not meet Requirement 2 (wide application encompassing as many types of measurement as pos-sible). Pearson r should be applied only to measurement scales which pro-vide comparable intervals, for it requires the computation of means and standard deviations, both of which require interval-scale measurements. The product moment r does involve specification of distance as well as di-rection. Indeed, the accurate specification of distance between data is quite important, as becomes particularly clear when we observe the effect which a single, markedly deviant, score can have on the value of r_p. Note that the formula $r_p = \dfrac{\sum z_X z_Y}{n}$ is actually an *arithmetic mean*. Therefore all of our remarks on the ambiguity of the mean on page 79 apply to r_p as well; that is, it is impossible to know, without examining the data which went into the calculation of a mean (or r_p), whether it has the value it does be-cause of a large number of cases near the mean or because of a single case far from the mean. Pearson r may have a small value simply because one case matches a high positive z-score with a high negative z-score; or the value of product moment r might be quite large merely because one case involves the matching of two high positive z-scores. The product moment

r, like the arithmetic mean (which it is), is markedly influenced by deviant cases, especially for a small n. On the other hand, rank order r, like the median, is not affected by markedly deviant cases, because both rank order r and the median are suited to ordinal scales, and therefore take into account direction but not distance.

Requirement 3 (fixed reference points) is, of course, met by the product moment r, as we have seen on page 195.

Requirement 4 (independence of sample size) is met because n is considered in the denominator of the formula.

Although it is not obvious from the discussion so far, r_p is highly useful in making predictions and thus meets Requirement 5. This feature of this correlation coefficient will be developed in detail in the mathematical section of this chapter.

The product moment r does have a good mathematical form (Requirement 6) and does lend itself readily to further elaboration and manipulation. This will become apparent in the mathematical section.

According to Requirement 7, the value of r_p should depend solely on the extent to which the two variables are related. To the question, does it meet this requirement? Our answer is a guarded, Yes. The extent to which two sets of z-scores match one another is a very good, although not perfect, measure of concomitant variation. There are three important points to keep in mind with respect to r_p; they result in the cautious, Yes, above.

Linearity

Pearson r is a direct reflection of the extent to which two variables are related in a linear fashion, but it is not a good measure of concomitant variation when the variables are related in a *curvilinear* manner. The graph in Figure 15 illustrates the fact that two sets of data can be related to one another in a curved-line fashion.

The calculation of Pearson r is based on a grouping of the scattergram points around a straight rather than around a curved line. There are methods for measuring the degree of relationship between two variables which are related to one another in a curvilinear fashion, but these methods will not be considered here (see references at end of chapter). The important point to be remembered is that if r_p is applied to variables which are related in a curvilinear way, there will be an underestimation of the degree of association; how great an underestimation depends on the degree of curvilinearity and the closeness of the relationship. (Note: Inspection of the scatter diagram provides an excellent means for determining whether the relationship is linear.)

Range

A further point to be kept in mind about the manner in which Pearson *r* reflects the concomitant variation between two variables is this: the greater the range of the data, the greater the opportunity for a high corre-

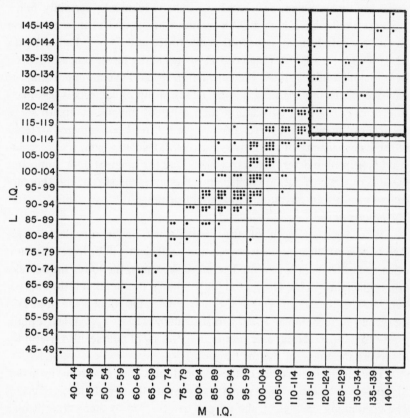

FIG. 22. A scatter diagram of the correlation between two forms (L and M) of the Stanford-Binet Intelligence test. From *Measuring intelligence* by Lewis M. Terman and Maud A. Merrill. Copyright 1937 by Houghton Mifflin Company and reprinted with their permission.

lation coefficient to appear. Conversely, the smaller the range of data, the less opportunity for a high correlation to appear. This fact can be demonstrated most easily by the illustration in Figure 22. Note that if the data were restricted to those in the box, there would be little opportunity for the scores to *covary*; if, on the other hand, the data were as varied as those in the remainder of the graph, there would be greater opportunity for co-variation to appear.

This feature of the product moment *r* has considerable practical importance. For example, suppose that an intelligence test were to be used as a predictor of success in school. If the subjects of this study were to include only honor students, neither the I.Q. scores nor the measure of success—say, achievement test scores—would vary much; certainly honor students would have high I.Q. scores and be successful in school. The situation would be analogous to that illustrated in the upper half of Figure 22. If, however, a larger range of I.Q. scores and a larger range of success were included in the study, the correlation would have an opportunity to increase. Thus, in general, a homogeneous group of subjects is less likely to give rise to a high correlation than a heterogeneous group. In short, the size of the obtained correlation coefficient must be evaluated in terms of the heterogeneity of the groups measured. (Note: Again, a scatter diagram is helpful in determining to what extent the range of data is affecting the size of the correlation coefficient. Of course, the size of the standard deviation is also a direct clue to amount of range.)

The Shapes of the Two Distributions

When one or both of the distributions under consideration are skewed, the product-moment correlation coefficient will be lower than it is when such skewness is absent. The more skewness, the lower the correlation coefficient will be. The reason for this lies in the fact that if the data are bunched together at one end of the distribution, the effect is the same as if the group were homogeneous. Consequently, a large r_p has less opportunity to appear. (Note: The scatter diagram is, of course, also useful for observing the shape of the distribution.)

What is the importance of these limitations? They simply indicate that the student must be cautious when working with the correlation coefficient. The correlation coefficient should not be accepted at face value; it may not directly reflect the concomitant variation between two variables. If at all possible, the data which went into the calculation of the correlation coefficient should be inspected. This is the safest and best method for making certain that the correlation coefficient has been interpreted correctly. (See Box 20.)

❮ Mathematically . . .

The problem with which we are concerned is one of those involved in the study of a population from more than a single viewpoint. Suppose, then that a group of *n* subjects has been tested in two ways. Let the scores of the first test be denoted by X's and those of the second test by Y's. A complete visual picture of the way in which the two variables fluctuate with respect to each other may be obtained by constructing a scatter diagram. The scatter diagram is a mathematical device in which each subject is repre-

---

B O X   2 0

Peer Judgments and Grades

As an example of what might be learned from a set of correlation coefficients, we present the following data.

Correlation coefficients between peer judgments and grade averages in medical school

PEER JUDGMENTS		GRADE AVERAGES				
	Class	First-year	Second-year	Third-year	Fourth-year	Cumulative
Willingness and ability to work independently	1954	.32	.34	.26	.21	.34
	1955	.47	.52	.51	.61	.63
	1956	.50	.54	.36	.35	.57
Likeability	1954	−.03	.04	.20	.04	.10
	1955	−.21	−.06	−.13	.20	−.07
	1956	−.10	−.06	−.13	.25	.00

(Adapted from *Teaching comprehensive medical care*, Hammond and Kern, et al., Harvard University Press, 1959.)

These correlation coefficients show the relation between student's judgments of one another and grade averages in medical school. There is a definite and persistent relationship between independent effort and grades. As may be seen from the table, these correlation coefficients range from .21 to .63, the median *r* being .47. But there is virtually no relation between likeability and grade averages. These correlations range from a −.21 to a +.25, the median *r* being −.03. Thus one may conclude that a student's likeability (as judged by his *peers*) is unrelated to the grades he receives from his teachers, but his willingness and ability to work independently (as judged by his peers) are related to the grades he receives.

sented by a point or dot, the position of each dot depending on the values of X and Y for the subject represented by the dot.

To construct the scatter diagram, a pair of perpendicular lines, one horizontal and the other vertical, are drawn. The intersection is called the "origin" and is denoted by O. The horizontal line is called the "X-axis" or the "axis of abscissas," and the vertical line is called the "Y-axis" or the "axis of ordinates." The scale appropriate to the variable X is then imposed on the X-axis and that appropriate to the variable Y on the Y-axis.

To locate the position of the point or dot which is to represent a given subject, the value of X for that subject is marked on the X-axis and the corresponding value of Y is marked on the Y-axis. The intersection of the vertical line through the X value and the horizontal line through the Y value is the required point. The process described here is nothing more than the plotting of points on graph paper containing a pair of perpendicular axes. The completed scatter diagram provides an almost perfect model of the data for visual analysis. If the large values of X are generally associated with large values of Y and similarly for small values of each, the array of dots will be strung out in a strip or band angling upward from left to right on the diagram. If large values of X correspond to low values of Y, a similar band or strip effect will be observed, except that it will angle downward from left to right. If there is no concomitant variation between X and Y, then no slanting band effect will appear; the array of dots will be so distributed that if a smooth loop is drawn about them, it will approximate an ellipse having axes parallel to the X- and Y-axes. The amount of elongation of such an ellipse relative to its width will be mainly due to the difference between the unit lengths used on the X-axis and the unit lengths on the Y-axis. The only other contributing factor to the elongation in this case is due to the inclusion of extreme or atypical cases in the sample being studied. If the ellipse is tilted or slanted either upward or downward to the right, however, both the angle of slant and the amount of elongation are influenced by the amount of correlation present between the variables.

The data of Table 42 are used to construct the scatter diagram in Figure 23.

In this example there is a large amount of concomitant variation. The upward slant of the band of dots in the diagram shows that students who scored high in English also scored high in vocabulary. The diagram may be used to make rough approximations of vocabulary grades if the English grades are known. For example, if a student's English grade is between 70 and 80, his vocabulary grade will be somewhere between 75 and 85.

TABLE 42

English and Vocabulary Grades for 18 Students

STUDENT NUMBER	ENGLISH GRADE	VOCABULARY GRADE
1	94	92
2	89	90
3	85	78
4	81	85
5	79	81
6	78	83
7	76	75
8	75	74
9	71	82
10	70	69
11	68	71
12	65	63
13	60	58
14	57	64
15	55	58
16	49	52
17	48	45
18	39	35

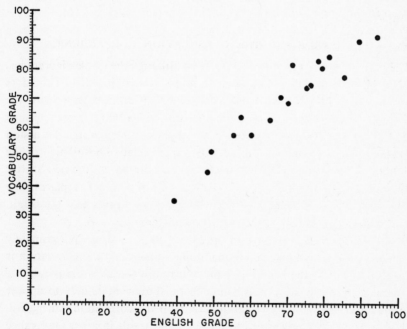

FIG. 23. Scatter diagram for the data of Table 42.

Visual analysis of the scatter diagram, while sufficient for some investigations, is not adequate for most studies. A refinement is required that will assign comparable numerical values to the results observed. The usefulness of such a refinement of analysis is especially apparent if the units in which the various variables are measured are quite different. In order to obtain such a refinement, a very common mathematical device is used: the data are transformed by certain operations into another set of data which, although different in some aspects, is completely similar to the original data in the properties being studied.

The transformation that will be used in the present case consists of applying two operations. The first is to subtract the mean of the X's from each X and the mean of the Y's from each Y. The result is, of course, to produce in place of each X and each Y the corresponding deviation from the mean. The scatter diagram of the deviations will look exactly like the original scatter diagram except that the two axes will pass through the point $(\bar{X}, \bar{Y})$ instead of the point $(0, 0)$. In fact, to obtain the scatter diagram of the deviations, it is only necessary to draw a vertical line through $\bar{X}$ on the X-axis and a horizontal line through $\bar{Y}$ on the Y-axis. The old axes may be erased or ignored, and the result will be the new scatter diagram.

CONSTRUCTING THE CORRELATION COEFFICIENT

The important point to notice here is that, although the whole diagram has been shifted and all the numbers changed, the relative position of the dots with respect to each other remains the same. The relative position of the dots is said to be *invariant under the transformation* that has been applied to the data. (At this point the student should be reminded of the discussion of standard scores on page 166.) Since it is the relative positioning of the dots that displays the presence or absence of correlation, the new scatter diagram will retain all the essential advantages of the one it replaces. The added usefulness of the new scatter diagram lies in the fact that the origin is now near the center of the array of dots (see Figure 24).

If there were no correlation present, there should be approximately the same number of dots in each quadrant. If some degree of correlation is present, however, the band effect previously discussed will be present: if the correlation is positive, this band effect will cause more dots to appear in the lower left and upper right quadrants; if the correlation is negative, the band will slope downward to the right and result in a preponderance of the points lying in the upper left and lower right quadrants. The plus and minus signs shown by pairs in the four quadrants of Figure 24 indicate the signs that will be associated with the coordinates of points in those quadrants. Because the right half of the horizontal axis and the upper half of the vertical axis are taken to be positive, all points in quadrant I will have two positive coordinates. This situation—using ($\bar{X}$, $\bar{Y}$) as the center of the scatter diagram—is produced by the mathematician because he sees the possibility of turning to his use the fact that the product of two numbers with like signs is positive and that of two numbers of unlike signs is negative. The contribution that each dot makes to the numerical measure

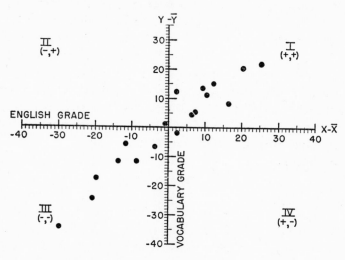

FIG. 24. Scatter diagram with the origin set at ($\bar{X}$, $\bar{Y}$).

of correlation will be taken to be the product of its coordinates. These coordinates are deviations from the means, some positive and some negative. If a dot lies in quadrant I (upper right) or quadrant III (lower left), the contribution will be positive. If the dot lies in quadrant II (upper left) or quadrant IV (lower right), its coordinates will have different signs and the contribution will be negative. If the sum of all the contributions is positive, the inference is that a band effect reaching from quadrant III to quadrant I is responsible; the more pronounced the band effect, the fewer dots there are in quadrants II and IV to make negative contributions. If the total of all the contributions is negative, the inference is that it is caused by a band effect sloping from quadrant II to quadrant IV and leaving comparatively few dots in quadrants I and III. If the total of the contributions is 0, the inference is that no band effect is present, and, hence, no correlation.

The contribution of each dot to the measure of correlation is $(X - \bar{X})$ $(Y - \bar{Y})$, where X and Y are the coordinates of the dot. The sum of all these contributions may be denoted by

$$\sum_{i=1}^{n} (X_i - \bar{X})(Y_i - \bar{Y})$$

This sum could be used as a measure of correlation, the use of which would provide a considerable improvement over visual analysis of the scatter diagram. Actually the sum above is not used, because it has two defects which are quite easily removed by a simple second operation which will complete the transformation of the original data into the data actually used for computation: (1) The result depends on the number, n, of contributions added to form the total. (2) The sum of the contributions is expressed in a combination of the units of X and the units of Y, which may be quite disparate, such as inches of rain and tons of hay per acre; it would therefore be well to eliminate the units of X and Y from the result and have a dimensionless number for the measure of correlation.

The measure of correlation can be made independent of the number of data by dividing each contribution $(X - \bar{X})(Y - \bar{Y})$ by n.

The problem of the units in terms of which the correlation coefficient is to be expressed is solved by eliminating such units altogether. The units in which deviations from the mean are expressed and those in which s is expressed are the same. If each deviation from the mean is divided by the appropriate standard deviation, the quotient will be a *dimensionless number;* that is, there will be no units associated with it. Each contribution $(X - \bar{X})(Y - \bar{Y})$ will for these reasons be divided by $ns_X s_Y$, where s_X and s_Y are, respectively, the standard deviations of the X's and the Y's. This is equivalent to substituting for the original coordinates (X, Y) of a dot in the scatter diagram, the coordinates $\dfrac{X - \bar{X}}{s_X}, \dfrac{Y - \bar{Y}}{s_Y}$. The subtraction of the means $\bar{X}$ and $\bar{Y}$, respectively, from the X's and Y's has the effect of moving the origin to the approximate center of the array of dots. Dividing by s_X and s_Y has the effect of changing the scales on the X-axis and Y-axis. If in Figure 24 each of the numbers on the X-axis and Y-axis were divided by s_X and s_Y, respectively, the result would be the final scatter diagram of the data used to compute r. Although the dots would be plotted on a different scale, *their relative positions would remain invariant.* The final scatter diagram, while different from that of the original data, retains all the properties of relative position present in the original. The point (X, Y) in the original scatter diagram is replaced by the point $\left(\dfrac{X - \bar{X}}{s_X}, \dfrac{Y - \bar{Y}}{s_Y}\right)$ in the final result. The correlation coefficient r is defined to be the mean of the products of the coordinates of each of the scatter-diagram points; that is,

$$r = \frac{1}{n} \sum_{i=1}^{n} \left(\frac{X_i - \bar{X}}{s_X}\right)\left(\frac{Y_i - \bar{Y}}{s_Y}\right)$$

A more convenient form is obtained by factoring the denominators out and placing them outside the summation sign. Then,

$$r = \frac{\sum(X_i - \bar{X})(Y_i - \bar{Y})}{n s_X s_Y}$$

or

$$r = \frac{\sum x_i y_i}{n s_X s_Y}$$

where x and y denote deviations from the mean; that is, $x_i = X_i - \bar{X}$ and $y_i = Y_i - \bar{Y}$.

As defined above, r has all the advantages previously stipulated and a few others as well. It is independent of the number of events, it is independent of the units of X and Y, and its value is directly related to the amount and slope of any band effect that may exist in the original scatter diagram. In addition, it has the advantage of being exactly the mean value of the products of the z-scores discussed in chapter 5 (see page 164), where the z-score corresponding to X was defined as being $\dfrac{X - \bar{X}}{s_X}$. The correlation coefficient may then be succinctly represented as $r = \dfrac{1}{n} \sum_{i=1}^{n} z_i z_i'$ where the z's are the z-scores for the X's and the z''s are the z-scores for the Y's. Another highly useful advantage of the definition evolved for r is that no r may be less than -1 or greater than $+1$. All correlation coefficients computed by this formula must lie between -1 and $+1$, inclusive. The proof of this fact, no matter what sets of X's and Y's are chosen, is mathematically beyond the scope of this book. The choice of s_X and s_Y to excise the units of X and Y from the formula for r was dictated by the desire to obtain the result in the form of z-scores and in the interval -1 to $+1$. Other constants would have served one or two of the objectives, but only the standard deviations satisfy all three requirements.

The Pearson product moment correlation coefficient is then, by definition,

$$r = \frac{\sum_{i=1}^{n} (X_i - \bar{X})(Y_i - \bar{Y})}{n s_X s_Y}$$

or

$$r = \frac{1}{n} \sum_{i=1}^{n} z_i z_i'$$

These forms, while displaying the structure of the quantity r, are not well adapted to computation. The computation of each mean deviation or each z-score is a tedious and time-consuming job at best. The following restatement of r is carried out to cast it into a mathematically equivalent form especially adapted for ease of computation.

First the expression $(X - \bar{X})(Y - \bar{Y})$ in the formula is expanded by ordinary algebraic multiplication so that the formula reads

$$r = \frac{\sum(XY - Y\bar{X} - X\bar{Y} + \bar{X}\bar{Y})}{n s_X s_Y}$$

The numerator is then, by means of distributing the $\sum$ symbol over the four terms of this general addend, expressed in the form of four sums:

$$r = \frac{\sum XY - \sum Y\bar{X} - \sum X\bar{Y} + \sum \bar{X}\bar{Y}}{n s_X s_Y}$$

By factoring a constant out of the second and third sums, the sums $\sum Y\bar{X}$ and $\sum X\bar{Y}$ can be written as $\bar{X}\sum Y$ and $\bar{Y}\sum X$, respectively. But $\sum Y = n\bar{Y}$, and $\sum X = n\bar{X}$; hence, $\sum Y\bar{X}$ and $\sum X\bar{Y}$ equal $n\bar{X}\bar{Y}$. By summing over the constant $\bar{X}\bar{Y}$, the last sum, $\sum \bar{X}\bar{Y}$, of the numerator can be written as $n\bar{X}\bar{Y}$. Using these equivalent forms for the last three sums in the numerator, r can be written as

$$r = \frac{\sum XY - n\bar{X}\bar{Y} - n\bar{X}\bar{Y} + n\bar{X}\bar{Y}}{n s_X s_Y}$$

$$r = \frac{\sum XY - n\bar{X}\bar{Y}}{n s_X s_Y}$$

If the means and standard deviations are already available, this form of r requires only that the sum of the products XY be computed and the results combined to produce r. If the means and standard deviations are not already available, the following equivalent form for r may be used to compute r from the original data. Starting from the form above,

$$ r = \frac{\sum XY - n\bar{X}\bar{Y}}{ns_Xs_Y} $$

$\bar{X}$, $\bar{Y}$, s_X, and s_Y are replaced by equivalent forms. $\bar{X}$ will be replaced by $\frac{1}{n}\sum X$, and s_X will be replaced by its equivalent,

$$ s_X = \frac{1}{n}\sqrt{n\sum X^2 - (\sum X)^2} $$

$\bar{Y}$ and s_Y will be similarly replaced, the result being

$$ r = \frac{\sum XY - n\left(\frac{1}{n}\sum X\right)\left(\frac{1}{n}\sum Y\right)}{n\frac{1}{n}\sqrt{n\sum X^2 - (\sum X)^2}\,\frac{1}{n}\sqrt{n\sum Y^2 - (\sum Y)^2}} $$

Now if both the numerator and denominator are multiplied by n, the value of the fraction is not changed, but the n's in the second term of the numerator all cancel out, as do all the n's of the denominator except those under the radical signs; the result is

$$ r = \frac{n\sum XY - (\sum X)(\sum Y)}{\sqrt{n\sum X^2 - (\sum X)^2}\,\sqrt{n\sum Y^2 - (\sum Y)^2}} $$

If it is recalled that $\sqrt{a}\sqrt{b} = \sqrt{ab}$ for any numbers a and b, this result can be put in its final form:

$$ r = \frac{n\sum XY - (\sum X)(\sum Y)}{\sqrt{[n\sum X^2 - (\sum X)^2][n\sum Y^2 - (\sum Y)^2]}} $$

Though to say that this is a simpler form of r is obviously false from some points of view, it is simpler from the viewpoint of the computer. All of the constituent parts are sums of the data, sums of the squares of the data, or sums of the cross-products XY of the data. Most modern desk calculators will accumulate all five of the required sums simultaneously with a single input of the original data. The values of $\bar{X}$, $\bar{Y}$, s_X, and s_Y are seen to be easy by-products of the computation.

Other forms of r have been developed for convenience in computing r from grouped data. The evolution of the basic formula for r into such computational forms is effected by substituting the grouped-data forms of the means and standard deviations into the appropriate places and simplifying the result algebraically. Such computations are rarely made, however, because of the widespread use of modern desk calculators, and they will therefore not be developed in detail here.

To illustrate the application of the formulas for r, suppose that a class of students has been tested in English, algebra, and history and that each student has been ranked for participation in extracurricular activities. In order to keep computations to a minimum, the class will be assumed to have only ten members, although this is rather too small a sample for most investigations. Let the data, which are fictitious, be as in Table 43.

TABLE 43

Five Sets of Test Scores Variously Correlated

STUDENT	ENGLISH X	ALGEBRA Y	HISTORY V	EXTRACURRICULAR W
A	72	76	54	1
B	81	78	74	10
C	52	60	80	7
D	95	88	74	5
E	68	70	63	9
F	75	79	66	2
G	85	80	84	3
H	69	65	58	4
J	48	40	45	6
K	89	85	60	8

To compute the correlations between various pairs of the four variables X, Y, V, and W, the following sums will be required.

$\sum X = 734$ $\sum Y = 721$ $\sum V = 658$ $\sum W = 55$

$\sum X^2 = 55,934$ $\sum Y^2 = 53,795$ $\sum V^2 = 44,638$ $\sum W^2 = 385$

$\sum XY = 54,725$ $\sum XV = 48,948$ $\sum XW = 4,014$ $\sum YV = 48,202$

$\sum YW = 3,924$ $\sum VW = 3,657$

Using r_{XY} to denote the correlation coefficient obtained by comparing the variables X and Y, the formula

$$r_{XY} = \frac{n\sum XY - (\sum X)(\sum Y)}{\sqrt{[n\sum X^2 - (\sum X)^2][n\sum Y^2 - (\sum Y)^2]}}$$

gives

$$r_{XY} = \frac{(10)(54725) - (734)(721)}{\sqrt{[10(55934) - 734^2][10(53795) - 721^2]}}$$

$$= \frac{18036}{\sqrt{(20584)(18109)}}$$

$$= .93$$

This is a very high level of correlation (remember, however, that the data are fictitious) and, if corroborating evidence could be adduced, would lend credence to a belief that the same factors lie behind success in English and algebra for these students. Using the computations provided above and the same formula as before, the other values of r suggested by the data are found to be as follows:

$$r_{XV} = .39 \qquad r_{XW} = -.06 \qquad r_{YV} = .49$$
$$r_{YW} = -.11 \qquad r_{VW} = .11$$

Of course, the correlation coefficient developed here will differ from 0 only to the extent that the band effect occurs in the scatter diagram. The axis of this band has been considered to be straight, and the whole structure of r is based on this property. It is possible that the dots of the scatter diagram may fall into a curved-band form. If this is the case, the Pearson product-moment correlation coefficient will be a poor statistic to use in the analysis of the data. The value of r will be quite low for such cases even though the band may be very narrow. Other types of correlation coefficients have been devised for use with curvilinearly correlated data. Their development requires the use of the calculus and is therefore beyond the scope of this book.

In the examples above, the variable W is of interest because it takes on each of the values 1 to 10 inclusive. As different as this range of values is from that of the other variables, no difficulty is experienced in computing and interpreting the various values of r. The formula developed is sufficiently general to envelop a very large class of cases.

RANK-ORDER CORRELATION COEFFICIENT

If two variables both run over a sequence of consecutive integers starting with 1, a special case exists, and a special form of r has been developed to cope with it. It is called the "rank-order correlation coefficient," although mathematically it is merely a special case of the Pearson product-moment correlation coefficient. The need for it arises when values cannot be or are not assigned to either variable on an interval scale. It may be that in such cases the subjects may be ranked first, second, . . . , with respect to two different properties or conditions to be studied. The ranks so assigned may be used just as are any other sets of scores in computing r by the formulas already discussed. The special nature of the data, however, allows a simplification of the formula. This simplification depends on a number of facts. First, since both X and Y run over the same set of numbers, although in a different order, it follows that $\sum X = \sum Y$. Moreover, it can be shown that the sum of the first n consecutive integers starting with 1 is $\frac{n(n+1)}{2}$ and that their mean is therefore $\frac{n+1}{2}$; hence, $\bar{X}$ and $\bar{Y}$ have the common value $\frac{n+1}{2}$. Finally, it is known from the theory of numbers that the sum of the squares of the first n consecutive positive integers is $\frac{n(n+1)(2n+1)}{6}$; it follows that $\sum X^2 = \sum Y^2 = \frac{n(n+1)(2n+1)}{6}$

Now,

$$s^2 = \frac{1}{n}\sum X^2 - \bar{X}^2$$

In the present case, then,

$$
\begin{aligned}
s^2 &= \frac{1}{n}\frac{n(n+1)(2n+1)}{6} - \left(\frac{n+1}{2}\right)^2 \\
&= \frac{(n+1)(2n+1)}{6} - \frac{(n+1)^2}{4} \\
&= \frac{2(n+1)(2n+1) - 3(n+1)^2}{12} \\
&= \frac{(n+1)(4n+2-3n-3)}{12}
\end{aligned}
$$

$$= \frac{(n+1)(n-1)}{12}$$

$$= \frac{n^2 - 1}{12}$$

and from this the standard deviation of the first n positive integers is found to be

$$s = \sqrt{\frac{n^2 - 1}{12}}$$

Substituting the values of $\bar{X}$, $\bar{Y}$, s_X, and s_Y thus obtained into the formula

$$r = \frac{\sum XY - n\bar{X}\bar{Y}}{n s_X s_Y}$$

gives
$$r = \frac{\sum XY - n\dfrac{n+1}{2}\dfrac{n+1}{2}}{n\sqrt{\dfrac{n^2-1}{12}}\sqrt{\dfrac{n^2-1}{12}}}$$

$$= \frac{\sum XY - \frac{1}{4}(n)(n+1)^2}{\frac{1}{12}(n)(n^2-1)}$$

(1)
$$= \frac{12\sum XY}{n(n^2-1)} - \frac{3(n+1)}{(n-1)}$$

The advantage of this formula is obvious in that only the sum of the products of the corresponding ranks is required in addition to the number, n, of subjects ranked.

Another form of the rank-order correlation coefficient can be obtained from the result above. To do so it is necessary to show that the term $\dfrac{3(n+1)}{(n-1)}$ in (1) can be expressed as

$$\frac{3(n+1)}{(n-1)} = \frac{6\sum X^2 + 6\sum Y^2}{n(n^2-1)} - 1$$

To do this, we use the fact that

$$\frac{3n+1}{n-1} = \frac{\dfrac{6n(n+1)(2n+1)}{6} + \dfrac{6n(n+1)(2n+1)}{6}}{n(n^2-1)} - 1$$

This last equation is easily verified by simplifying the right-hand side. Then

$$\frac{3(n+1)}{(n-1)} = \frac{6\sum X^2 + 6\sum Y^2}{n(n^2-1)} - 1$$

Substituting this value into (1) gives

$$r = \frac{12\sum XY - 6\sum X^2 - 6\sum Y^2}{n(n^2-1)} + 1$$

$$= \frac{-6\sum(X^2 - 2XY + Y^2)}{n(n^2-1)} + 1$$

$$= \frac{-6\sum(X - Y)^2}{n(n^2-1)} + 1$$

$$= 1 - \frac{6\sum d^2}{n(n^2-1)}$$

where d is the rank difference ($X - Y$). This is the form sought. Its advantage lies in the fact that only the differences in ranks are needed to get the result. Moreover, the only products to be added are squares, and modern desk calculators will accumulate squares with a minimum of time and effort. (Most workers with numbers take the small amount of time necessary to learn the first twenty-five squares. No other information forms such an adequate basis for mental arithmetic calculations as these first few squares. For easy applications and techniques, see the list of elementary factor forms of any elementary algebra text.)

As an example of the application of the rank order correlation coefficient the data of Table 43 will be recast entirely as rankings. In each academic subject the scores will be ranked, with the highest score in each instance being first. The data, then, are as in Table 44.

Note that in history two equal scores are tied for third ranking. It has been found expedient and useful to give each such score the average of ranks 3 and 4. If three scores were tied for, say, twelfth ranking, each would be given a ranking of $\frac{12 + 13 + 14}{3} = 13$. Higher level ties are treated similarly.

Using the formula

$$r = 1 - \frac{6\sum d^2}{n(n^2-1)}$$

TABLE 44

Four Rankings of a Set of Ten Students

STUDENT	ENGLISH X	ALGEBRA Y	HISTORY V	EXTRACURRICULAR W
A	6	6	9	1
B	4	5	3½	10
C	9	9	2	7
D	1	1	3½	5
E	8	7	6	9
F	5	4	5	2
G	3	3	1	3
H	7	8	8	4
J	10	10	10	6
K	2	2	7	8

the various rank order correlation coefficients are as follows:

$$r_{XV} = .40 \qquad r_{XW} = .08 \qquad r_{YV} = .41$$
$$r_{YW} = .12 \qquad r_{VW} = -.14 \qquad r_{XY} = .98$$

Comparing these values with those obtained previously, it is seen that somewhat different results are obtained. The reason for this lies in the fact that actual measurements—scores—contain more information than do rankings. In Table 43 student J has scores in English, algebra, and history that are quite a distance from the others; these distances are taken into account in the product-moment computation of r. However, in the rankings student J is placed only one rank away from the next highest score, no matter how much higher it may be. Only direction, not distance, is considered, and the result is that the rankings convey an impression of more or less homogeneity than is actually the case. Thus, the rank-order correlation coefficient does not measure concomitant fluctuation between two variables as well as in the case where distance as well as direction is taken into consideration.

The last formula affords an opportunity to analyze the correlation coefficient with respect to its values and their range. If both sets of ranks are identical, it is clear that each d will be 0; then $r = 1 - 0 = 1$. If the rankings are simply the reverse one of the other, the d's will consist of the numbers $n - 1, n - 3, n - 5, \ldots, n - 5, n - 3, n - 1$. That the sum of the squares of this set of numbers is always $\dfrac{n(n^2 - 1)}{3}$ is an elementary exercise in the theory of numbers. Substituting into the formula gives

$$r = 1 - \frac{6\dfrac{n(n^2 - 1)}{3}}{n(n^2 - 1)}$$
$$= 1 - 2 = -1$$

which is to be expected when the two rankings are exact inverses one of the other.

It should be realized that a correlation coefficient does not uniquely characterize a particular set of data. There are a great many sets of possible data which will produce the same values of r. In some senses these different sets of data have differing degrees of correlation, but not in regard to the criteria by which the formula was designed. With respect to these criteria, the degrees of correlation will be the same if the values of r are the same. Consider for instance the trivial but revealing example presented in Table 45.

TABLE 45

Variously Correlated Arrangements of the Digits 1, 2, 3, and 4

X	U	V	W	Y
1	1	1	2	3
2	3	4	3	1
3	4	2	1	2
4	2	3	4	4

The correlation coefficients r_{XU}, r_{XV}, r_{XW}, and r_{XY} are all equal to .4. It is tempting to conclude that U, V, W, and Y will, by pairs, have correlation coefficients of 1 (that is, be perfectly correlated with one another), since they all correlate the same with X. This is far from the truth: such a conclusion is never justified when dealing with correlation coefficients. In the present example, for instance, $r_{UY} = -.6$, $r_{UW} = -.4$, and $r_{VW} = +.6$, which shows a considerable variation in correlation.

THE REGRESSION EQUATION

If two variables were found to be perfectly correlated with $r = +1$, all of the points of the scatter diagram would lie on a straight line. The band effect discussed in the development of the correlation coefficient would be maximum in this case. Moreover, it would be possible to determine exactly the value of one 'member of a pair of measurements if the value of the other member of the pair were known. For example, consider the case of a merchant who decides that he will sell his merchandise at one and a half times the wholesale cost. Figure 25 shows graphically how the retail price compares with the wholesale price.

The graph is constructed by computing the retail prices for several different wholesale prices and plotting the results on a set of axes properly labeled and marked off in relevant units (dollars and cents in this case).

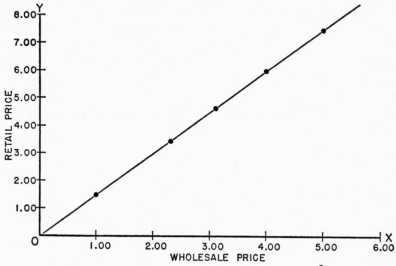

FIG. 25. The graph of the regression equation $Y = \frac{3}{2} X$.

Each wholesale price determines a retail price, and these numbers are taken to be the coordinates of a point in the plane. Several such points constitute a scatter diagram with all of its points lying on a straight line, and the graph is completed by drawing this line through the plotted points. The graph may then be used in lieu of repeated calculations for the determination of retail prices. It will be found, for instance, that the point on the line just above the wholesale price $2.50 is on a level with the retail price $3.75 = $1\frac{1}{2} \times $2.50, and similarly for other cases. Although no connotation of futurity is intended, the retail price is said to be predicted from a knowledge of the wholesale price. If some letter—say, X—is used for wholesale price and another—Y—is used for retail price, their relation may be stated as

(1) $$Y = \tfrac{3}{2} X$$

Now (1) is the equation of the line graphed in Figure 25. The line is straight because the equation $Y = \frac{3}{2}X$ contains only first-degree terms. Graphs of equations having terms of higher degree, such as X^2, Y^3, or XY, will ordinarily be curvilinear rather than straight. It is clear from Figure 25 and from equation (1) that an increase of 1 unit in X is accompanied by an increase of $\frac{3}{2}$ in Y; that is, the line rises one and a half units for each increase of one unit to the right; for this reason, $\frac{3}{2}$ is called the *slope* of the line. (The ratio $\frac{3}{2}$ is also called the *rate of change*.) Had the merchant decided to double his wholesale price, the slope of the graph would have been 2, and its equation would be

$$(2) \qquad\qquad Y = 2X$$

Note that if the merchant obtains an item at no cost, his pricing formula requires him to give it away; that is, the graph goes through the origin point. To avoid this, suppose that he decides to add \$.50 to every price computed by formula (1). His pricing formula then becomes

$$(3) \qquad\qquad Y = \frac{3}{2}X + .50$$

The graph of this formula would be the same as in Figure 25 except that every point will be .5 higher. The effect of the addition will thus be to raise the line by just the added amount. Then, when $X = 0$, $Y = .5$. The value .5 is called the "Y-intercept" of the graph, since it is the value on the Y-axis that is cut by the line.

It appears, then, that by properly choosing the coefficient of X and adding the right amount, the line may be made to assume any degree of slope and to cut the Y-axis at any desired place. In effect,

$$(4) \qquad\qquad Y = mX + b$$

is the most general equation of a straight line having slope m and Y-intercept b.

Whenever such a line can be drawn through all the points of a scatter diagram, having knowledge of one variable is equivalent to having exact knowledge of the other. Such exactness will only be possible when the two variables are perfectly correlated with $r = \pm 1$. Since perfect correlations are quite rare, it is necessary to evolve means whereby the value of one variable may be estimated from the value of the other when the correlation is less than perfect. The linear regression equation has been designed to fill this need: it is a linear equation of the form $Y = mX + b$ wherein the slope m and the Y-intercept b are chosen so that the line lies as nearly down the middle of the band effect as possible. It is that one line which comes nearest to, or fits best, all the points of the scatter diagram—in the sense that if the vertical distances, or deviations, of each of the points of the scatter diagram from the regression line are noted and squared, then the sum of these squared deviations is less than would be the case for any other line; such a line is said to fit best in the sense of *least squares*.

The methods used for determining the two numbers m and b for such a line are found in a first-year calculus course. It is important for the student to know, however, that m can be expressed in the form $r\dfrac{s_Y}{s_X}$, and b can be expressed as $\bar{Y} - r\dfrac{s_Y}{s_X}\bar{X}$. The regression equation for predicting Y from X is then

$$(5) \qquad \begin{aligned} Y' &= mX + b \\ &= \left(r\frac{s_Y}{s_X}\right)X + \left(\bar{Y} - r\frac{s_Y}{s_X}\bar{X}\right) \end{aligned}$$

where Y' is used to indicate that not Y, but an estimate of Y is intended. The terms $r\dfrac{s_Y}{s_X}X$ and $r\dfrac{s_Y}{s_X}\bar{X}$ combine into $r\dfrac{s_Y}{s_X}(X - \bar{X})$, so that (5) may be expressed as

$$(6) \qquad Y' = r\frac{s_Y}{s_X}(X - \bar{X}) + \bar{Y}$$

and

$$(7) \qquad Y' - \bar{Y} = r\frac{s_Y}{s_X}(X - \bar{X})$$

From these equations, it is apparent that the best prediction of Y depends not only on the corresponding value of X, but also on the means and standard deviations of X and Y and on the amount of correlation r between X and Y. Formula (7) is particularly useful since it gives predictions of the mean deviations $Y' - \bar{Y}$ in terms of the mean deviations $X - \bar{X}$ of X. If $x = X - \bar{X}$ and $y' = Y' - \bar{Y}$, then (7) becomes

$$(8) \qquad y' = r\frac{s_Y}{s_X}x$$

If it is desired to predict X rather than Y, the formulas above are altered by interchanging X and Y throughout. Thus,

$$(9) \qquad X' - \bar{X} = r\frac{s_X}{s_Y}(Y - \bar{Y})$$

and

$$(10) \qquad x' = r\frac{s_X}{s_Y}y$$

Equations (6) and (7) are called *regression equations of Y on X*, and (9) is a form of the *regression equation of X on Y*. There are thus two regression lines for every pair of variables. Their intersection will always occur at the point $(\bar{X}, \bar{Y})$—that is, the means of the two distributions composing the scatter diagram. This is apparent from equations (8) and (10), since a deviation of 0 from the mean makes x or y zero, and consequently y' or x' equals 0 also.

As an example of the use of the regression equation, the data of Table 46 will be used.

TABLE 46

Twenty-five Pairs of Highly Correlated Data

X	Y	X	Y	X	Y	X	Y	X	Y
56	65	64	72	71	76	81	76	90	92
59	52	65	63	71	64	84	81	92	89
60	57	68	58	73	70	85	87	94	91
62	55	70	60	75	73	87	90	95	96
62	60	70	74	77	80	89	85	97	93

The necessary calculations are as follows: $\bar{X} = 75.88$, $\bar{Y} = 74.36$, $s_X = 12.39$, $s_Y = 13.30$, and $r = .93$. The regression line of Y on X is then

$$(11) \qquad Y' = .93\,\frac{13.30}{12.39}\,(X - 75.88) + 74.36$$
$$= .998X - 1.368$$

and that for X on Y is

$$(12) \qquad X' = .93\,\frac{12.39}{13.30}\,(Y - 74.36) + 75.88$$
$$= .866Y + 11.48.$$

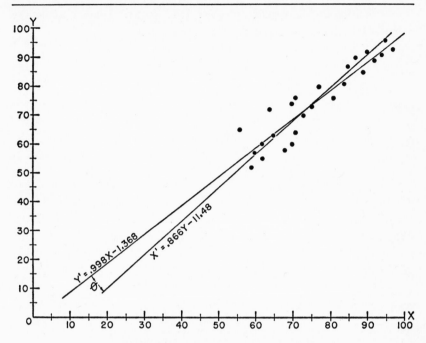

FIG. 26. Regression lines for the data of Table 46.

The scatter diagram for the data is given in Figure 26, and the two regression lines are plotted there as well.

Note the angle θ (theta) which is measured counterclockwise from the Y' line to the X' line and thus depends on r, s_X, and s_Y, the exact relation being

$$(13) \qquad \qquad \text{Tan } \theta = \frac{1 - r^2}{r} \frac{s_X s_Y}{s_X^2 + s_Y^2}$$

From this it will be seen that if $r = \pm 1$, the numerator will be 0, indicating that $\theta = 0$ and hence that the two lines coincide. If r should be 0, indicating no correlation between X and Y, then the denominator of Formula (13) becomes 0; this can occur only if $\theta = 90°$. Thus, when no correlation exists between X and Y the two lines are perpendicular. The factor $\frac{s_X + s_Y}{s_X^2 s_Y^2}$ will always be greater than 0, and not greater than $\frac{1}{2}$.

Errors of estimates

Whenever an estimate is made, the question of its accuracy arises. If no information as to the accuracy of the estimate is available, the estimate is of little value. The error of estimate is the difference between an actual value and the estimate of that value. In the case of the regression equation of Y on X, estimates Y' of Y are made according to the formula

$$(14) \qquad Y' = r\frac{s_Y}{s_X}(X - \bar{X}) + \bar{Y}$$

If e is the error of estimate, then

$$(15) \qquad e = Y - Y'$$

or

$$(16) \qquad e = Y - \left(r\frac{s_Y}{s_X}(X - \bar{X}) + \bar{Y}\right)$$

If (14) is used to make estimates of all of the Y's the resulting errors of estimate consitute a set of numbers having a mean and a standard deviation. The mean estimate of error is denoted by $\bar{e}$, and the standard deviation, called the *standard error of estimate*, is denoted by s_e.

The values of $\bar{e}$ and s_e describe the distribution of errors by showing their point of central tendency and the degree of dispersion about that point. If s_e is quite small, the errors of estimate will cluster closely about their mean; if s_e is large, the errors will be dispersed over a considerable range.

In order to compute $\bar{e}$ and s_e, it is necessary to recall a few formulas and results previously established. In the chapter on the mean it was shown that in any distribution the sum of the deviations from the mean is zero; that is,

$$(17) \qquad \Sigma(X - \bar{X}) = 0$$

The formula

$$(18) \qquad r = \frac{\Sigma(X - \bar{X})(Y - \bar{Y})}{n s_X s_Y}$$

will be required, as well as

$$(19) \qquad s^2 = \frac{1}{n}\Sigma(X - \bar{X})^2$$

Now,

$$\bar{e} = \frac{1}{n}\sum_{i=1}^{n} e_i$$

$$= \frac{1}{n}\Sigma(Y - Y') \qquad \text{(from equation (15))}$$

$$= \frac{1}{n}\Sigma Y - \frac{1}{n}\Sigma Y' \qquad \text{(by distributing the } \Sigma \text{ symbol over the general addend)}$$

(20) $$= \bar{Y} - \bar{Y}' \qquad \text{(by definition of the mean)}$$

It thus appears that the mean of the errors of estimate is the difference between the actual mean $\bar{Y}$ and the mean $\bar{Y}'$ of the estimates. If, instead of equation (15), equation (16) is used above, the result is

$$\bar{e} = \frac{1}{n}\Sigma e$$

$$= \frac{1}{n}\Sigma\left(Y - \left(r\frac{s_Y}{s_X}(X - \bar{X}) + \bar{Y}\right)\right) \qquad \text{(by equation (16))}$$

$$= \frac{1}{n}\Sigma\left((Y - \bar{Y}) - r\frac{s_Y}{s_X}(X - \bar{X})\right) \qquad \text{(by rearranging terms)}$$

$$= \frac{1}{n}\left[\Sigma(Y - \bar{Y}) - \Sigma r\frac{s_Y}{s_X}(X - \bar{X})\right] \qquad \text{(by distributing the } \Sigma \text{ symbol over the general addend)}$$

$$= \frac{1}{n}\left[\Sigma(Y - \bar{Y}) - r\frac{s_Y}{s_X}\Sigma(X - \bar{X})\right] \qquad \text{(by factoring out the constant } r\frac{s_Y}{s_X}\text{)}$$

$$= 0 \qquad \text{(by equation (17) applied to each of the two sums)}$$

The result is that $\bar{e} = 0$ whenever predictions or estimates of Y are made using the regression equation. The result (20) now can be given additional meaning. Since $\bar{e} = \bar{Y} - \bar{Y}'$ and $\bar{e} = 0$, it follows that the mean $\bar{Y}'$ of the estimates is equal to the mean $\bar{Y}$ of the Y's; that is,

(21) $$\bar{Y}' = \bar{Y}$$

The value of $\bar{e}$ having been found to be zero, the computation of s_e^2 is quite easy. By equation (19),

$$s_e^2 = \frac{1}{n}\sum(e - \bar{e})^2$$

$$= \frac{1}{n}\sum e^2 \quad \text{(since } \bar{e} = 0)$$

$$= \frac{1}{n}\sum\left(Y - \left(r\frac{s_Y}{s_X}(X - \bar{X}) + \bar{Y}\right)\right)^2 \quad \text{(by equation (16))}$$

$$= \frac{1}{n}\sum\left((Y - \bar{Y}) - r\frac{s_Y}{s_X}(X - \bar{X})\right)^2 \quad \text{(by rearranging terms)}$$

The squared quantity is now multiplied out and the result is

$$s_e^2 = \frac{1}{n}\sum\left[(Y - \bar{Y})^2 - 2r\frac{s_Y}{s_X}(Y - \bar{Y})(X - \bar{X}) + \frac{r^2 s_Y^2}{s_X^2}(X - \bar{X})^2\right]$$

$$= \frac{1}{n}\sum(Y - \bar{Y})^2 - \frac{2r s_Y}{n s_X}\sum(Y - \bar{Y})(X - \bar{X}) + \frac{r^2 s_Y^2}{n s_X^2}\sum(X - \bar{X})^2$$

where the $\sum$ symbol has been distributed over the general addend and some constants factored out of the resulting sums. Then

$$s_e^2 = s_Y^2 - 2r s_Y^2 \frac{\sum(Y - \bar{Y})(X - \bar{X})}{n s_X s_Y} + r^2 s_Y^2$$

Here the first term, $\frac{1}{n}\sum(Y - \bar{Y})^2$, is equated with s_Y^2 according to equation (19). The second term has been multiplied by $\frac{s_Y}{s_Y} = 1$ in order to show that it contains $\frac{\sum(Y - \bar{Y})(X - \bar{X})}{n s_X s_Y} = r$ as a factor. The last term has $\frac{1}{n}\sum(X - \bar{X})^2$ replaced by s_X^2, which cancels out. Then

$$s_e^2 = s_Y^2 - 2r^2 s_Y^2 + r^2 s_Y^2$$

$$= s_Y^2 - r^2 s_Y^2$$

$$= s_Y^2(1 - r^2)$$

and

(22) $$s_e = s_Y\sqrt{1 - r^2}$$

This result shows that the dispersion of the errors of estimate is closely related to the dispersion of the Y's. If the correlation coefficient is 0, then $s_e = s_Y$. As the correlation coefficient becomes larger, $1 - r^2$ becomes smaller, as does s_e. When $r = .87$, the factor $\sqrt{1 - r^2}$ is approximately $\frac{1}{2}$. Very high correlations are necessary to reduce s_e to less than half of s_Y.

Equation (22) may be solved for r, the result being

(23)
$$r^2 = 1 - \frac{s_e^2}{s_Y^2}$$

or

(24)
$$r = \sqrt{1 - \frac{s_e^2}{s_Y^2}}$$
$$= \frac{\sqrt{s_Y^2 - s_e^2}}{s_Y}$$

If r in the regression equation is replaced by

$$\frac{\sqrt{s_Y^2 - s_e^2}}{s_Y}$$

the equation assumes the form

$$Y' = \frac{\sqrt{s_Y^2 - s_e^2}}{s_X}(X - \bar{X}) + \bar{Y}$$

If X is being estimated instead of Y, the entire treatment above must be altered by interchanging X and Y throughout.

SUMMARY

The behavioral sciences, then, do have methods for describing the degree of association between two variables—despite the variability in the distribution of events. To be sure, the methods available are not foolproof; correlation coefficients require thoughtful and critical examination of the data they represent. Consequently, every good research worker will carefully examine the data which gave rise to a given coefficient in order to understand how and why that coefficient came to be as high or low as it did.

The good research worker will be cognizant of the properties of the correlation coefficient and will examine the data in light of his knowledge

BOX 21

Correlation and Causality

There is a propensity on the part of most of us to infer a causal relationship between two events whenever we perceive them to be associated. But close association in time or place may be just that and nothing more. Association in itself is not proof of a causal relationship. A high degree of association as indicated, say, by a large correlation coefficient is not proof of a causal relationship, for the correlation coefficient merely quantifies the degree of association. The correlation coefficient can do no more —assertions of causal connections must rest on other evidence. The reason we must emphasize this point is that most of us jump too quickly to the conclusion that "correlation means causation."

In order to drive this point home, it has become commonplace for instructors to describe situations in which there is a high degree of association but in which it would be absurd to assert a causal connection. One such absurdity often cited is that of the correlation between the number of cases of infant diarrhea per month and the viscosity of the tar roads in southern states. Obviously neither of these phenomena is the cause of the other. But such illustrations go too far. To assert a causal relation here would be absurd only because we *already know* what causes diarrhea and what changes the viscosity of the roads. Behavioral scientists, on the other hand, are using the correlation method to explore the unknown.

It is precisely because we do *not* know what kinds of behavior are related to other kinds of behavior that we are investigating the degree of association between two variables in the first place. "What leads to what?" is the very question we wish to answer. And it is for that reason that the behavioral scientist will frequently stumble over the causality question. There is no way of knowing *in advance* that the correlation between two variables may really be due to a third variable which is related to both (as is the case in the example of the roads and diarrhea). This is exactly the kind of thing that has to be discovered.

While it is important to understand that the correlation coefficient merely provides a quantitative measure of the degree of association between two variables, we must also understand that the scientist must interpret the correlation coefficient—he must say what it means. In doing so, it is inevitable that he will make mistakes. Causation *will* be mistakenly asserted on the basis of correlation. But these mistakes are corrected by further research. True, correlation does not prove causation. On the other hand, nothing ventured, nothing gained.

of these properties. He will, for example, realize that all correlation coefficients must fall within the *limits* of $+1.00$ and -1.00. He will realize
that the original *raw score units* will not have affected the size of either the
rank-order or product-moment correlation coefficient, for one is expressed
in terms of ranks and the other in terms of standard scores $\left(\dfrac{X - \bar{X}}{s}\right)$. He
will be aware of the fact that the product-moment correlation coefficient
reports the degree of association in terms of a *straight line*, and that,
should an examination of the data show that a curved line best expresses
the nature of the association between the two variables, the product-
moment correlation coefficient will underestimate the actual degree of
association. He will be aware of the fact that the size of correlation coefficients is affected by the *range* of scores. Further, he will examine his
data in order to discover to what extent they are asymmetrical and thus
decreasing the value of r_p which would have been obtained had the distribution been symmetrical. He knows that the form of the distribution
has no effect on rank order r. He knows that correlation is not identical
with causation. (See Box 21.)

Most important, however, is the fact that a good research worker
will scrutinize the original data for incongruities, oddities, and irregu-
larities so that he will not rest his case on a correlation coefficient which is
based on faulty data. One of the most important steps in the work of the
behavioral scientist is the checking of his basic data at every stage. And
nowhere is this step more important than in the computation of the correlation coefficient, for no statistical technique is more susceptible to freakish
errors. Unless it is used with a critical eye, the correlation coefficient is
truly, as one scientist bitterly put it, "a tool of the devil." Used wisely, it is a
powerful analytic tool.

Suggestions for Further Reading

All of the references listed at the end of Chapter 3 will provide
further discussion of correlational methods. For more detailed discussions
of correlational methods the student should consult the following:

KENDALL, M. G. 1955. *Rank correlation methods.* New York: Hafner.
SIEGEL, S. 1956. *Nonparametric statistics for the social sciences.* New
York: McGraw-Hill.

WALKER, H., and LEV, J. 1953. *Statistical inference.* New York: Holt. For a general discussion of causality, the student should consult CHURCHMAN, C., and ACKOFF, R., 1950. *Methods of inquiry.* St. Louis: Educational Publishers.

For a commentary on the life of Sir Francis Galton, as well as one of his original papers, the student should consult Part VI of Vol. II of Newman's *World of Mathematics* (see reference at end of Chapter 2).

See also references listed at the end of Chapter 5 for descriptions of various applications of the correlation coefficient to problems of psychological research.

PROBLEMS

1. Explain in a short paragraph how it is possible for the values of two variables to correspond in a more or less systematic way without the existence of any causal relationship between the variables.

2. Suppose that Mr. Ambus arrives every week day at the bus depot within two minutes before or after 8:00 a.m. On the other side of town, Miss Busam arrives every week day at the public library between 8:25 a.m. and 8:30 a.m. Under what additional circumstances, if any, would you say that one of these events could be used to predict the other?

3. If two variables fluctuate together so that a high value of one is always associated with a high value of the other, then a high correlation exists. Would you say, on the contrary, that a complete lack of correlation would require that a high value of one variable never be associated with a high value of the other? Explain your answer.

4. One example of a numerical measure having no units or dimensions associated with it is the scale of percentages. Can you think of any other numerical measures having no associated units?

5. For each of the seven requirements of a good measure of association between two variables, give as good a reason as you can in one sentence for the requirement.

6. If Anne, Ben, Connie, and Dan rank, respectively, first, second, third, and fourth as extemporaneous speakers, how many different rankings of the four as orators are possible? For every such possible ranking find $\sum d^2$. To which rankings do the minimum and maximum values of $\sum d^2$ belong?

7. The formula $r = 1 - \dfrac{6\sum d^2}{n(n^2 - 1)}$ may be written as $r = 1 - \dfrac{6}{n^2 - 1}$ $\left(\dfrac{1}{n}\sum d^2\right)$, wherein the portion in the parentheses is observed to be the mean of the squares of the rank differences. Using this fact as a point of departure, discuss rank order r with respect to requirement number 4.

8. If the highest five scores on a test were 93, 89, 89, 85, and 83, what were the corresponding ranks?

9. Suppose the scores of ten subjects are 56, 53, 53, 49, 49, 49, 45, 40, 38, and 38. What are the corresponding ranks?

10. Find $\sum uv$ for the following data:

i	1	2	3	4	5	6	7	8	9	10
u_i	1	6	2	7	3	8	4	9	5	10
v_i	5	−1	3	−6	6	−1	−2	−1	3	−6

11. There are six different ways in which the three numbers 2, 5, and 10 may be paired with the numbers 3, 5, and 8. Compute the mean and standard deviation for each set of three numbers, and use these values to convert the data into z-scores. Then compute r_p for all six possible pairings.

12. What is wrong with limiting one's consideration to the most intelligent segment of the population in making a study of the correlation between business success and intelligence?

13. If high correlation does not necessarily signify a causal relationship, then of what use is the correlation coefficient? Your answer to problem 2 may provide a starting point for the discussion of this question.

14. Make a scatter diagram for the following data:

i	1	2	3	4	5	6	7	8	9	10	11	12	13	14	15	16
X_i	4	4	5	5	6	7	7	7	8	9	9	10	11	11	12	13
Y_i	4	6	3	8	7	3	5	8	7	4	9	6	5	9	5	7

15. Compute the means $\bar{X}$ and $\bar{Y}$ for the data of problem 14, and make a new table replacing each X and Y with its deviation from its mean. Make a scatter diagram from the table of deviations from the means.

16. Compute the standard deviation of the X's and the standard deviation of the Y's in problem 14. Construct a new table by dividing $X_i - \bar{X}$ of problem 15 by s_X and, similarly, $Y_i - \bar{Y}$ by s_Y. Use the resulting table of values to construct a scatter diagram.

17. The scatter diagram of problem 16 should have its points closer together than they were in problems 14 and 15. By what factor are the horizontal distances between points reduced? By what factor are the vertical distances in the diagram reduced?

18. Use the formula $r = \dfrac{1}{n}\sum\dfrac{(X - \bar{X})(Y - \bar{Y})}{s_X s_Y}$ and the data of problem 16 to compute r. Note that each of the data in problem 16 has been converted to a z-score and that the formula shown here calls for the computation of $\sum z_X z_Y$.

19. Reduce the formula $r = \dfrac{\sum(X - \bar{X})(Y - \bar{Y})}{n s_X s_Y}$ to a more convenient computational form. The purpose of this problem is to test whether or not you can do this transformation without consulting the detailed steps given in the text. If review is necessary, review the similar treatment of the formula for the standard deviation for ideas on how to proceed.

20. Compute r for the data of problem 14 using the formula $r = \dfrac{\sum XY - n\bar{X}\bar{Y}}{n s_X s_Y}$. Compare with problem 18.

21. Repeat problem 20 using the formula

$$r = \frac{n\sum XY - (\sum X)(\sum Y)}{\sqrt{[n\sum X^2 - (\sum X)^2][n\sum Y^2 - (\sum Y)^2]}}.$$

22. Check the values of the correlation coefficients as given on page 211.

23. Write the numbers 1, 2, 3, 4, 5, and 6 across the page and then just under these numbers write the same ones in reverse order, 6, 5, 4, 3, 2, and 1. Now if the vertical pairs of numbers are added, six totals of 7 will be obtained, giving 42; this is just twice the sum of the numbers in the first row. Repeat this process for 1, 2, . . . , 10, and then generalize your results to obtain a formula for $1 + 2 + \cdots + n$.

24. Find rank order r for the rankings:

X	1	2	3	4	5	6	7	8	9	10	11	12	13	14	15	16
Y	4	11	3	12	2	1	13	7	14	6	5	15	10	16	9	8

25. Repeat problem 24 with $Y = 4$ and $Y = 16$ interchanged.

26. Compute rank order r for the six different pairs of variables in Table 44. Check your results against the values given in the text.

27. Find the rank order correlation coefficient for each of the three possible pairs of rankings given below.

	A	B	C	D	E
Running	1	2	3	4	5
Jumping	4	2	1	5	3
Throwing	3	2	5	1	4

28. Make scatter diagrams for the three pairs of rankings in problem 27. How do the diagrams correspond with your computations?

29. Prove or disprove the following statement: If two sets of rankings each have the same correlation coefficient with respect to a third set of rankings, then the first two are perfectly correlated with each other.

30. Write the equation and draw the graph of the straight line whose slope is $5/4$ and whose Y-intercept is -2.

31. Repeat problem 30 for a slope of -3 and a Y-intercept of 5.3.

32. Find the regression equation of Y on X for the data of Table 37.

33. Find the regression equation of X on Y for the data of Table 37.

34. Draw the graphs of the equations found in problems 32 and 33. Estimate from your graph the coordinates of the point of intersection.

35. Use equation 22 to find the value of r that will give $s_e = \dfrac{s_Y}{3}$.

36. If the variance s_Y^2 of Y is 12 and the standard error of estimate is 3, what is the value of r?

37. Can the standard error of estimate be improved (reduced) by enlarging the sample? Why?

38. Repeat the derivation of $s_e = s_Y\sqrt{1 - r^2}$ using the more easily handled x and y in place of $(X - \bar{X})$ and $(Y - \bar{Y})$, respectively.

39. What are some of the deeper pitfalls awaiting the careless user of r_p and r_r?

PART

I I

Inductive Inference

INTRODUCTION

THE TECHNIQUES presented in Part I for describing the data of a survey or experiment are indispensable. But they are not enough. Although these techniques do cope successfully with variability, they do not, by themselves, provide a means for solving the major problem with which we opened this book—the problem of *inductive inference*.

The student will recall from Chapter 1 that only a limited number of observations are available to the scientist. He cannot observe all relevant instances—now and forever—of the phenomena which he is studying. But to limit one's conclusions only to those specific events observed is annoying and unsatisfactory, because the scientist wishes to generalize from his experiments: he wishes to present results which will have general significance, which will be applicable over and beyond the specific subjects and conditions actually studied. (Such highly general results, of course, lead toward scientific laws.)

The problem of inductive inference takes two specific forms so far as the behavioral scientist is concerned. When the behavioral scientist is undertaking a "natural history" study, one form is involved; when he sets out to discover laws of behavior, another form is involved. In the naturalistic undertaking the investigator aims at obtaining an accurate estimate of the actual—or true—value in a population; that is, he may wish to know what is the average intelligence of the children in a given area, how many voters are Republicans, how many children drink milk, or how many high school seniors are planning to go to college. The task for the investigator attempting a naturalistic study is to get an accurate estimate of the true value in question. Because he cannot examine every case, the investigator must make an inference from those cases observed to those not observed. His procedure is to make an *estimate*—an inference on the basis of a sample of individuals drawn from the population in which he is interested.

Naturally the question will arise as to how good the estimate is—how close it approximates the true value—for such estimates are always subject to error. *An important function of the statistical method is to provide a rigorous, logical procedure whereby the estimate can be made with a high probability such that the error made, if any, is quite small.*

However, when studying the conditions which affect behavior, as in an experiment, the problem of inductive inference arises in a different form. The problem resolves itself to this: Are the results of the study true regularities? Would they appear if the study were endlessly repeated? Or are they mere accidental random combinations of events which happened to occur in this specific experiment?

To take a simple illustration, suppose that a psychologist who wishes to discover whether condition A or condition B results in more rapid learning arranges for one group of subjects to learn under condition A and another to learn under condition B; after the appropriate number of learning sessions, he compares the achievement of the two groups. There will, of course, be a good deal of variability among the individuals in each group, and, therefore, it will be appropriate to use some measure of central tendency (such as the mean achievement score) to compare the groups. Suppose that the mean achievement score of one group was higher than that of the other, but the distribution of scores overlapped: Was the apparent difference due to a regular, systematic relation between the conditions and achievement? Will the relation appear regularly, and can it be relied upon? Or was the difference merely due to some peculiar happenstance and, therefore, not to be relied upon? A decision must be reached as to which interpretation is correct. *A primary function of the statistical method is to provide a rigorous, logical procedure for making this decision.*

It may well occur to the student that no "method," statistical or otherwise, is really necessary to make a decision of this kind. If the research is thoughtfully carried out, should not the experiment itself make clear whether the data represent lawful, regular events? Is it not the task of the experiment itself to provide the answer to this question? The answer is, No—for two reasons. First, every study produces a distribution of events, with a standard deviation larger than 0. Although there may be differences of opinion as to the source of variability, the behavioral scientist must cope with the fact that he will find variability in his data. Small differences between the mean scores of two groups, between the percentages for and against various issues, and the like, will raise the question of accidental differences immediately. But even large differences have to be evaluated in terms of the amount of variability in the distributions. The ideal situation would be one in which it was possible to draw the line—to say that in *this* study one may lay the results to an accidental combination of events, but in *that* study the findings are a result of factors which are systematically related to one another. A good method for making this decision should approach this ideal as closely as possible.

The second reason that an experiment requires statistical analysis has to do with inductive inference. The behavioral scientist cannot include in any given experiment all the individuals in which he is interested. He may be interested in studying human beings, but he cannot study all of them. No amount of experimental skill and rigor can avoid this problem. Clearly, a method is needed which will cope successfully with the necessity to make inferences from those individuals included in the study to those not included. Of course, this method must be logically sound and generally applicable. Let us consider the nature of this method briefly and in general terms.

The scientist formulates a hypothesis, carries out an experiment to test its validity, and analyzes the results. But those scientists who use random-sampling techniques in order to make an inductive inference (and the behavioral scientist is one of these) must face the fact that they may draw the wrong conclusion about their results simply by reason of variations due to random sampling. Therefore, there is always some risk attached to their decisions about the outcome of the experiment—whether, for example, the hypothesis has been confirmed or not. Because of our knowledge of randomness, however, it is possible to calculate the *amount of risk involved*. Indeed, it is possible to set the amount of tolerable risk in advance, and to design the experiment so that the decision may be made with no more risk than is desirable.

Note that the method is based primarily on our knowledge of *the behavior of random events*. Moreover, the method is an outgrowth of the fact that the form of a series of random events can be predicted with considerable accuracy. This point is crucial, for it is knowledge about random events which enables the scientist to ascertain the risk involved in drawing a given conclusion from the results of an experiment.

This procedure may seem strange and certainly invites incredulity. That is as it should be; it *is* a strange procedure. But the student will find not only that there is no other way to proceed but that this way is a very good way indeed. The remaining chapters show why such a procedure provides a good approach to the problem of variability and inductive inference, and why the concept of randomness is fundamental to this approach.

The improbable is inevitable.

R. A. FISHER

CHAPTER

7

A MODEL OF
RANDOMNESS

IN ORDER to achieve a clear understanding of the statistical method, it is necessary to take a close look at a key concept, *randomness*. It is our knowledge of randomness upon which everything else depends.

"Randomness" refers to a set of events in which one event has no predictable effect on the next. Games of chance involve events of this kind, provided they are honestly run. Knowledge of the outcome of one throw of a die, one turn of the wheel, or one toss of the coin in no way aids in our prediction of what the next throw, turn, or toss will reveal. "Randomness," in other words, refers to events which are independent and unrelated to one another. *Independence* is a crucial condition of randomness. Thus, when a scientist wishes to create a *random sample*, he must not only be certain that he draws his sample in such a way that each item in the sample is drawn *independently* of every other item but also that each item has an *equal likelihood* of appearing in the sample. Otherwise, he cannot claim to have met the conditions of randomness. (See Box 22.)

A principal fact about random events is that, although each event taken *singly* is unpredictable, certain *collections* of random events have highly predictable forms. The most prominent of these predictable forms, although by no means the only one, is known as the "normal probability curve," to which we shall give a great deal of consideration later in this

---

B O X 2 2

Random Thoughts Are Impossible

". . . nothing is so alien to the human mind as the idea of randomness. It is true that we can conceive of randomness in a negative way as devoid of pattern or form. And we can think of sequence that appears to lack system, and therefore has an unpredictable character, the unpredictability being due either to the limitations of the human mind or to the intrinsic nature of the material. But we ourselves cannot perceive, think, decide, or act in a random manner. When we construct so-called randomizers, mechanical or electronic, or when we prepare series of numbers which we believe are random in the above sense, we do so by withdrawing our mental participation from the randomizing process. The moment we intervene we introduce an element of pattern. Try to utter or write down a series of numbers or words 'at random'; you will find that the resulting series is not random at all but marked by certain patterns or meaningful linkages between the items. A sequence of choices made by the youngest child who can understand speech invariably has a pattern. Even if he merely has to decide in which hand a sweet is hidden, his successive selections of right or left hand will reveal a pattern of preferences which is characteristic of children of his age in the particular circumstances of the experiment. There will of course be variation from child to child, but the choices will never be random."

Cohen, J. 1960. *Chance, skill and luck.* Harmondsworth: Penguin Books.

---

chapter. A further highly significant fact about randomness is that the various forms which collections of random events assume may be nicely described, or represented, by mathematical equations. This is another, and very important, example of what was noted in Chapter 2—concrete events in the world of things may become represented by symbols in the world of ideas. And, of course, such representations of events may have greater or lesser degrees of correspondence with concrete events.

Mathematicians have provided scientists with several formulas or equations for describing various forms of randomness. We shall refer to these equations as models, because "model" is a simple word for indicating that each equation represents an ideal form of a distribution of random events. Such models exist in their perfect form only in the world of ideas. Their counterparts in the world of things may approach but seldom achieve this perfection. But it is the perfect form, the model, which is most useful to us, because it tells us what we need to know—how a set of events will be distributed under idealized conditions of randomness.

Before discussing how such models are employed, we will describe the general nature of the normal probability model because of its wide application in the remaining chapters. (The student should not, however, overlook the fact that there are many models of randomness. Too often it is assumed that the normal probability model is the only one.)

THE NORMAL PROBABILITY MODEL

Although the mathematical rationale of the normal probability model is not developed here because it involves a knowledge of calculus (not presupposed by this book), the Bernoulli model, which is based on the binomial expression $(p + q)^n$ approaches the normal probability model and will be sufficient for our purposes. It is through the binomial model, then, that a view of the normal probability model will be attained here.

The binomial expression

In the binomial expression $(p + q)^n$ the symbol p refers to the probability of one kind of event (such as the probability of "heads" in coin tossing), q refers to the probability of nonoccurrence of that same event ("tails"), and n refers to the number of repetitions of the event (tosses of the coin, or coins, under conditions of randomness). When the expression $(p + q)^n$ is expanded, for example, with $n = 2$, it results in $(p + q)^2 = p^2 + 2pq + q^2$. Each term (such as p^2) states the frequency with which a specific random event should occur *relative* to the total number of events; that is, each term states the *relative frequency* with which a specific random event should occur—according to the theory of the binomial expression.

A simple concrete example will make this clearer. Consider the random events which occur in tossing two pennies repeatedly. The alternative events are heads (p) or tails (q). Since each event, heads *or* tails, is equally likely, the probability of heads (p) equals one half, and the probability of tails also equals one half. The number of pennies is n—in this case, two. According to the expansion of the binomial expression for this situation where $p = \frac{1}{2}, q = \frac{1}{2}$, and $n = 2$, we find that

$$(\tfrac{1}{2} + \tfrac{1}{2})^2 = (\tfrac{1}{2})^2 + 2(\tfrac{1}{2})(\tfrac{1}{2}) + (\tfrac{1}{2})^2$$
$$= \tfrac{1}{4} + \tfrac{1}{2} + \tfrac{1}{4}$$

This asserts that the relative frequency of occurrence of two heads (p) is $\frac{1}{4}$ (or once in four trials), the relative frequency of a head and a tail (pq) is $\frac{1}{2}$ (once in two trials), and the relative frequency of two tails (q) is $\frac{1}{4}$ (once in four trials) under idealized conditions of randomness. We shall consider in detail the arithmetic involved in this expression later; the point to observe here is that a relation exists between the above theoretical statement—an expression in the world of ideas—and a set of events, *random events*, in the world of things.

We now present a larger expansion of the binomial $(p + q)^n$ in order to show that as n increases, the number of outcomes increases. Thus, for example, when n is increased from 2 to 5, the binomial expression becomes

$$(p + q)^5 = p^5 + 5p^4q + 10p^3q^2 + 10p^2q^3 + 5pq^4 + q^5$$

With reference to coin-tossing again, where $p = q = \frac{1}{2}$, the above expansion asserts that five heads should occur with a relative frequency of $(\frac{1}{2})^5$, or $(\frac{1}{2}) (\frac{1}{2}) (\frac{1}{2}) (\frac{1}{2}) (\frac{1}{2})$, which is $\frac{1}{32}$.

The relative frequency of $\frac{1}{32}$ means that, should five coins be tossed repeatedly, one of thirty-two of the trials should result in all five coins appearing as heads. To repeat, the binomial expansion states the frequency with which a given random event (such as five heads) should occur relative to the total number of events (thirty-two) under idealized conditions of randomness.

How often will five coins appear as four heads and one tail under idealized conditions of randomness? The second term of the binomial expansion states that the probability of obtaining four heads and one tail when five coins are tossed is $5p^4q$, or $5 (\frac{1}{2})^4 (\frac{1}{2})$, or $\frac{5}{32}$. Thus four heads and one tail should appear in five out of thirty-two of the trials.

How often should five coins appear in the form of three heads and two tails? The third term of the binomial expansion gives the probability of this event as $10p^3q^2$, or $10(\frac{1}{2})^3(\frac{1}{2})^2$, which is equal to the ratio $\frac{10}{32}$; thus, the binomial model asserts that ideally, in ten of thirty-two of the tosses, or trials, the random event three heads and two tails should occur. Obviously, this event is ten times more likely to occur than five heads, which should occur in one of thirty-two of the trials. To put these fractions in terms of percentages merely requires the division of 1 by 32, or 5 by 32, or or 10 by 32 and multiplication by 100: when this is done, it may be said that the relative frequencies of the various possible outcomes are 3.125 per cent for five heads, 15.625 per cent for four heads, and so on. *The larger the number of times the five coins are tossed, the more closely these percentages approach the percentages in the ideal form.*

The complete expansion of the binomial $(p + q)^{10}$ is displayed in the first column of Table 47 for the case where the actual events are heads and

TABLE 47

The Eleven Terms of $(H + T)^{10}$

RELATIVE FREQUENCY
OF EVENTS

$H^{10} = \frac{1}{1024}$	1 chance in 1,024 of all coins falling heads
$10H^9T^1 = \frac{10}{1024}$	10 chances in 1,024 of 9 heads and 1 tail
$45H^8T^2 = \frac{45}{1024}$	45 chances in 1,024 of 8 heads and 2 tails
$120H^7T^3 = \frac{120}{1024}$	120 chances in 1,024 of 7 heads and 3 tails
$210H^6T^4 = \frac{210}{1024}$	210 chances in 1,024 of 6 heads and 4 tails
$252H^5T^5 = \frac{252}{1024}$	252 chances in 1,024 of 5 heads and 5 tails
$210H^4T^6 = \frac{210}{1024}$	210 chances in 1,024 of 4 heads and 6 tails
$120H^3T^7 = \frac{120}{1024}$	120 chances in 1,024 of 3 heads and 7 tails
$45H^2T^8 = \frac{45}{1024}$	45 chances in 1,024 of 2 heads and 8 tails
$10H^1T^9 = \frac{10}{1024}$	10 chances in 1,024 of 1 head and 9 tails
$T^{10} = \frac{1}{1024}$	1 chance in 1,024 of all coins falling tails

tails, and therefore $p = .5$ and $q = .5$ (H and T—for heads and tails—being used in the table instead of p and q), and the number of trials is 10. The data of the table are presented graphically in Figure 27. Each outcome is plotted on the horizontal axis, and the frequency of its expected occurrence is indicated on the vertical axis.

A dotted line has been drawn through the center points of the bars of the histogram.

It is important that the reader not be confused by the arithmetic in the above paragraphs, and that he remember the significant feature of the discussion—*a correspondence exists between a mathematical expression (the binomial expansion) and the frequency of occurrence of specific random events in the world of things.*

The student's attention must also be called to the way in which the correspondence between this model and real events occurs; noting carefully the *form* of the dotted line in Figure 27, the student will perceive the clear resemblence of this line to the familiar "normal curve" of heights, weights, intelligence test scores, the "grade curve," and so forth. The reason for this is that as the *binomial expression is expanded, the results begin to approximate the normal curve.* The greater the value of n in the expression $(p + q)^n$—that is, as the number of trials increases—the closer the ap-

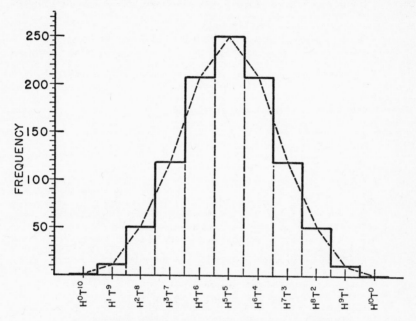

FIG. 27. The histogram and frequency polygon of theoretical frequencies of heads and tails of 10 coins tossed 100 times (see Table 47).

proximation of the results to the normal curve. The binomial model predicts the frequency of specific random phenomena, and the predictions, although not perfect, are very good ones.

A further example of the relation between the binomial expansion and the normal curve is provided in Figure 28, which shows the results obtained when a set of twelve coins was tossed 4,096 times. On each toss the number of heads which appeared ranged from none to twelve. The thirteen terms of $(p + q)^{12}$ with $p = q = \frac{1}{2}$ give the relative frequencies with which each of these thirteen outcomes is *predicted* to occur under ideal conditions where randomness alone has produced the outcomes. The

actual frequencies of the thirteen possible outcomes are given by the
dotted-line frequency polygon in Figure 28, and the expected frequencies
(relative frequencies multiplied by 4,096) are shown in the solid polygon.
The student should compare the actual frequencies with the theoretical
(ideal) frequencies—that is, those expected on the basis of the binomial
expansion.

There are two points to be noted here: first, the close correspondence
between the actual outcomes and those predicted by the binomial model,

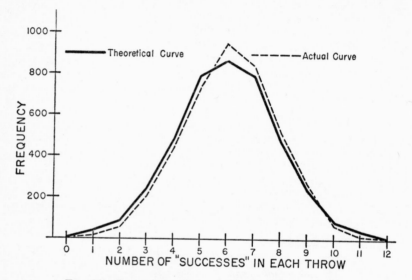

FIG. 28. Comparison of frequencies predicted by the
Bernoulli model with actual frequencies obtained by
throwing 12 coins 4,096 times.

and, second, once again, the close resemblance between the curves in Figure 28 to the normal curve. The binomial expansion approximates the normal curve ever more closely as the number of trials increases.

In summary, the mathematical expression $(p + q)^n$ provides a good
description of certain random phenomena. When these random phenomena are sufficiently numerous, the frequency curve of the random phenomena approximates the normal probability curve. Moreover, the more numerous the data, the more closely the results approximate the normal
curve. In short, *when the data become sufficiently numerous, the form of the
distribution of random phenomena becomes constant and predictable.* And
with enough trials even "the improbable is inevitable." (See Box 23.)

The fact that random events in the world of things can be adequately represented by a mathematical expression has immense practical value. For it then becomes possible to set up tables so that the relative frequency

---

B O X   2 3

From Chaos, Order

The attention of many people has been engaged by the fact that as we increase the number of random observations, the distribution curve of these random observations more closely approximates the perfectly symmetrical normal distribution curve. As L. C. Tippett, the British statistician points out, this apparent paradox of increasing order emerging from increasing chaos has from time to time given rise to metaphysical speculation. Thus people of the eighteenth century saw in the regularity found among individual variation evidences of a divine order. Sir Arthur Eddington saw in the concomitant unpredictability of *individual* random events and the complete predictability of a large population of random events some comfort for those who want to believe in free will and scientific law at the same time.

Sir Francis Galton, one of the foremost scientists of the nineteenth century, and the inventor of a number of statistical methods used by behavioral sci-entists, observed with wonder the manner in which order emerges from the apparent chaos of random events.

"I know of scarcely anything so apt to impress the imagination as the wonderful form of cosmic order expressed by the 'Law of Frequency of Error.' The law would have been personified by the Greeks and deified, if they had known of it. It reigns with serenity and in complete effacement, amidst the wildest confusion. The huger the mob, and the greater the apparent anarchy, the more perfect is its sway. It is the supreme law of Unreason. Whenever a large sample of chaotic elements are taken in hand and marshalled in the order of their magnitude, an unsuspected and most beautiful form of regularity proves to have been latent all along."

Tippett, L. *Sampling and the standard error,* in Newman, J. R. 1956. *The world of mathematics.* New York: Simon and Schuster.
Galton, F. 1894. *Natural inheritance.* New York: Macmillan.

(probability) of any specific random event may be ascertained immediately. This feature is due to two specific characteristics of the normal probability model, which will be described in the next section. Before leaving this section, however, we wish to remind the student that all the models of randomness discussed in this book are ideal forms approximated more and more closely as the number of trials is increased.

Using the normal probability model

Two characteristics of the normal probability curve make it simple to use. First, as the reader will recall, the curve is *symmetrical;* the mean, median, and mode are at exactly the same point—they have exactly the same value—and, therefore, the left half of the curve is a mirror image of the right half (see page 132). Second, the standard deviation bears an exact relation to the area under the curve. In order to clarify this relation, it is necessary to discuss various portions of the area enclosed between the curve and the X-axis. It will be convenient for this purpose to apply the term *ordinate* to any line segment rising perpendicularly from the horizontal axis to the curve. The line which joins the peak of the curve to the point just below it on the axis is called the *ordinate at the mean.*

Now the relation referred to above between the standard deviation s and the area under the curve is as follows. The area between the ordinates at $X = \mu$ and $X = \mu + \sigma$ is a fixed portion of the whole area. To one decimal place, it is 34.1 per cent of the entire area. Since the curve is symmetrical with respect to the ordinate at $X = \mu$, the area between the ordinates erected one standard deviation to either side of the mean is very nearly 68.2 per cent of the whole area. Approximately 95 per cent of the area is included between the ordinates at $X = \mu \pm 2\sigma$. For almost all practical applications, 99.99 per cent of the area is included between the ordinates at $X = \mu \pm 3\sigma$. Tables have been computed whereby the area between any two ordinates is easily computed; see Table A in the Appendix, which gives the areas between the ordinates at μ and $\dfrac{X - \mu}{\sigma} = z$ for various values of z from 0 to 3. And because the curve is symmetrical—that is, the areas for negative values of z are the same as for the corresponding positive values of z—only the positive values of z are presented in Table A.

The reader will be familiar with the above facts concerning the standard deviation and the normal probability curve by virtue of the discussion of these points in Chapters 4 and 5 (see page 131 and Figure 11), and the above remarks are intended merely to recall them to mind. The remainder is important, however, for when the normal probability table is used in connection with random phenomen, it is precisely the relation between the standard deviation and the area of the curve which furnishes the key to its use as a model of randomness.

Thus, when considering the normal probability model, each point on the X-axis can be considered to differ from the mean by a number of standard deviations. Corresponding to this number of standard deviations, a definite portion of the area under the curve is associated. Now, keeping in mind that a frequency curve, such as the normal curve, may be considered to be the limiting form of a histogram having a very large number of very narrow bars, this fraction of area can be interpreted as a fraction of all possible cases. (Remember that it is characteristic of histograms that *their area is equal to the number of data.* See Chapter 2, page 59.) In other words, various portions, or areas, of the normal curve may be thought of as relative frequencies, or probabilities. The probability that a value of X between two given points will occur is equal to the proportion of area contained between the ordinates at those two points: thus, the probability that a randomly selected datum from a normal population will not differ from the mean by more than one standard deviation is .682 (68.2 per cent of the area of the curve lies between μ and plus or minus one standard deviation. See Box 24.)

By way of example

Suppose that a group of children has been given a test of arithmetic: the distribution of scores is normal, the mean of the distribution is 50, and the standard deviation is 10. What is the relative frequency (probability) of children chosen at random obtaining a score between 50 and 60 —that is, between the mean (50) and one standard deviation to the right of the mean ($+10$)? When the distribution of scores approximates the normal probability curve, we need only to look at the normal probability table; there we find that when $\dfrac{X - \bar{X}}{s}$, or z, is equal to 1 (which is the value of z in the above case, for $\dfrac{60 - 50}{10} = 1$), 34.1 per cent of the cases will lie between the mean and one standard deviation unit to the right of it. Because 34.1 per cent is roughly equivalent to one third, approximately one of every three cases is expected to lie between the mean and a point one standard deviation above the mean. Thus, the probability is approximately ⅓ that *cases drawn at random will lie between the mean and a point one standard deviation above it.* In the above illustration the chances are about one in three that cases drawn at random will have a score which lies between 50 and 60.

Consider a different question. What is the probability that children in the above hypothetical example will have a score which lies *beyond* a given point? In other words, what is the relative frequency of various

---

B O X   2 4

Probability

Despite the fact that the concept of probability has been under the scrutiny of philosophers, mathematicians, and scientists for some 300 years, it has successfully resisted being reduced to a single, perfectly clear definition. To some, probability implies a degree of uncertainty about future events ("Will it rain tonight?") or a degree of uncertainty about whether some event took place ("Did Caesar cross here?"). When probabilities are assigned to these kinds of statements, they are called "subjective probabilities," for the reason that the probability lies with the person who holds the belief rather than in the event. For, after all, rain will or will not fall tonight, and Caesar did or did not cross here. There is no uncertainty in the event itself, only in our knowledge about it.

To others the term probability may also be attached to a scientific hypothesis; thus, one might attach a probability of .8 (or .3) to the proposition that a child's creative ability is fully determined by the time he reaches age six. The degree of probability assigned is reached by following Hume's suggestion that "a wise man proportions his belief to the evidence." It has been argued that this is merely another form of subjective probability on the ground that the proposition itself can only be true or false.

To the mathematician, however, the term "probability" has different meanings. Most impor-

---

scores beyond a specific point? To take a specific example, what is the relative frequency of occurrence of scores more than two standard deviations above the mean. Inspection of Table A in the Appendix shows that approximately 47.5 per cent of the cases are expected to lie *between* the mean and a point two standard deviations above the mean. Since 50 per cent of all cases lie to the right of the mean, approximately 2.5 per cent $(50 - 47.5 = 2.5)$ of the cases will be expected to have scores beyond a point two standard deviations to the right of the mean. (Because the curve is symmetrical, 2.5 per cent of the cases are also expected to lie beyond two standard deviations to the *left* of the mean.)

Before concluding this section, the student should be reminded that there are other models of randomness aside from the normal probability model. Certain of these will be discussed later in this book.

---

tant of these is the concept of probability as a relative frequency, which the student will recognize is the sense in which the term is employed here. It should be emphasized that the frequency concept of probability is not applicable to events which are *unique,* but to those which occur repeatedly. And it is this feature which permits the mathematical development of the theory of probability which underlies the whole of the statistical method.

Polya provides an amusing example of "How not to interpret the frequency concept of probability."

"The [doctor] shook his head as he finished examining the patient. 'You have a very serious disease,' said the [doctor]. 'Of ten patients who have got this disease only one survives. . . . But you are lucky. You will survive, because you came to me. I have already had nine patients who all died of it.' "

Do the subjective and frequency theories of probability conflict? C. S. Peirce (a frequentist) took the position that ". . . the whole utility of probability is to insure us in the long run." But J. M. Keynes (a subjectivist) noted that ". . . in the long run, we shall all be dead." The student who pursues the study of probability will find himself at once in the midst of highly significant unresolved logical, scientific, and even moral issues. A good place to begin is Part VII, Volume II, of J. R. Newman's *The world of mathematics,* to be followed by a conference with a philosopher in order to discover which avenues should be explored next. Try it.

Polya, G. 1954. *Patterns of plausible inference.* Princeton: Princeton University Press.

By way of summary

Understanding the concept of randomness is fundamental to understanding the statistical method. "Randomness" refers to a set of events in which one event has no predictable effect on another. However, although *single* random events are unpredictable, certain *collections* of random events assume highly predictable forms. The purpose of this chapter is to illustrate the nature of the most prominent form of these collections—

the normal probability curve—and the extent to which certain actual random events approximate this ideal mathematical form. (See Box 25.)

The correspondence between certain actual random events and the

---

BOX 25

Gambling

Although it may be surmised that the student of probability is not likely to be a gambler (having more faith in his knowledge of relative frequencies than in luck), we cannot expect that the reader will be able to suppress completely whatever tendencies he may share with his fellow man to indulge in a game of chance. Therefore we offer two pieces of advice to those who will succumb to temptation. The first is from John Maynard Keynes, the famous British economist, and is quite general in nature. The second is quite specific. Neither is guaranteed to increase your fortune in the slightest.

Keynes gives a mathematical proof that "the poorer a gambler is, relatively to his opponent, the more likely he is to be ruined." Furthermore, if one's opponent has resources of an infinite amount, ruin is therefore certain. Continuing the argument, he points out that "The infinitely rich gambler is the public. It is against the public that the professional gambler plays, and his ruin is therefore certain." Keynes then considers (possibly with tongue in cheek) some of the implications of this conclusion, thus: "[However], . . . no gambler plays, as this argument supposes, forever. At the end of any finite quantity of play, the player, even if he is not the public, *may* finish with winnings of any finite size. The gambler is in a worse position if his capital is smaller than his opponent's—at poker, for instance, or on the Stock Exchange. This is clear. But our desire for moral improvement outstrips our logic if we tell him that he *must* lose. Besides it is paradoxical to say that everybody individually must lose and that everybody collectively must win. For every individual gambler who loses there is an individual gambler or syndicate of gamblers who win. The true moral is this, that poor men should not gamble and that millionaires should do nothing else.

---

normal probability curve was shown to be very close, and to become closer as the number of events becomes very large. As a result, tabled values of the normal probability curve may be employed to ascertain the relative frequency (probability) of various actual random events. Such a table is of great practical value. It is easy to use because one half of the curve is a mirror-image of the other (thus, only half of the values need to be tabled), and because the standard deviation is the measure of the dis-

---

But millionaires gain nothing by gambling with one another, and until the poor man departs from the path of prudence the millionaire does not find his opportunity. If it be replied that in fact most millionaires are men originally poor who departed from the path of prudence, it must be admitted that the poor man is not doomed with certainty. Thus the philosopher must draw what comfort he can from the conclusion with which his theory furnishes him, that millionaires are often fortunate fools who have thriven on unfortunate ones."

The second piece of advice concerns what is known as the "gambler's fallacy." This fallacy is well known to all students of probability and statistics; yet surprisingly enough few gamblers seem to be aware of it, and they greet the notion with considerable scepticism. The gambler's fallacy is that he believes that the probability of an event's occurrence changes with the occurrence of the preceeding events. Thus, a gambler playing at roulette, for example, may observe that on the last six turns of the wheel the ball has fallen in a red pocket. "Aha," he muses "we are about ready for a black." Perhaps he is cautious. He waits for another turn of the wheel. Red again! Now he has no doubts whatever. Red has appeared seven times in a row. On the next turn the ball *must* fall in the black! He splurges, bets all his chips on the black. Does he win? We cannot answer that, unfortunately. But we can say this: The gambler's hopes were based on a mistaken premise— for the odds against a black on the crucial turn of the wheel remained exactly what they were on *any* turn of the wheel. Each event, each turn of the wheel (assuming that it is honest) involves exactly the same probability for the red or the black as any other turn, for each turn is independent of every other turn. The probability of the occurrence of an event is not dependent upon the outcome of previous events—providing the events occur at random. And randomness, of course, is the essential element of gambling.

Keynes, J. 1921. *A treatise on probability*. London: Macmillan and New York: St. Martin's Press.

---

tance along the base line of the curve. Thus, in order to ascertain the relative frequency of the occurrence of specific random events, it is only necessary to locate their distances from the mean of the distribution in terms of the standard deviation.

❨ Mathematically . . .

To attain the degree of generality needed, and to provide a convenient mathematical basis for the development of the student's knowledge of models of randomness, the concept of a *set* will be considered first.

SETS

Mathematically, a *set* is a collection or aggregation of objects. The objects may be anything whatever—people, numbers, ideas, or even other sets. In order to specify a set exactly, either of two methods may be used: the objects, called the *elements* of the set, may be listed in complete detail; or, if such a listing is not feasible, a rule may be developed which when applied to any object whatever will classify the object as an element or as a nonelement of the set.

For example, the set, *A*, of all odd numbers between 1 and 10 may be defined either by actually listing all of these numbers ($A = \{1, 3, 5, 7, 9\}$) or by the expression "all odd numbers between 0 and 10." In some cases the set *must* be defined by the rule; for example, the infinite set, *B*, of *all* odd numbers cannot, of course, be listed in detail. A convenient notation for this is $B = \{x|x$ is an odd number$\}$, which is read, "*B* is the set of all *x*'s such that *x* is an odd number." It is also possible that the rule by which a set is defined may be satisfied by no object: such a set is called an *empty* or *null* set, denoted by the symbol ϕ. The set of all people who are 200 years of age is such an empty set. Although it may appear strange to consider sets which have no elements, the concept is extremely useful, as will be shown shortly.

Combining of sets

Two or more sets may be combined into a single set by means of an operation analogous to the addition operation for numbers. However, because sets are not numbers, and because there are essential differences in the two operations, a different name and symbol are used for combining sets. Thus, mathematicians talk about the *union* of sets. The union of two sets *A* and *B* is denoted by $A \cup B$ and consists of all the elements that are in either *A* or *B* or in both *A* and *B*. The following examples will serve to show both the similarities and differences which this method of combining sets has with ordinary addition.

Let $A = \{r, s, t, u, v\}, B = \{m, n, p, t, v\}$, and $C = \{k, l, m, p\}$. Then the unions $A \cup B$, $A \cup C$, and $B \cup C$ are as follows:

$$A \cup B = \{m, n, p, r, s, t, u, v\}$$
$$A \cup C = \{k, l, m, p, r, s, t, u, v\}$$
$$B \cup C = \{k, l, m, n, p, t, v\}$$

Note that the set $A \cup B$ has eight elements, although A and B each have five. The reason for this is that those which appear in both A and B are shown just once in $A \cup B$. In the case of $A \cup C$ the sets A and C have no common elements, and hence the five elements of A and the four elements of C form a union of nine elements. (Sets such as A and C, which have no element in common, are said to be *disjoint* or *mutually exclusive*.)

It is possible to form the union of three sets by forming the union of two of them and then forming the union of the resulting set with the third set; that is, the union of the sets A, B, and C is $(A \cup B) \cup C$. Since it does not matter which pair of sets is selected for the first union, the parentheses are usually omitted and the result written $A \cup B \cup C$. The process can obviously be extended to four or more sets.

A second operation by which sets may be combined to produce other sets is that of *intersection*. The *intersection* of two sets A and B is the set of all elements which are in both A and B. In the examples given above, with intersection denoted by $\cap$,

$$A \cap B = \{t, v\}$$
$$A \cap C = \phi$$
$$B \cap C = \{m, p\}$$

$A \cap B$ has only the elements t and v because only these elements are *common* to both A and B. Note that the disjoint sets A and C have as their intersection the null or empty set ϕ. For this reason, disjoint or mutually exclusive sets are frequently referred to as "sets with a null intersection."

As with unions, three sets may be combined into an intersection by first choosing any two of them, forming their intersection, and then intersecting this result with the third set. Extension of the process to four or more sets is as easily done.

To further exemplify the ideas of union and intersection, consider the three sets of geometric points denoted below by A, B, and C. Each circle encloses a set of points in the plane. Some points lie in only one of the three sets, some lie in two sets, and some lie in all three sets. The regions have been numbered for easy reference. The number 6 thus stands for all the points in the sixth region. The union $A \cup B$ consists of 1, 2, 3, 4, 5, and 6, while the intersection $A \cap B$ consists of 2 and 5. The intersection of two sets is, in fact, their "overlap." The union of two sets may be thought of as their "combined total expanse." Note in the figure that the only points common to A, B, and C are those in region 5; thus, $A \cap B \cap C$ is the proper expression for region 5.

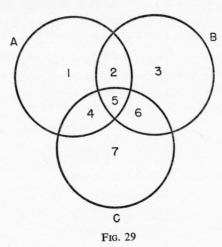

FIG. 29

Measure of a set

The concepts of set, element, union, and intersection, along with a few others not immediately necessary here, form the basis for an algebra of sets. This algebra of sets, called *set theory*, is of fundamental importance in practically all of modern mathematics. In particular, for the immediate purpose, it furnishes an excellent beginning point for the development of a theory of probability.

For such a development, the concept of the *measure of a set* must be considered. The measure of a set is a number which serves to quantify some property which the set has by virtue of the elements it contains. It is important to observe here that, although the measure of a set is determined by its elements, it is not a property of the elements but of their aggregate, the set. The property to be measured may rest on any aspect of the elements which is subject to quantification. The simplest measure of a set is the number of elements it contains. Other frequently useful measures are the *sums* of the weights, areas, ages, or incomes of the elements in the set. The measure of a set E will be denoted by $m(E)$ which is read "measure of E."

Without specifying just what measure is being used, it is possible to develop a highly useful property of all set measures. This property is best stated in the form of a theorem.

Theorem 1. If A and B are any sets, then $m(A \cup B) = m(A) + m(B) - m(A \cap B)$.

In proving this theorem, it must be kept in mind that A, B, $A \cup B$, and $A \cap B$ are sets and that their measures are numbers. It is thus appropriate to use the signs $+$ and $-$ in their usual sense when we wish to denote operations performed on the measures. The sum $m(A) + m(B)$ includes the measure contributions of every element of both A and B. Of, course, those elements which are in both A and B also contribute to both $m(A)$ and $m(B)$. But these are exactly those elements in $A \cap B$. By subtracting $m(A \cap B)$, all of the duplicate contributions are deleted and $m(A) + m(B) - m(A \cap B) = m(A \cup B)$ exactly. If $A \cap B = \phi$, then $m(A \cap B) = 0$, and, hence, for disjoint sets the theorem has the simple form $m(A \cup B) = m(A) + m(B)$.

As an example of this theorem, let the measure of a set be the number of its elements, and consider the sets $A = \{a, b, c, d, e, f\}$ and $B = \{a, c, e, g, h\}$. Then $A \cup B = \{a, b, c, d, e, f, g, h\}$ and $A \cap B = \{a, c, e\}$. According to the theorem,

$$
\begin{aligned}
m(A \cup B) &= m(A) + m(B) - m(A \cap B) \\
&= 6 + 5 - 3 \\
&= 8
\end{aligned}
$$

which checks with the fact that $A \cup B$ does have exactly eight elements. The theorem proved here is no more than a precise statement of a relation that is quite frequently dealt with by almost everyone: if two guest lists are made for a reception, for example, it is common knowledge that the number of invited guests is the total of the two lists less the number of duplications, if any. The phrase "less the duplications, if any" refers to the measure of the "intersection" of the two lists and recognizes that this intersection may be empty. By reasoning similar to the above, it can be shown that for three sets, A, B, and C, $m(A \cup B \cup C) = m(A) + m(B) + m(C) - m(A \cap B) - m(A \cap C) - m(B \cap C) + m(A \cap B \cap C)$. The subtracted measures are, as before, to eliminate duplicate contributions to the total measure. They result, however, in a double deletion of those in $A \cap B \cap C$ and hence these contributions are added in again at the end. Using area as the measure, this result can easily be verified for the sets A, B, and C represented by intersecting circles above.

Some additional set concepts

The concepts of the mathematical theory of sets can be applied to the results of experiments in such a way as to help us evaluate these results. Before doing so, however, we must consider three new concepts: outcome space, the principle of indifference, and event.

Outcome space

The outcomes of an experiment can be considered to be a set. The set which the outcomes comprise will be given the special name, *outcome space*, and will be denoted by I (sometimes also called "the universe of discourse"). For example, in an experiment designed to determine how many tails will occur if 100 coins are tossed, the outcome must be one of the whole numbers from 0 to 100 inclusive; these 101 numbers constitute the outcome space or the universe of discourse for this experiment. If the 100 coins are to be repeatedly tossed and it is desired to find the *mean number* of tails per toss, the outcome could be any number, whole or fractional, from 0 to 100; in this case the outcome space would have an infinity of elements.

The measure to be applied to this set (the outcome space) is that of "frequency weights"; that is, each outcome of the experiment is assigned a number proportional to the *expected* frequency of that outcome. These numbers are called the frequency weights of the outcomes, or elements of the outcome space I. The measure of any subset of I can be found by adding the expected frequencies assigned to its elements. For an example of the addition of frequency weights, consider the case of the two flipped coins discussed earlier (page 240). There it was pointed out that the relative frequency of two heads is $\frac{1}{4}$, that the relative frequency of one head and one tail is $\frac{1}{2}$, and that the relative frequency of two tails is $\frac{1}{4}$. From this information the relative frequency of the outcome "at least one head" can be computed by adding the $\frac{1}{4}$ for two heads to the $\frac{1}{2}$ for one head and one tail. Also, the relative frequency of the outcome "both are the same" is obtained by adding the $\frac{1}{4}$ for two heads and the $\frac{1}{4}$ for two tails. In this way, relative frequencies for complex and ramified outcomes (subsets of I) may be constructed from the frequency weights assigned to a complete set of the simplest outcomes (to the elements of I).

Principle of indifference

The *principle of indifference* is employed in order to determine the expected frequencies, or frequency weights, of various outcomes. The principle states that in the absence of knowledge concerning outcome frequencies, each outcome will be assumed to occur with equal frequency.

For example, if a coin is to be flipped, the outcome will be heads or tails; if no knowledge is available as to the fairness of the coin, the principle of indifference requires that equal frequency weights be assigned to heads and tails. As a further example, consider the throw of a die: with no knowledge of the die other than that one of its six faces must lie upward, the principle of indifference requires that no one of the six possible outcomes be preferred in the assignment of outcome frequency weights; hence, each of the outcomes 1 to 6 inclusive would be assigned weight 1. It is important to note that the basic assumption here is that the outcome will be determined by randomness alone, and that "randomness" personified is indifferent as to which possible outcome "it" will choose.

It is apparent that the principle of indifference may be applied in experiments which have been designed so that no one of its outcomes is favored over any of the others. However, it is not always possible to frame or construe an experiment so that the principle of indifference can be directly applied. In such cases the principle of indifference may be modified to give frequency weights which are not based on complete "indifference" or ignorance as to outcome. The knowledge that complete indifference is not operative may derive either from prior similar experiments or from the physical objects of the experiment and accepted theories of the behavior of such objects.

The following example illustrates the modification of the principle of indifference. If one card is to be drawn from a bridge deck, the outcomes may be limited to two, a spade or a nonspade. Since the nonspades outnumber the spades three to one, the principle of indifference is not directly applicable. It seems reasonable, even without prior card-drawing experience, to assume that "chance" will favor a nonspade outcome. If the experiment were to be repeated a large number of times, the resulting outcomes would form a random sequence of spades and nonspades *but not in equal numbers*. The principle of indifference is modified in this case to give frequency weights of 1 and 3. The important point to observe here is that the principle of indifference may be modified according to experience and objective evidence.

To sum up, the set of all possible outcomes of an experiment constitutes the outcome space (I) of the experiment, and the principle of indifference, appropriately modified, is used to assign frequency weights to each outcome of the experiment.

Event

We turn now to the third concept, that of an event. Any *subset* of the outcome space is called an *event*. A subset of I is, of course, any part of the elements of I considered as another set. The idea of a subset includes the two extreme cases ϕ and I as special cases. Consider the experiment of flipping a coin twice. The possible outcomes are

$$HH, HT, TH, TT$$

where H denotes heads and T denotes tails; I thus has four elements. Applying the principle of indifference directly, the weight 1 is assigned to each element of I. The event of "unlike flips" is the subset $\{HT, TH\}$. The event "at least one head" is the subset $\{HH, HT, TH\}$. Several other events may be considered as well. The event "both flips are heads" consists of the single element $\{HH\}$. It is important to note that HH may be considered either as an element of I or as a subset of I. (When considered as a subset of I, the braces $\{\ \}$ should be used to indicate that a set is being considered.)

PROBABILITY

Having presented the concepts of outcome space, the principle of indifference, and the idea of event, we can now define the concept of the probability of an event in these terms.

The probability of an event E is the measure of the event E divided by the measure of the outcome space I. The "measure" referred to in this definition is based on the principle of indifference and on frequency weights as described above. Using this definition in the case of flipping a coin twice, the probability of the event $E = \{HH, TT\}$ is

$$P(E) = \frac{m(E)}{m(I)} = \frac{2}{4} = \frac{1}{2}$$

What is being said here with the aid of symbols is that the combined relative frequencies of all possible outcomes satisfying the condition that both flips are the same is equal to one half of the combined relative frequencies of all the points of the *sample space* (another name for the universe of discourse). Similarly, the probability of at least one head in two flips of a coin is

$$P(E) = \frac{m(E)}{m(I)} = \frac{3}{4}$$

where $E = \{HH, HT, TH\}$ and $m(E) = 3$, since each element of I has the weight 1 assigned to it.

The probability $P(\phi) = \dfrac{m(\phi)}{m(I)} = 0$ corresponds to impossibility. If every possible outcome is included in I, then it is impossible that one of them not occur. Hence, whenever a calculation yields a 0 probability, the conclusion must be that the event involved is impossible.

On the other hand, $P(I) = \dfrac{m(I)}{m(I)} = 1$ corresponds to certainty because at least one of the outcomes in I must occur. The two extremes 0 and 1, corresponding to impossibility and certainty, respectively, thus bound between them the probabilities of all possible events.

Although an experiment may have various possible outcomes, any particular experiment can end with only one outcome; if that outcome is an element of the event in question, then the event is said to have occurred. For example, the event $\{HH, TT\}$ will be said to have occurred if both coins fall with the same face up.

The assignment of frequency weights to the elements of I as a basis for the measure of events depends to a large extent on the nature of the experiment. If special knowledge is available, either from theory or experience, it is used to modify the principle of indifference. It is good practice to design experiments so that the indifference principle may be directly applied. Such equal assignments of relative frequency weights to all outcome space points lead to the most easily handled models of randomness. In this case all outcomes are assigned weight 1, and the probability of an event becomes the number of elements in the event divided by the number of elements in I. Thus, the simplest of all measures is used, that which merely counts the elements involved.

This completes the basic mathematical framework relating set theory to probability. Although this framework is capable of a very extensive elaboration, it will be extended here only to include those situations which have to do (1) with the probability that at least one of two or more specified events will occur and (2) with the probability that two events will occur simultaneously.

Probability of the union of two events

The probability that at least one of two specified events will occur is, in the language of set theory, called the *probability of the union of two events*. The phrase refers to the probability that one or the other or both will occur. Keeping in mind that *an event is a subset of all the possible experimental outcomes*, consider two events—say, E and F. Since E and F are both subsets of I, so also are $E \cup F$ and $E \cap F$. It is thus possible to consider $P(E \cup F)$—that is, the probability of the event $E \cup F$. Now, since $E \cup F$ is all of the outcomes in I which are in either E or F, if either E or F occurs, it is proper to say that $E \cup F$ has occurred. The problem then is to determine $P(E \cup F)$ in terms of the individual probabilities of E and F. By definition, $P(E \cup F) = \dfrac{m(E \cup F)}{m(I)}$. By the theorem on measures,

$$m(E \cup F) = m(E) + m(F) - m(E \cap F)$$

It follows that

$$P(E \cup F) = \frac{m(E) + m(F) - m(E \cap F)}{m(I)}$$

$$= \frac{m(E)}{m(I)} + \frac{m(F)}{m(I)} - \frac{m(E \cap F)}{m(I)}$$

(1) $$= P(E) + P(F) - P(E \cap F)$$

It appears from this result that the probability of "either E or F" depends not only on $P(E)$ and $P(F)$ but on whether or not E and F have elements in common. If $E \cap F = \phi$, the last term of (1) is 0, and the probabilities $P(E)$ and $P(F)$ are merely added together. If $E \cap F \neq \phi$, then the last term of (1) is not 0 and must be reckoned with in the calculation. In the case of $E \cap F = \phi$, E and F are disjoint or mutually exclusive. From this follows the special formula

$$P(E \cup F) = P(E) + P(F)$$

provided that $E \cap F = \phi$ (E and F are mutually exclusive events).
By way of example

As an example of this additive theorem on probabilities, consider a group of 100 people sixty of whom are males, twenty boys, and fifteen girls. What is the probability that a randomly selected person will be an adult or a male? It is first necessary to find $m(I)$. There being no knowledge of any bias in the method of choice, the principle of indifference is directly applicable. Hence, if frequency weight 1 is assigned to each of the 100 people, $m(I) = 100$. Next, the event "an adult will be selected" must be considered; this event will be denoted by A. From the data given it is easy to discover that since there are 35 boys and girls, there must be 65 adults and hence $m(A) = 65$. The data also show that since there are sixty males, if M denotes the event "a male will be chosen," $m(M) = 60$. Then $A \cup M$ is the event of an adult or a male being chosen. From the additive theorem on probabilities,

$$
\begin{aligned}
P(A \cup M) &= P(A) + P(M) - P(A \cap M) \\
&= \tfrac{65}{100} + \tfrac{60}{100} - \tfrac{40}{100} \\
&= .65 + .60 - .40 \\
&= .85
\end{aligned}
$$

The probability $\tfrac{40}{100}$ arises from the fact that twenty of the sixty males are boys. Thus, there are exactly forty people who are simultaneously male and adult, and when one of these forty is chosen, the events A and the event M both occur at the same time. The probability .85 may be interpreted as meaning that if this experiment were to be repeated a large number of times, 85 per cent of the choices would be either adults or males.

Of course, "adults or males" can be interpreted as "adult females or males." The sets W (for women) and M are disjoint sets, and the problem could be expressed as

$$
\begin{aligned}
P(W \cup M) &= P(W) + P(M) \\
&= \tfrac{25}{100} + \tfrac{60}{100} \\
&= .85
\end{aligned}
$$

Here the $\tfrac{25}{100}$ results from the presence in the universe of discourse of twenty-five women. There is no third term to subtract because the set $W \cap M$ of people who are both women and males is the null set; W and M are mutually exclusive. It is always best to frame a probability problem in terms of mutually exclusive (disjoint) events if it is possible to do so.

Probability of the joint occurrence of two events

The appearance of $P(E \cap F)$ in the additive theorem for probabilities makes it necessary to extend the theory to include the probability of the simultaneous occurrence of two events. $P(E \cap F)$ means "the probability that both E and F will occur," whereas $P(E \cup F)$ means "the probability that one or the other or both of E and F will occur."

To compute $P(E \cap F)$, it is necessary to note that $E \cap F$ is a subset of E. This is easy to see from Figure 30, where the shaded area represents $E \cap F$ and is contained entirely within E. It is possible then to consider E as a special outcome space and $E \cap F$ as an event in that outcome space.

With this viewpoint, $P(E \cap F) = \dfrac{m(E \cap F)}{m(E)}.$ Such a probability is given the name of a *conditional probability*. The reason for using the word "conditional" is that limiting the outcome space to the set E is equivalent to setting the condition that the event E must have occurred prior to any

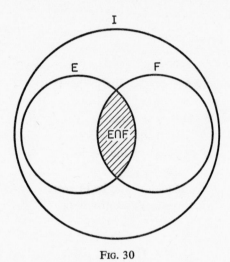

FIG. 30

consideration of the probability of $E \cap F$. For this reason the notation $P(F|E)$ is used and is read "the probability of F given that E has occurred." The notation $P(F|E)$ is thus a convenient way to specify the outcome space as well as the event being considered.

In order to find the probability of the event $E \cap F$, it is only necessary to write

$$P(E \cap F) = \frac{m(E \cap F)}{M(I)}$$
$$= \frac{M(E)}{M(E)} \cdot \frac{M(E \cap F)}{M(I)}$$
$$= \frac{M(E)}{M(I)} \cdot \frac{M(E \cap F)}{M(E)}$$

The right member of the last equation has a particularly simple form if it is stated in terms of probabilities rather than measures. It is, of course, $P(E) \cdot P(F|E)$, so that the result is $P(E \cap F) = P(E) \cdot P(F|E)$.

This result may be interpreted in the form of the following theorem.

Theorem: The probability of the event $E \cap F$ is equal to the probability of E times the probability of F assuming that E has already occurred. This is called the theorem on conditional probabilities.

An interesting special case arises if $E \cap F = \phi$: the occurrence of E precludes the possibility of any outcome in the event F. Then $P(F|E) = 0$, and, consequently,

$$P(E \cap F) = P(E)P(F|E) = 0$$

This result conforms to the fact that the set $E \cap F$ being void has no elements to contribute to its measure, and therefore

$$P(E \cap F) = P(\phi) = \frac{m(\phi)}{m(I)} = \frac{0}{m(I)} = 0.$$

Of less interest is the special case that arises when $E = F$. Then $E \cap F = E \cap E = E$. According to the formula,

$$P(E \cap E) = P(E)P(E|E)$$
$$= P(E)$$

since

$$P(E|E) = \frac{m(E)}{m(E)} = 1$$

The expression for $P(E \cap F)$ obtained here permits a more detailed statement of the additive theorem for probabilities:

$$P(E \cup F) = P(E) + P(F) - P(E \cap F)$$

becomes

$$P(E \cup F) = P(E) + P(F) - P(E)P(F|E)$$

There is a close connection between the questions of the probability of the event $E \cap F$ in a single experiment and the probability that the two separate events E and F will both occur as the outcomes of two different experiments performed consecutively. To show this connection, the case of two separate experiments will be discussed.

Suppose that an urn contains five red and three black balls and that the experiments will each consist of making one draw. Letting R and B denote the events of a red draw and a black draw, respectively,

$$P(R) = \frac{m(R)}{m(I)} = \frac{5}{8}$$

and

$$P(B) = \frac{m(B)}{m(I)} = \frac{3}{8}$$

are the probabilities associated with the first draw, or experiment. The second draw, or experiment, will have the same probabilities as the first one, *provided* that the first draw is returned to the urn before the second draw is made. If such a replacement is *not* made, however, the first draw will alter the outcome space for the second draw. Depending on whether the first ball drawn was red or black, the probabilities for the second experiment will be $P(R|R)$ and $P(B|R)$, or $P(R|B)$ and $P(B|B)$; that is, the probabilities for the second draw must be modified to take into account what has already happened. The probability that a red will be drawn first is $P(R)$. The probability that a black draw will occur after one red ball has been drawn is $P(B|R)$.

The number $P(R)$ can be regarded as the fraction or proportion of times that a red ball would be drawn first if the pair of experiments were to be repeated a large number of times. Some of these many red draws would be succeeded by reds on the second draw, and some would be succeeded by blacks. The proportion of red draws that would be followed by black draws is exactly $P(B|R)$. It thus appears that the proportion of red-black sequences is a fraction of a fraction of all the possible two draw sequences; it is, in fact, $P(R) \cdot P(B|R)$.

This result can be stated as a theorem.

Theorem: The probability that two events E and F will occur in the stated order is $P(E) \cdot P(F|E)$.

It will be noted that this is the same result as that obtained for $P(E \cap F)$. If the occurrence of E has no effect on the outcome space of F, the two events are said to be *independent*, and $P(F|E) = P(F)$. This would be the case in the above example if the first draw were to be replaced in the urn before the second draw is made. In this case the theorem has the simple form:

Theorem: The probability that two independent events E and F will occur in the stated order is $P(E) \cdot P(F)$.

The last two theorems taken together form what is called the *multiplicative theorem for probabilities*. Applied to the problem of the red and black balls discussed above, two cases are to be distinguished with the following results.

CASE 1: Replacement of the first draw is not made. Letting $P(RB)$ denote the probability of a red and black in that order and similarly for the other possible pairs RR, BR, and BB, the probabilities are

$$P(RB) = P(R) \cdot P(B|R) = \tfrac{5}{8} \cdot \tfrac{3}{7} = \tfrac{15}{56}$$
$$P(RR) = P(R) \cdot P(R|R) = \tfrac{5}{8} \cdot \tfrac{4}{7} = \tfrac{20}{56}$$
$$P(BR) = P(B) \cdot P(R|B) = \tfrac{3}{8} \cdot \tfrac{5}{7} = \tfrac{15}{56}$$
$$P(BB) = P(B) \cdot P(B|B) = \tfrac{3}{8} \cdot \tfrac{2}{7} = \tfrac{6}{56}$$

It is no accident that $P(RB) = P(BR) = {}^{15}\!/_{56}$, since the denominators will in all cases be the same while the numerators will be $m(R)$ and $m(B)$, only their order being changed. Since every possible outcome RB, RR, BR, and BB was considered, it is expected that their probabilities will total 1, and this is seen to be the case.

CASE 2: Replacement of the first draw is made.

$$P(RB) = P(R) \cdot P(B) = \tfrac{5}{8} \cdot \tfrac{3}{8} = \tfrac{15}{64}$$
$$P(RR) = P^2(R) = \tfrac{5}{8} \cdot \tfrac{5}{8} = \tfrac{25}{64}$$
$$P(BR) = P(B) \cdot P(R) = \tfrac{3}{8} \cdot \tfrac{5}{8} = \tfrac{15}{64}$$
$$P(BB) = P^2(B) = \tfrac{3}{8} \cdot \tfrac{3}{8} = \tfrac{9}{64}$$

The two sets of probabilities are thus seen to be quite different according to whether or not the first experiment alters the outcome space for the second experiment.

Additive and multiplicative theorems on probabilities are of great importance because by means of them the probabilities of highly complex events can be computed in terms of quite simple events involving outcome spaces with very few elements. Complex events may be considered as unions or intersections of simpler events. In some cases it may be convenient to construe an event as a union of intersections of other events or as an intersection of unions.

Suppose, for example, that a group of 100 people consists of sixty males forty of whom are adults and forty females twenty-five of whom are adults. What is the probability that two persons selected at random will consist of an adult and a child in that order? The problem will be solved in two ways, each of which illustrates a different way of reducing the complex event E in question into a combination of simpler events. First, E will have occurred if any of the following events occur:

E_1, a man and a boy are chosen
E_2, a man and a girl are chosen
E_3, a woman and a boy are chosen
E_4, a woman and a girl are chosen

Each of these four simpler events is disjoint with the other three, so that only one of them, if any, can occur. Also, there is no way for E to happen without one of the four also happening, which means that the events E_1, E_2, E_3, and E_4 exhaust all the possibilities. Having divided E into disjoint, exhaustive events, the additive theorem implies

(1) $$P(E) = P(E_1) + P(E_2) + P(E_3) + P(E_4)$$

The problem of terms such as $P(E_1 \cap E_2)$ is avoided by having chosen mutually exclusive (disjoint) sets. Now the problem of evaluating $P(E_1)$ is construed as finding the probability that two events will occur together—that is, that a man will be selected and that a boy will be selected. Denoting these events by M and B, respectively, and applying the multiplicative theorem,

$$P(E_1) = P(M)P(B|M)$$

Using W for the event of a woman being chosen and G for the case of a girl, it is found similarly that

$$P(E_2) = P(M)P(G|M)$$
$$P(E_3) = P(W)P(B|W)$$
$$P(E_4) = P(W)P(G|W)$$

Then the first simplification of the problem resolves (1) into the form

(2)

$$P(E) = P(M)P(B|M) + P(M)P(G|M) + P(W)P(B|W) + P(W)P(G|W)$$

Each of the probabilities in (2) is easily found from the data given. The result is

$$P(E) = \frac{40}{100} \cdot \frac{20}{99} + \frac{40}{100} \cdot \frac{15}{99} + \frac{25}{100} \cdot \frac{20}{99} + \frac{25}{100} \cdot \frac{15}{99}$$
$$= \frac{800 + 600 + 500 + 375}{9900}$$
$$= \frac{91}{396}$$

which is the required probability. The same result would have been obtained if the event consisting of all possible adult-child pairs had been considered with respect to the outcome space consisting of all pairs of two persons. This would have involved an outcome space of measure 4,950.

Another approach to the problem is as follows. Let A denote the event of an adult, and let C be the event of a child. Then, applying the multiplicative theorem first this time, one obtains

(3) $$P(E) = P(A)P(C|A)$$

The second level of simplification is obtained by noting that $A = M \cup W$ (man or woman) and $C = B \cup G$ (boy or girl). Noting also that $M \cap W = \phi$ and $B \cap G = \phi$, $P(A)$ can be expressed as

$$P(A) = P(M) + P(W)$$

Similarly,

$$P(C|A) = P(B \cup G|A)$$
$$= P(B|A) + P(G|A)$$

Then equation (3) becomes

(4)
$$P(E) = [P(M) + P(W)][P(B|A) + P(G|A)]$$
$$= P(M)P(B|A) + P(M)P(G|A) + P(W)P(B|A) + P(W)P(G|A)$$

The terms of this sum are the same as those computed for (2) above, and the result is the same. The event E required that an adult and a child be selected in that order. Had the order of selection not been of importance, four more sets would have been required in the first solution to take care of the pairs in which a child preceded the adult. The second solution would have involved adding the term $P(C)P(A/C)$ into equation (3). Since a child-adult pair can be formed only by reversing an adult-child pair, the answer in this case would have been twice $9\frac{1}{3}96$, or $9\frac{1}{1}98$.

Permutations and combinations

A sufficiently broad basis, except in one area, has now been completed for the development of the specific and highly useful model of randomness, called the *binomial* or *Bernoulli distribution*. The topic necessary to complete the ground work is that of permutations and combinations. The usefulness of these concepts lies in the ease with which the measures of many sets may be determined with their use.

Permutations

A *permutation* of a set of objects is a sequential ordering of the objects. The two letters a and b have two possible orderings or permutations, ab and ba. If three letters are permuted in all possible ways, six permutations result: abc, acb, bac, bca, cab, and cba.

It is intended here to find a simple formula whereby is found the number of ways in which a set of objects may be permuted. Specifically, the question is, How many permutations are there of n objects permuted r at a time? An example in more familiar terms is that of asking how many three-letter "words" can be formed from the five letters a, b, c, d, and e if no letter is used more than once in any one word. (Any ordering of any three letters is to be considered a word here.) This problem will be solved with a method which will then be generalized to handle the general case of n objects permuted r at a time. The method is to subdivide the set of all permutations into subsets, which in turn will be divided into smaller subsets; this process is continued until the whole set has been so divided into smaller subsets that its structure and number of elements become apparent.

Let S, then, be the set of all three-letter words that can be formed from a, b, c, d, and e with no duplicate letters in any one word. Let S_a be the subset of all such words that begin with a, and let S_b, . . . , S_e be similarly defined. No two of these five subsets will contain any word in common, and every word in S must appear in one of them. The sets S_a, . . . , S_e are thus disjoint, exhaustive subsets. Now let S_a be subdivided into four disjoint, exhaustive subsets: S_{ab}, S_{ac}, S_{ad}, and S_{ae}. Every word whose first two letters are ab is in S_{ab}, and similarly for the other three subsets. Let each of the original five subsets be similarly divided. There are then twenty subsets of S each characterized by the two first letters of the words in it. Each of these twenty subsets contains exactly three words: that is, S_{ab} contains abc, abd, and abe; S_{db} contains dba, dbc, and dbe; and so on.

The point is that, having specified the first two letters in each subset, there remain only three letters from which to choose the third.

If the twenty subsets are now subdivided into smaller subsets with all three letters specified for each one, there will be sixty subsets finally, each containing exactly one element. Sixty words of three letters can thus be formed from five different letters. Since three-letter words are required, three successive subdivisions were made. The original set S was divided into five parts, each of these five into four parts, and each of the four into three parts. The final subsets contained one word each. There being $(5)(4)(3) = 60$ subsets, this must also be the answer to the problem.

Applying this method to the general case of n objects taken r at a time, the first subdivision is one of n parts. Each of the n subsets is divided into $n - 1$ parts. After the second subdivision, there are $n(n - 1)$ subsets. After the third subdivision there will be $n(n - 1)(n - 2)$ subsets, and so on until r subdivisions have been made. At the end of this time, each subset will contain exactly one permutation. The result, using $P(n, r)$ to denote the number of permutations of n objects taken r at a time, is then

$$P(n, r) = n(n - 1)(n - 2) \ldots$$

where the product is carried on until there are r factors in the product. By trying out a few numerical examples, it will be found that this formula may be written as

$$P(n, r) = n(n - 1)(n - 2) \ldots (n - r + 1)$$

According to the formula, the number of ways that eight objects may be permuted or ordered four at a time is

$$P(8, 4) = (8)(7)(6)(5)$$
$$= 1,680$$

If all eight objects are to be used in each permutation, the result is

$$P(8, 8) = (8)(7)(6)(5)(4)(3)(2)(1)$$
$$= 40,320.$$

A special notation has been devised to indicate a product whose factors run consecutively downward to 1 as in $(8)(7)(6)(5)(4)(3)(2)(1)$. This product is written $8!$, the exclamation point taking the place of all smaller whole numbers which follow as factors. Thus,

$$1! = 1$$
$$2! = (2)(1) = 2$$
$$3! = (3)(2)(1) = 6$$
$$4! = (4)(3)(2)(1) = 24$$
$$5! = 5(4!) = 120$$
$$6! = 6(5!) = 720$$
$$7! = 7(6!) = 5040$$

and so on. The expression $n!$ is read "n factorial." Factorials increase in value with great rapidity: 1,000! has over 2,650 digits, for example. The use of factorials makes it possible to simplify the formula for $P(n, r)$. Noting that

$$P(n, r) = n(- 1)(n - 2) \ldots (n - r + 1)$$

it is clear that, if the sequence of factors were continued, the next one would

be $n - r$. It is possible then to multiply $P(n, r)$ by $\dfrac{(n - r)(n - r - 1) \ldots (3)(2)(1)}{(n - r)(n - r - 1) \ldots (3)(2)(1)}$ without changing its value; the result is $\dfrac{n!}{(n - r)!}$, which is the simplified result required. Applying this formula to the case of ten objects permuted 3 at a time gives

$$P(10, 3) = \frac{10!}{7!}$$
$$= \frac{(10)(9)(8)(7)(6)(5)(4)(3)(2)(1)}{(7)(6)(5)(4)(3)(2)(1)}$$

The entire denominator cancels, leaving

$$P(10, 3) = (10)(9)(8) = 720$$

which corresponds to the original formula. The longer formula is best for computational purposes, while the shorter formula affords notational advantages. The theory of permutations has an interesting and extensive further development, but the foregoing is sufficient for the immediate purpose.

Combinations

Somewhat similar to permutations are combinations. A *combination* is a subset of objects whose order is not of interest, whereas a permutation is a subset the order of whose elements is of essential interest.

The nature of combinations is well illustrated by the following "dinner party" problem. A host, being unable to accommodate seven of his friends at a single dinner, decides to invite them three at a time to different dinners until he has exhausted all the different combinations of three guests. The question is, How many dinners must he have? The absence of order as a consideration here is made clear by observing that inviting guests A, B, and C in different orders will not constitute different dinner parties. Stated specifically, the problem is to find out how many ways seven objects can be taken (not permuted) three at a time. The problem is solved by first considering the problem to be one of permutations. Having done this, let any three of the seven guests—say, B, C, and F—be singled out. The list of permutations contains exactly $P(3, 3) = 6$ permutations of the three letters B, C, and F. Each of these six permutations is made up of the same combination of letters. The same would be true if any other combination of letters had been selected. It appears, then, that the number of combinations is equal to $P(7, 3)$ divided by the number of ways in which any subset of three can be permuted three at a time. This divisor is $P(3, 3) = 3!$; that is,

$$
\begin{aligned}
C(7, 3) &= \frac{P(7, 3)}{P(3, 3)} \\
&= \frac{7!}{(7 - 3)!3!} \\
&= \frac{7!}{4!3!} \\
&= 35
\end{aligned}
$$

The same reasoning can be extended to the general case of n objects taken r at a time. Any r objects contribute $P(r, r) = r!$ permutations to the totality of all permutations of n objects permuted r at a time. The set of all permutations is thus partitioned into subsets each of which contains $r!$ permutations of the r objects peculiar to that subset. The general formula for combinations of n different objects taken r at a time is then

$$
\begin{aligned}
C(n, r) &= \frac{P(n, r)}{P(r, r)} \\
&= \frac{n!}{(n - r)!r!}
\end{aligned}
$$

For example, the number of combinations of nine guests taken two at a time is

$$C(9, 2) = \frac{9!}{7!2!}$$
$$= 36$$

Notice that nine guests taken seven at a time results in

$$C(9, 7) = \frac{9!}{2!7!}$$
$$= 36$$

At first this may seem odd, but it is clear that, since every choice of two guests involves a rejection of seven, $C(9, 2) = C(9, 7)$. In fact, the same reasoning leads to the conclusion that $C(n, r) = C(n, n - r)$ for all cases. This conclusion is verified by writing out the formula in each case; that is

$$C(n, r) = \frac{n!}{(n - r)!r!} = \frac{n!}{r!(n - r)!} = C(n, n - r)$$

The number of combinations of n objects taken r at a time is always less than the corresponding number of permutations if $r > 1$. There is only one way to take six objects six at a time, but there are 720 permutations of six letters permuted all at a time.

The binomial expansion

There is a close connection between the expansion of the binomial power $(p + q)^n$ into its several terms and the formula $C(n, r)$ developed for counting combinations. To display this connection, several specific examples of $C(n, r)$ are shown below along with expansions of $(p + q)^n$ for $n = 1, 2, 3, 4,$ and 5. Keeping in mind that $C(n, r) = \frac{n!}{r!(n - r)!}$, and, for convenience, defining 0! to be 1, the following are easily verified:

$C(1, 0) = 1 \quad C(1, 1) = 1$
$C(2, 0) = 1 \quad C(2, 1) = 2 \quad C(2, 2) = 1$
$C(3, 0) = 1 \quad C(3, 1) = 3 \quad C(3, 2) = 3 \quad C(3, 3) = 1$
$C(4, 0) = 1 \quad C(4, 1) = 4 \quad C(4, 2) = 6 \quad C(4, 3) = 4 \quad C(4, 4) = 1$
$C(5, 0) = 1 \quad C(5, 1) = 5 \quad C(5, 2) = 10 \quad C(5, 3) = 10 \quad C(5, 4) = 5 \quad C(5, 5) = 1$

By actual multiplication the results for $(p + q)^n$ are as follows.

$(p + q) = p + q$
$(p + q)^2 = p^2 + 2pq + q^2$
$(p + q)^3 = p^3 + 3p^2q + 3pq^2 + q^3$

$$(p + q)^4 = p^4 + 4p^3q + 6p^2q^2 + 4pq^3 + q^4$$
$$(p + q)^5 = p^5 + 5p^4q + 10p^3q^2 + 10p^2q^3 + 5pq^4 + q^5$$

It is clear that each of these expansions starts with p^n and that in subsequent terms p appears with successively lower exponents. As the exponents of p decrease, those of q increase, so that the sum of the exponents in any term is always n. A comparison of the coefficients with the values of $C(n, r)$ given above shows that every coefficient is some $C(n, r)$. In fact, all of the $C(n, r)$ with $n = 5$ compose the coefficients of $(p + q)^5$. Similarly, the $C(4, r)$, $(r = 0, 1, 2, 3, 4)$, appear as the coefficients of $(p + q)^4$.

By means of the relations observed here, it appears that $(p + q)^6$ may have the form $C(6, 0)p^6 + C(6, 1)p^5q + C(6, 2)p^4q^2 + C(6, 3)p^3q^3 + C(6, 4)p^2q^4 + C(6, 5)pq^5 + C(6, 6)q^6$. Evaluating the $C(n, r)$ symbols makes this read $p^6 + 6p^5q + 15p^4q^2 + 20p^3q^3 + 15p^2q^4 + 6pq^5 + q^6$, which is correct and may be verified by multiplying $(p + q)^5$ by $(p + q)$. It is proved in most algebra texts that the rules observed here for the assignment of exponents and coefficients are valid for all $(p + q)^n$ when n is a whole positive number.

Using these rules and the relation $C(7, r) = \dfrac{7!}{r!(7 - r)!}$, the expansion of $(p + q)^7$ is $\dfrac{7!}{0!\,7!}p^7 + \dfrac{7!}{1!\,6!}p^6q + \dfrac{7!}{2!\,5!}p^5q^2 + \dfrac{7!}{3!\,4!}p^4q^3 + \dfrac{7!}{4!\,3!}p^3q^4 + \dfrac{7!}{5!\,2!}p^2q^5 + \dfrac{7!}{6!\,1!}pq^6 + \dfrac{7!}{7!\,0!}q^7$. With arithmetic simplifications, this is $(p + q)^7 = p^7 + 7p^6q + 21p^5q^2 + 35p^4q^3 + 35p^3q^4 + 21p^2q^5 + 7pq^6 + q^7$. Note that, with the factorial notation, each coefficient is constructed out of the exponents of the term with which it is associated. For example, the term with p^2q^5 has $\dfrac{(2 + 5)!}{2!\,5!}$ for its coefficient, and all the other coefficients may be similarly constructed.

Using the fact that any coefficient may be constructed if the exponents of p and q are known, it is possible to construct any single term of any binomial expansion without first working up through the preceding terms. Suppose, for example, that the term in $(p + q)^{25}$ which contains q^7 is desired. It is known that the term will have p^{18} in it, because the exponents of p and q must total 25. The coefficient must then be $\dfrac{(18 + 7)!}{18!\,7!} = 480{,}700$.

The required term is then $480{,}700p^{18}q^7$. Such individual terms are of interest because they constitute probability computations.

If several terms of a binomial expansion are desired, it is possible to avoid the considerable amount of arithmetic involved in computing $C(n, r)$ for each term by using any term already obtained to generate the next term. Suppose that the term $\dfrac{n!}{r!(n-r)!} p^{(n-r)}q^r$ has been obtained. If this term is multiplied by $\left(\dfrac{n-r}{r+1}\right)\left(\dfrac{q}{p}\right)$, the result is $\dfrac{n!\,(n-r)}{r!\,(r+1)\,(n-r)!}$ $p^{n-r-1}q^{r+1}$. This simplifies to $\dfrac{n!}{(r+1)!(n-r-1)!} p^{n-r-1}q^{r+1}$ which is the next term in the expansion. For example, the term of $(p+q)^{12}$ containing p^4q^8 is $\dfrac{12!}{4!\,8!} p^4q^8 = 495\, p^4q^8$. Multiplying by $\left(\dfrac{12-8}{8+1}\right)\left(\dfrac{q}{p}\right)$ gives $\left(\dfrac{4q}{9p}\right)(495\, p^4q^8) = 220\, p^3q^9$ as the next term. The numerical factor by which a term is multiplied to get the next always turns out to be the exponent of p divided by one more than the exponent of q. The $\dfrac{q}{p}$ part of the multiplier merely causes the power of p to decrease by one and that of q to increase by one. (Extensive tables of binomial coefficients are available.)

One other method of finding binomial coefficients is convenient for small values of n but become laborious for large n; this is Pascal's Triangle, which is illustrated in Box 26.

The binomial expansion has been developed here in terms of p and q each of which is taken to be a positive proper fraction representing a probability. All that has been said, however, is valid for the expansion $(x+y)^n$ where x and y are any numbers whatever.

The rather long form of a binomial expansion can be shortened by use of the $\sum$ symbol. For example:

$$(p+q)^{15} = \sum_{r=0}^{15} C(15, r)p^{n-r}q^r$$

If r is given successively the values 0, 1, 2, . . . , 15 and the terms thus obtained are connected with plus signs, the result is the full expansion of $(p+q)^{15}$. Each time r is increased by 1, the $C(n,r)$ symbol is changed to the next case, $n-r$ decreases by 1, and the next term is formed.

Computing probabilities

The binomial expansion has been developed here for two reasons: it is a very useful tool for computing probabilities, and it leads naturally into a consideration of the normal probability distribution. As an example of the usefulness of the binomial expansion in solving problems in probability,

---

B O X 2 6

Pascal's Triangle

The triangular array of numbers called Pascal's triangle was known to Napier (*circa* 1600) and to other earlier mathematicians, but Pascal's use of it (*circa* 1650) in his contributions to the development of the theory of probability made the device peculiarly his own. The first ten rows of the triangle appear below and are seen to be the co-efficients of the first eight powers of the binomial $(x + y)$. Observe that in each row each number (except the first and last which are ones) is the sum of the two nearest above it. Note the symmetry which this rule of construction produces about the centers of the rows. The array may be carried on to any desired number of rows.

```
                  1
                1   1
              1   2   1
            1   3   3   1
          1   4   6   4   1
        1   5  10  10   5   1
      1   6  15  20  15   6   1
    1   7  21  35  35  21   7   1
  1   8  28  56  70  56  28   8   1
1   9  36  84 126 126  84  36   9   1
```

The student who wishes to check his understanding of the construction of Pascal's triangle should calculate the values for the next row and check his results with the data in Table 47.

---

consider the following problem. A test contains a section consisting of five multiple-choice questions. There are three choices for each question, only one of which is correct. What is the probability that a student answering blindly will be able to guess three correct answers out of the five? Instead of considering the rather complicated event "three out of five correct guesses," the problem is considered as five trials of the simpler event "a correct guess on one problem." Since the answer is either right or wrong, each trial or problem is capable of just two outcomes, one of which must occur. Also, the probability of a correct answer is $\frac{1}{3}$ on every trial. It is assumed that the five choices made have no effect on one another. Denoting a right answer by R and a wrong answer by W, the five trials could turn out to be $WWRRR$. Since these are independent events, the probability of their joint occurrence is the product of their individual probabilities; that is, $P(WWRRR) = \frac{2}{3} \cdot \frac{2}{3} \cdot \frac{1}{3} \cdot \frac{1}{3} \cdot \frac{1}{3} = \frac{4}{243}$. The sequence $WRRRW$ also satisfies the requirement of three right answers. Since the two sequences cannot both occur at the same time, the probability of either happening is the sum of their individual probabilities. Now $P(WRRRW) = \frac{4}{243}$ also, since only the order and not the value of the individual probabilities is different than in the former case. It is clear that there are several other ways in which three right answers could be obtained. In fact, there are as many ways as there are ways to locate the two W's in the five trials. But this is simply $C(5, 2) = \dfrac{5!}{3!2!} = 10$. Each one of these ways to get three correct answers has probability $(\frac{1}{3})^3(\frac{2}{3})^2 = \frac{4}{243}$. The total probability is then $C(5, 2)p^3q^2 = \frac{40}{243}$ where $p = \frac{1}{3}$ and $q = \frac{2}{3}$. But this is clearly a term of $(p + q)^5$. The other terms of $(p + q)^5$ give the probabilities of other numbers of correct guesses. The probability of five correct guesses is $p^5 = (\frac{1}{3})^5 = \frac{1}{243}$. The probability of just one correct guess is given by the term of $(p + q)^5$ which has pq^4 in it; this term is $C(5, 1)pq^4 = 5(\frac{1}{3})(\frac{2}{3})^4 = \frac{80}{243}$. It is clear that if all the possibilities ranging from no correct guesses (q^5) to five correct guesses are added up, the result must be 1. This follows from the fact that every term of $(\frac{1}{3} + \frac{2}{3})^5$ is used, and $(\frac{1}{3} + \frac{2}{3})^5 = 1^5 = 1$. Denoting by $P(k)$ the probability of k correct guesses, the results are, in order,

$$P(0) = q^5 = \frac{32}{243}$$
$$P(1) = C(5, 4)pq^4 = \frac{80}{243}$$
$$P(2) = C(5, 3)p^2q^3 = \frac{80}{243}$$
$$P(3) = C(5, 2)p^3q^2 = \frac{40}{243}$$
$$P(4) = C(5, 1)p^4q = \frac{10}{243}$$
$$P(5) = C(5, 0)p^5 = \frac{1}{243}$$

These five numbers give the relative frequency or probability of each of the several possible outcomes. They constitute the *Bernoulli* or *binomial distribution* of the outcomes of the experiment. James Bernoulli (1654–1705) was the first to apply binomial expansions to probability problems. An experiment is said to consist of Bernoulli trials if it, like the problem above, has the following properties:

1. The experiment is or can be construed to be a series of trials each of which has just two possible outcomes.
2. The separate trials are all independent of one another. What happens on a given trial can have no effect on the other trial outcomes.
3. The probabilities for individual trials remain the same from trial to trial.

As another example of Bernoulli trials, suppose that ten coins are tossed together on a table and that the probabilities of various numbers of heads are required. Though the experiment here does not consist of repeated trials but of a single action, it is nevertheless easy to construe the experiment as a sequence of ten Bernoulli trials. Each trial must fall either heads or tails, and the probabilities, $\frac{1}{2}$ for each, remain the same from trial to trial. The fall of one coin in no way affects any other. All the conditions are satisfied for Bernoulli trials, and the appropriate binomial expansion gives the distribution of relative frequencies (probabilities) of the various numbers of heads possible. This distribution is given in Table 48. The probability of a head is denoted by $p = \frac{1}{2}$ and that of a tail by $q = \frac{1}{2}$.

TABLE 48

Probabilities for ten Bernoulli trials with $p = q = \frac{1}{2}$

$$P(10) = C(10, 0)p^{10} = \tfrac{1}{1024} = .001$$
$$P(9) = C(10, 1)p^9q = \tfrac{10}{1024} = .010$$
$$P(8) = C(10, 2)p^8q^2 = \tfrac{45}{1024} = .044$$
$$P(7) = C(10, 3)p^7q^3 = \tfrac{120}{1024} = .117$$
$$P(6) = C(10, 4)p^6q^4 = \tfrac{210}{1024} = .205$$
$$P(5) = C(10, 5)p^5q^5 = \tfrac{252}{1024} = .246$$
$$P(4) = C(10, 6)p^4q^6 = \tfrac{210}{1024} = .205$$
$$P(3) = C(10, 7)p^3q^7 = \tfrac{120}{1024} = .117$$
$$P(2) = C(10, 8)p^2q^8 = \tfrac{45}{1024} = .044$$
$$P(1) = C(10, 9)pq^9 = \tfrac{10}{1024} = .010$$
$$P(0) = C(10, 10)q^{10} = \tfrac{1}{1024} = .001$$

| | Total | 1 | 1.000 |

In reading the histogram (Figure 27, page 243) corresponding to the data of Table 48, it is convenient to regard each bar as being one unit wide. The height or relative frequency is then in each case equal to the area of the bar. The total area enclosed is thus 1, since the sum of the relative frequencies is 1. The symmetry about the center bar is due to choosing $p = q = \frac{1}{2}$. The histogram would be somewhat skewed if $p = \frac{1}{3}, q = \frac{2}{3}$ had been chosen. The distribution described may be denoted by $B(10, \frac{1}{2})$, which indicates the Bernoulli distribution based on ten trials each having $p = \frac{1}{2}$. There are, of course, many other experiments having the same outcome distribution, but from the statistical point of view all are equivalent and can be characterized by the symbol $B(10, \frac{1}{2})$.

Even though the number of possible outcomes on a given trial may be greater than two, the Bernoulli model may be used if the question is properly framed. Suppose, for example, that twenty persons selected at random are to be polled on a political question. If from previous surveys it is known that 40 per cent of the population to be sampled are Democrats, 35 per cent Republicans, and 25 per cent of other parties or of no party, what is the probability that the sample of 20 will include, say, nine Democrats? Even though each of the twenty trials can end in more than two ways, the binomial expansion can be used in view of the question that is asked. It is only necessary to group all the possible outcomes other than Democrats into one set. Viewed in this way, the outcome of each trial is either a Democrat or a non-Democrat. The probability of a Democrat may be denoted by p and that of a non-Democrat by $1 - p = q$. Then the twenty-one terms of $(p + q)^{20}$ give the probabilities of various numbers of Democrats that could be chosen. The probability of obtaining nine Democrats in the sample of twenty is then, with $p = .40$ and $q = .60$, $P(9) = \dfrac{20!}{9!11!}p^9q^{11}$.

Normal probability distribution

The arithmetic involved in computing the value of binomial terms such as $\dfrac{20!}{9!11!}$ $(.40)^9(.60)^{11}$ is quite tedious. These calculations may be avoided by making use of a very interesting property of binomial expansions, the proper mathematical development of which is beyond the scope of this book. With the aid of the calculus, it can be shown that as the number of trials becomes large, the frequency polygon of the Bernoulli distribution looks very much like a certain continuous curve about which a great deal is known. This continuous curve, which we have discussed earlier, is known as the *normal probability curve*. When the number of trials is sufficiently large to make the normal curve a good approximation to the Bernoulli frequency polygon, the easier calculations associated with the normal curve are used.

As the number of trials increases from five to ten to twenty, the Bernoulli histograms increasingly assume the shape of the normal curve. If the number, n, of trials is increased to 30 or more and if p is greater than about .05, the Bernoulli histogram is an extremely close approximation of the normal curve. It is known that as n tends to very high numbers, the correspondence tends to become more perfect.

In order to take advantage of the fact that a binomially distributed variable behaves very like a normally distributed variable, it is only necessary to know the mean and standard deviation of the binomial distribution. Because the theoretically exact values of the mean and standard deviation are to be considered here, the symbols σ and μ will be used instead of s and $\bar{X}$. It is found by advanced methods that the Bernoulli distribution $B(n, p)$ has $\sigma = \sqrt{npq}$ and $\mu = np$ where, as usual, $q = 1 - p$.

To see the usefulness of this information, consider the following typical problem. It is known that 30 per cent of all applicants for a certain class of jobs are accepted and that 70 per cent are rejected. Of course, because of random sampling errors, the division is seldom exactly 30/70 for any given 100 applicants. The effect of random sampling errors can be observed by asking, "What is the probability that the number accepted out of 100 applicants will be between twenty-eight and thirty-two inclusive?"

Using the binomial distribution only, this problem may be solved by adding the five terms of $(.3 + .7)^{100}$ which give the relevant probabilities. The amount of work involved in computing even one of these, say $C(100, 28)(.3^{28})(.7^{72})$ is prohibitive. Instead, compute

$$\mu = (100)(.3) = 30$$

and

$$\sigma = \sqrt{(100)(.3)(.7)} = 4.58$$

The next step is to convert the interval of interest, 28–32, into standard units using these statistics. At this point, it should be noted that a continuous distribution, the normal, is being used in lieu of a discrete distribution, the binomial. For this reason, the number 28 is considered to begin at 27.5 and to end at 28.5; that is, any number in this interval, when rounded off to the nearest integer, will be 28. The interval of interest is then, more properly, 27.5 to 32.5. Then,

$$z_1 = \frac{27.5 - 30}{4.58} = -.55$$

$$z_2 = \frac{32.5 - 30}{4.58} = +.55$$

The normal probability table gives the value .2088 for $z = .55$. Hence the probability is $2(.2088) = .4176$ that the number of applicants accepted will be between the noninclusive limits 27.5 and 32.5.

As a further example, let the probability of exactly 500 heads out of 1,000 tosses of a coin be computed. The mean number of heads to be expected per 1,000 tosses is $\mu = 1,000(\frac{1}{2}) = 500$, and the standard deviation is $\sigma = \sqrt{1,000(\frac{1}{2})(\frac{1}{2})} = 15.81$. The discrete number 500 occupies in the continuous scale of the normal distribution the interval from 499.5 to 500.5. Converting these limits into standard units, one has

$$z_1 = \frac{499.5 - 500}{15.81} = -.0316$$

$$z_2 = \frac{500.5 - 500}{15.81} = +.0316$$

The normal probability table shows that the area extending from $-.0316\sigma$ on the left of the mean to $.0316\sigma$ on the right of the mean is .0252 (interpolation is necessary here, since z is computed to more than two decimal places). Even though 500 is the most likely outcome, its probability is very small, as shown here.

Both of the examples above use intervals centered on the mean, but the method is not limited to such intervals.

To illustrate this, consider the probability of accepting a number of applicants between 245 and 260, inclusive, if the probability of accepting any one is .4 and 600 applicants are interviewed. The mean and standard deviation of the approximating normal curve are $\mu = 600(.4) = 240$ and $\sigma = \sqrt{600(.4)(.6)} = 12$. The interval of interest in terms of standard units is then from z_1 to z_2 where

$$z_1 = \frac{244.5 - 240}{12} = .375$$

and

$$z_2 = \frac{260.5 - 240}{12} = 1.708$$

The normal probability table gives .1462 for $z_1 = .375$, and .4562 for $z_2 = 1.708$, again using interpolation. The required probability is then $.4562 - .1462 = .3100$. Subtraction is used here because the value for z_2 includes all the area of the curve from the center over to z_2, whereas only the area from z_1 to z_2 is desired.

The usefulness of the binomial model is thus preserved for values of n

for which completely detailed computation would be prohibitively extensive. It takes no more effort to compute a probability based on $n = 10,000$ than it does to compute one based on $n = 30$ or 40.

Suggestions for Further Reading

The student will find a somewhat different approach to the concept of probability taken in the references provided at the end of Chapter 3. All of these present general, but brief, introductions to probability theory.

More advanced mathematical treatments of probability may be found in the following:

FELLER, W. 1950. *An introduction to probability theory and its applications.* New York: Wiley.

PARZEN, E. 1960. *Modern probability theory and its applications.* New York: Wiley.

Among the many interesting essays about probability are these:

CHURCHMAN, C. W. 1948. *Theory of experimental inference.* New York: Macmillan.

GOOD, I. J. 1959. Kinds of probability. *Science,* 20, 129, 443-447.

NEWMAN, J. R. 1956. The world of mathematics (especially Vol. 2, Part VII, The laws of chance). New York: Simon and Schuster.

POLYA, G. 1954. *Patterns of plausible inference.* Vol. 2. Princeton: Princeton University Press.

REICHENBACH, H. 1951. *The rise of scientific philosophy.* Berkeley: University of California Press.

RESTLE, F. 1961. *The psychology of judgment and choice.* New York: Wiley.

PROBLEMS

1. Will the following process produce a sequence of random digits? Roll a red and a green die together and record nothing if the green number is 6. Otherwise, record 1 less than twice the green number if the red number is odd and 2 less than twice the green number if the red number is even.

2. A two-digit number may be generated by using the rule in problem 1 once for the first digit and once for the second digit. Generate 100 two-digit numbers using this rule.

(a) What could be said of this random sample of the first 100 numbers if no random sampling errors occurred?

(b) Classify your results in ten class intervals, and list those intervals which reveal random sampling errors.

(c) Combine your results with those of up to five other students and repeat part (b). Do the random sampling errors seem to be as numerous or as serious as in the smaller sample?

3. As an example of an equation designed to describe a particular model of randomness, consider the equation $f(p) = 3p^4 - 8p^3 + 6p^2$. This equation gives the probability that an event E having probability p will occur at least twice in four trials.

(a) Let $p = \frac{1}{2}$ and find the probability that at least two out of four flipped coins will be heads.

(b) Let $p = \frac{1}{6}$ and find the probability that at least two out of four rolls of a die will be fives.

(c) The probability that a randomly chosen integer will be divisible by 3 is $\frac{1}{3}$. Let $p = \frac{1}{3}$ and find the probability that at least two out of four randomly chosen numbers will be divisible by 3.

4. If a coin is tossed a few times, it is unlikely that 50 per cent of the results will be heads. Flip a coin 100 times and stop at 10, 20, 30, . . . , 100 tosses to compute the percentage of heads at that point. Notice how the percentages tend to stay nearer to 50 per cent as the data grow more numerous. Combine your results with those of other students and compute percentages for 100, 200, . . . , 1,000 tosses to observe an even more sharp convergence of the percentages to 50 per cent. Collecting the data can be shortened by tossing 10 coins at a time.

5. Let $\mu = 75$ and $\sigma = 5$ for a normally distributed population. Find the relative frequency of the population which lies in each of the following intervals: (a) 60–65, (b) 65–70, (c) 70–75, (d) 75–80, (e) 80–85, (f) 85–90.

6. What property of a normal curve makes it possible to supply the answers to parts (d), (e), and (f) of problem 5 on the basis of computations already done for the preceding parts of the problem?

7. How large must a value be to be in the upper 10 per cent of a normally distributed population with $\mu = 40$ and $\sigma = 10$?

8. Give an example of a universe of discourse that would include the set of all sculptors, the set of all musicians, and the set of all finger

painters. Try to make your answer as limited to these sets as possible.

9. Exhibit the set, A, of all whole nonmultiples of 3 between 6 and 15 by displaying the elements between a pair of braces.

10. Let A be as in problem 9, and let $B = \{2, 4, 6, 8, 10, 12, 14, 16\}$. Find $A \cup B$ and $A \cap B$.

11. Let J be the set of all odd numbers, and find $J \cap (A \cap B)$ where the set $A \cap B$ is obtained from problem 10.

12. Let K have six elements and L have ten elements.
    (a) What is the least possible number of elements in $K \cup L$?
    (b) What is the greatest possible number of elements in $K \cup L$?
    (c) What is the least possible number of elements in $K \cap L$?
    (d) What is the greatest possible number of elements in $K \cap L$?

13. Using the diagram on page 254, list the numbered regions that are included in: (a) $A \cup B$, (b) $A \cap B$, (c) $(A \cup B) \cup C$, (d) $A \cup (B \cup C)$, (e) $(A \cap B) \cap C$, (f) $A \cap (B \cap C)$, (g) $A \cup (B \cap C)$, (h) $A \cap (B \cup C)$.

14. In a group of people there are ten who like candy, six who like cake, and four who like both. Use the theorem on measures of sets to compute the number of people in the whole group.

15. In a sample of 100 families it is found that eighty-five do not own a small car and that thirty-six do not own a large car. How many families have no car?

16. The extension of the theorem on measures of sets to the case of three sets is $m(A \cup B \cup C) = m(A) + m(B) + m(C) - m(A \cap B) - m(A \cap C) - m(B \cap C) + m(A \cap B \cap C)$.
    Use this result to solve the following problem: All of the 140 students in a school were given some tests; eighty took tests in reading, fifty in arithmetic, twenty-five in history, fifteen in history and arithmetic, thirty in reading and arithmetic, and forty in all three subjects. How many students were tested in reading and history but not in arithmetic?

17. The set of all integers that are both odd and even is the null set, since no number can satisfy all the requirements for inclusion in the set. Give another characterization of the null set by so restricting membership in the set that no elements qualify.

18. The expression for $m(A \cup B \cup C)$ used in problem 16 may be derived from the expression for $m(M \cup N)$; it is only necessary to use the set $[A \cup B]$ in place of M, and C in place of N. Complete the derivation of the expression for $m(A \cup B \cup C)$.

19. In a lottery one ticket is to be drawn to determine the winner. Apply the principle of indifference or modifications of it to assign frequency weights to each person in the set of all ticket holders if (a) no person has more than one ticket, (b) any person may hold from one to five tickets, (c) no person may hold more than one ticket, but up to three people may share a ticket.

20. If a coin is flipped three times, there are eight possible outcomes; that is, eight three-letter "words" may be spelled using the two letters H and T, these "words" representing the elements of the outcome space of the experiment. Let each such element be given a frequency weight of 1.

    (a) List the elements of the outcome space.

    (b) List the elements of the event "two of the flips will be heads." What is the measure of this event?

    (c) List the elements of the event "at least two of the flips will be heads." What is the measure of this event?

    (d) List the elements of the event "at most two of the flips will be heads," and give the measure of the event.

    (e) The *complement* of an event, E, is the event which contains all elements not in the event E. Find the complementary events for the events described in (b), (c), and (d), and give their measures.

21. Use the definition of a probability to compute the probabilities of the events described in (b), (c), and (d) of problem 20.

22. Using the definition of the complement of an event given in problem 20(e), show that $P(E') = 1 - P(E)$, where E' denotes the complement of E.

23. Let S be the set of all spades in a deck of playing cards, and let F be the set of all face cards.

    (a) What cards are in the set $S \cap F$?

    (b) What cards are in the set $S \cup F$?

    (c) What is the probability that a single draw from the deck will be both a spade and a face card?

    (d) What is the probability that a single draw will be either a spade or a face card?

24. What is the probability that a card drawn at random from a deck of playing cards will be red but not a face card?

25. Suppose an urn contains twelve red, twenty black, and twenty-eight white balls. Two balls are to be drawn from the urn, the first not being replaced before the second is drawn.

(a) What is the probability that the two draws will be red and white in that order?

(b) What is the probability that the two draws will be white and red in that order?

(c) Why must the probability for the second draw in each case have to be expressed as a conditional probability?

26. The probabilities that it will rain tomorrow in New York and Los Angeles are .3 and .4, respectively. What is the probability that (a) it will rain in both cities? (b) it will rain in neither city? (c) it will rain only in New York? (d) it will rain only in Los Angeles? Explain why these four probabilities must total 1.

27. A businessman estimates that the probability that his store will be robbed during the year is .05 and the probability that he will suffer fire damage is .04. What is the probability (a) that one or the other of these two losses will occur? (b) that both kinds of loss will occur?

28. If the probability that a guest will arrive by plane is .5 and that he will arrive by train is .2, what is the probability that he will arrive by neither plane nor train?

29. Let S be the set of all four-letter "words" that can be formed by the letters a, b, c, and d, no letter being used more than once in any one word. Let S_a be the subset of words whose first letter is a and let S_b, S_c, and S_d be defined similarly for the letters b, c, and d.

(a) List all the words in S and separate them into the four subsets S_a, S_b, S_c, S_d.

(b) Break each of the four subsets S_a, . . . , S_d into three subsets according to the second letters of the words.

(c) Continue the process started in (a) and (b) until each final subset has just one word in it.

30. The product $(n)(n-1) \ldots (n-r+1)$ has exactly r factors. Verify this fact by (a) letting $n = 12$, $r = 5$, and displaying the factors and (b) letting $n = 23$, $r = 7$, and displaying the factors.

31. (a) In how many ways is it possible to stack six books on a shelf in the usual way?

(b) If two of the books in (a) must be next to each other, how many ways may the books be stacked?

32. How many different committees of four members may be chosen from among nine people?

33. Evaluate $C(10, 4)$ and $C(10, 6)$, and explain why the results are the same. State the general principle of symmetry illustrated here.

34. Verify the table of $C(n, r)$ given on page 272. The principle of symmetry discussed in problem 33 may be used to reduce the computation.

35. Write out in detail the expansion of $(p + q)^{10}$.

36. Write the term of $(p + q)^{25}$ which contains q^{11}.

37. Use the method given for generating any binomial term out of the preceding one to find the term after $C(10, 4)p^6q^4$ in $(p + q)^{10}$. Show that $\frac{6}{5}C(10, 4) = C(10, 5)$.

38. Verify $(p + q)^9 = \sum_{r=0}^{9} C(9, r)p^{9-r}q^r$ by expanding the sum into its several terms.

39. Find the probability that in ten rolls of a die, there will be (a) three rolls of 4 or less and seven rolls of 5 or more.

    (b) five rolls of 4 or less and five rolls of 5 or more.

    (c) eight rolls of 4 or less and two rolls of 5 or more.

40. Using the mean 68 inches and the standard deviation 2.5 inches as given in the text for heights, find

    (a) the value of 64 inches in standard units.

    (b) the value of 74 inches in standard units.

    (c) the probability that a randomly chosen man will have a height between the mean height and 64 inches.

    (d) the probability that a randomly chosen man will have a height between the mean height and 74 inches.

    (e) the probability that a randomly chosen man will have a height between 64 and 74 inches.

41. Noting that 47.5 per cent of the normal curve area lies above the interval between the mean μ and the point $\mu + 1.96\sigma$, find how tall a man must be to be in the tallest 2.5 per cent of the population. Use the statistics as given in problem 40.

42. What per cent of all heights lie in the following intervals? (a) $\mu - \sigma$ to $\mu + \sigma$, (b) $\mu - .5\sigma$ to $\mu + .5\sigma$, (c) $\mu - \sigma$ to $\mu + .5\sigma$, (d) $\mu - .5\sigma$ to $\mu + \sigma$, (e) $\mu - 1.5\sigma$ to $\mu + 2\sigma$, (f) μ to 2.58σ, (g) $\mu - 1.96\sigma$ to $\mu + 1.96\sigma$, (h) $\mu - 2\sigma$ to $\mu + 2\sigma$.

Chance, the ever-present rival conjecture.

CHAPTER

8

RANDOM SAMPLING DISTRIBUTIONS

THE OBSERVATION has frequently been made that science increases its power and significance as more and more abstract, unobservable entities are discovered and usefully employed. The same holds true for our understanding of the statistical method. We shall see, and it will be the main purpose of the chapter to point out, that our ability to cope with the problem of inductive inference increases when abstractions rather than concrete events are dealt with.

For example, in the preceding chapter the behavior of such specific, easily observable random events as tosses of coins and throws of dice was used as an example to aid in the development of the concept of a model of randomness. As a matter of fact, the earliest explorers of random phenomena studied this very type of event precisely because it was easy to observe and record (and because understanding these events has always had a certain practical importance). But the real power of a model of randomness lies, not in its ability to describe accurately the behavior of random events which we can see, but in its power to describe accurately the behavior of random phenomena which we *cannot* see. The unobservable random phenomena which concern us are the *random sampling distributions* of means, standard deviations, proportions, correlation coefficients, and the like. The previous chapter discussed the concept of *randomness*. We begin this chapter with a discussion of a more familiar subject—*sampling*.

SAMPLING

The crucial concept to be grasped is that of a *random sample*. Although this is a simple idea, and the reader will be well acquainted with the concept by virtue of his experience with public opinion polls, random sampling is actually relatively new. Its full employment did not occur until the behavioral scientists' need for a rigorous method of inductive inference became pressing. The pressure developed out of the process of selecting subjects for study in biological, psychological, and educational experiments and in connection with investigations made by urban and rural sociologists.

For example, psychologists at the turn of the century often used no more than four or five subjects in their experiments, and sometimes only one. As might be expected from our present knowledge of variability, results obtained from four or five subjects were either found to be puzzling because of the variability among the subjects, or because a second experiment using another four or five subjects produced results different from the first. Of course, such differences in the results of experiments led to controversy. Many psychologists were not aware of the fact that differences in results might well be due to accidental variations in the *selection of subjects*—that is, in sampling. Eventually, however, it was perceived that variability among subjects was to be expected, and that it was both more profitable and more scientific to cope with variability than to deny it. Coping with variability, as we have seen, means describing a distribution of results in terms of central tendency and variability, at the least. Although the employment of such descriptive techniques as the mean and standard deviation clarified results of experiments by removing the confusion engendered by variability within a distribution, the use of these techniques did not provide explanations of why one investigator's results differed from another's. By 1920, however, the more advanced psychologists, sociologists, and educational researchers had recognized that it was necessary for each investigator to select his subjects at random if he wanted the results of his experiments or surveys to be *comparable* with those of others. Even more important was the recognition that subjects would have to be selected at random (and in sufficient numbers) if the scientist wanted the results of his investigation not to be limited merely to the specific people who happened to be included in the study, but to be applicable to *all similar subjects*. There are, therefore, two reasons for the random selection (random sampling) of an adequate number of subjects: (1) to provide for comparable groups of subjects and (2) to generalize the results of an experiment beyond the specific subjects included in the experiment—that is, to make an inductive inference. Random sampling makes both comparability and generalization possible.

Random samples and biased samples

It is perfectly apparent that any given sample will resemble *more or less* the population from which it was drawn. The "more or less" is important, for it is equally apparent that the sample will tend to resemble the population "more" if it is a genuinely random sample and "less" if it is not random.

In order for a sample to be considered random, every person, or element, in the population must have an equal opportunity of appearing in the sample. A biased sample, on the other hand, results from a sampling procedure which does not permit each person an equal opportunity of being included—in which some persons are more likely to be included than others. Biased samples, in short, have *systematic* error. Selecting persons at random does not imply haphazard selection, however. The procedure used to sample the population must be carefully thought through so that bias does not inadvertently appear. Bias—that is, systematic error—usually occurs as a result of drawing names from sources which do not list everyone in the population under consideration (telephone directories, for example, include only those who can afford telephones) or from inadequate selection techniques (failing to track down those not at home, for example). It is important to note that once the population has been defined, it is necessary to draw the elements of the sample *at random*. No matter what restrictions are placed on the population—that is, no matter how narrowly it may be defined—the final step, that of choosing the subjects to be studied, *must* include the process of random selection. In this way only random errors account for the divergence of the value of any statistic, such as the mean of a sample, from the true value in the population, such as the true mean of the population.

It should be mentioned here that random sampling is "easier said than done," and that difficult technical problems are encountered when-

---

BOX 27

Population Sampling

True random sampling is a difficult, technical procedure beset with pitfalls, and for this reason the problem can only be mentioned here. However, the interested student will find a good treatment of this problem in the reference listed at the end of this box.

The following passage from *Theory and Problems of Social Psychology* sets forth concisely the initial problem in population sampling: "The first step in the sampling process is the definition of the population. What group, in other words, is being studied? When it is reported that 65 per cent of the people favor a given issue, does this refer to 65 per cent of the entire American population—men, women, and children—to adults only, to eligible voters only, or to whom? When it is stated that a certain per cent of American workers holds

a given attitude, does this refer to every American who works or only to skilled workers or only to union members or to the officers of unions or to whom? And if a research article reports that the correlation between attitude toward Russia and attitude toward England is .40 for a group of 75 college sophomores, to what population is this supposed to be generalizable—to all college sophomores, to all college students, to all Americans, or to whom?" In short, the investigator must be prepared to define precisely the population to which the results apply.

But, of course, he must do more than that. He must employ those techniques of population sampling which enable him to make the inference, the generalization, from sample to population without *systematic error*. Some types of sampling are sim-

---

ever a serious attempt is made to carry out random sampling. (See Box 27).

But even truly random samples do not resemble the population from which they are drawn in every specific instance. There is, however, a crucial difference between failure of a biased sample to resemble the population and that of a random sample. The difference lies in the kind of error found in each sample. Because the biased sample is in *systematic* error, the error is more often found in one direction than another. Therefore, a biased sample provides systematically a biased representation of the population, and the resulting inaccuracy prevents comparison with and generalization to other groups unless one knows specifically what the bias

---

ple random sampling, stratified random sampling, and cluster sampling.

Simple random sampling is fundamental to every random sampling technique. It provides an equal opportunity for every element in the population to appear in the sample. Tables of random numbers are employed to aid in the procedure. (*Note:* In sampling from files, when, say, every fifteenth case is drawn, the *initial* case must be selected at random; otherwise, the selections are not random selections.)

Stratified random sampling involves the division of the population into various strata—by sex, age, income groups, etc.— and then sampling randomly within these strata. Stratified samples are used when the investigator has reason to believe that opinions are related to a certain characteristic of the population—say, income. By stratifying along income levels, and thereby making certain that suf-

ficient numbers are present in the various income strata (which might not occur in simple random sampling) the investigator increases his sampling efficiency.

Cluster sampling is essentially a geographical technique that is often used to avoid the difficulties and expense which may be involved in the two techniques mentioned above. When lists or files are not readily available, cluster sampling is often employed; therefore it is most often used in large scale surveys. Larger units, such as schools, or areas such as city blocks, or census tracts, may be randomly drawn and then simple or stratified sampling carried out within these units. The statistical analysis of the data is complex, but the method works well and is in frequent use.

Krech, D. and Crutchfield, R. 1948. *Theory and problems of social psychology.* New York: McGraw-Hill. Copyright, 1948. McGraw-Hill Book Company, Inc.

---

is. On the other hand, because the random sample selects individuals at random, it is inaccurate only by chance; its errors are unsystematic, *random errors.* Comparison and generalization are not prevented in this case because the *size of the random error can be ascertained* and taken into consideration when making comparisons and generalizations.

How are the sizes of random errors ascertained? Here our knowledge of models of randomness plays a critical role, for a model of randomness provides the information which allows the amount of random error to be ascertained. Generally speaking, the normal-probability model indicates how often the sample will be exactly like the population, how often it will be slightly different, and how often it will be widely different. In brief, a model of randomness will tell us how often a random sample statistic will differ by various amounts from the true value of the statistic in the population, as a result of random sampling errors.

By way of summary

A random sample permits the inductive inference that *what is true of the sample is true of the population from which it was drawn*. That is why both the concept of randomness and the procedure of sampling are fundamental to inductive inference—the process of reasoning from the particular (the sample) to the general (the population from which the sample was drawn).

If a random sample is drawn, it represents without bias—without *systematic* error—the population from which it was drawn. Because a random sample does not include all the members of a population, however, it remains subject to error. But the errors of a random sample are random. And the relative frequency of occurrence of random errors of different sizes may be calculated because models of randomness describe the relative frequency of specific random phenomena.

Here, then, is the key to the problem of inductive inference. Because models of randomness describe the relative frequency of occurrence of random events, it is possible to describe the relative frequency with which a sample (individuals studied) will differ from the population from which it was drawn (similar individuals *not* studied) by various amounts because of the operation of random sampling errors. We now turn to the details of this procedure as it is related to the estimation of true values in the population.

SAMPLING DISTRIBUTIONS AND ESTIMATIONS

In this section the fundamental concepts of random sampling distributions are set forth in connection with the "natural history" type of research in which the scientist wishes to discover the true value of, say, a mean in a population.

First, two definitions must be made in order to simplify the discussion. In the preceding section we pointed out that a random sample "resembled" the population from which it was drawn. At this point we must be more specific and discuss the *way* in which the sample resembles the population. Thus, samples may be described in terms of means, standard deviations, correlation coefficients, and proportions, but, of course, populations from which samples are drawn may also be described in the same terms. In order to be clear as to whether we are referring to the sample or population, separate terms are used for each. Thus, the means, standard deviations, and so on, of a sample are called *statistics*, and the true values of the mean, standard deviation, and so on, of the population are called *parameters*. The value of this distinction will become more apparent as we proceed.

The random sampling distribution of the mean

How is it possible to refer the results from a sample to the normal probability model so that we may ascertain how often a statistic (such as a mean) will differ from the parameter (the true mean in the population) by various amounts? In order to answer this question, we shall consider first the relation between the normal probability model and the arithmetic mean. Although the relation between the model and the arithmetic mean is a very simple one, it is most intriguing. The relation is this: *The form of the frequency distribution of an infinite number of sample means drawn at random is that of a normal probability curve* (unless the population from which the samples were drawn is markedly asymmetrical). Thus, the tabled values of the normal probability model describe the frequency distribution of sample means as well as concrete random events. This fact is, of course, of tremendous importance. (*Note:* The student should see the similarity between the remarks here and those in pages 240–247 in Chapter 7.)

In order to illustrate this point, let the reader imagine for a moment a large container full of thousands of slips of paper on each of which a number has been written. The numbers may represent any variable— such as heights or weights of a group of people—which is normally distributed. Suppose that we draw a slip of paper and record the number written on it; we then continue to do this until we have recorded the numbers from 10 slips. At this point we compute a statistic, the mean of the ten. We shall say that we have computed the mean of a sample of ten persons. Now suppose we repeat this procedure until we have drawn 100 such samples of ten persons each and computed the mean for every sample. When the means of these samples are plotted, they will form a frequency distribution which will be a close approximation to a *normal probability curve;* the larger the number of samples used, the closer the approximation will be. *Of equal significance is the fact that the mean of the distribution of sample means will be very close to, if not identical with, the actual mean of the population, the parameter.*

Consider a further example. Suppose a behavioral scientist drew at random 200 samples and measured the intelligence (ordinarily a normally distributed variable) of each person in each of the samples. If he then com-

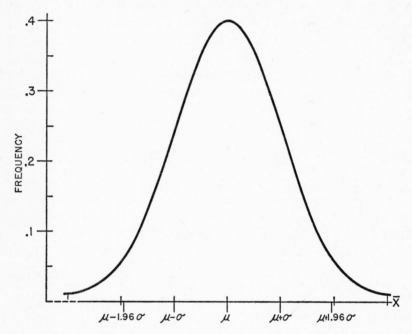

Fig. 31. The form of the random sampling distribution of means.

puted the mean intelligence test score in each of the 200 samples, the resultant frequency distribution of means would form a normal curve, as illustrated in Figure 31 above. Of course, the distribution of sample means would have a standard deviation and a mean, the standard deviation in this case being called the *standard error of the mean*. The mean of the distribution of the 200 sample means (a statistic) would be almost identical with the true mean intelligence test score (a parameter) in the population from which the samples are drawn. Furthermore, the larger the number in each of the samples, and the larger the number of sample means, the more closely would the mean of the distribution of sample means approximate the true mean.

These facts are of crucial importance. Because the distribution of sample means corresponds to the normal probability model, we can employ our knowledge of the characteristics of the model. Such knowledge makes it possible to discover how often the means of samples drawn at random will be in error by a given amount—that is, will diverge by any given amount from the true mean in the population. For we have already shown that within the normal curve 68 per cent of all outcomes will diverge from the mean by not more than plus or minus one standard deviation. In the specific case of sample means, then, 68 per cent of all sample means will be included within plus or minus one standard error of the true mean; that is, because the mean of the distribution of sample means is, in the "idealized" mathematical model, identical with the true mean of the population, the normal probability model tells us that 68 per cent, or roughly two thirds, of all sample means drawn at random will fall within plus or minus one standard error of the true mean.

Using the random sampling distribution of the mean

We know that approximately two thirds of the sample means will fall within plus or minus one standard error of the mean. This means that the chances are approximately two to one that *any one* sample mean will fall within those limits. And because approximately 95 per cent of the sample means will fall between plus and minus two standard errors of the mean, the chances are approximately nineteen to one that any sample mean will fall within that range.

Consider again the example of the psychologist who drew 200 samples, measured the intelligence test scores of each person in each sample, and then computed the mean intelligence test score of each sample. Suppose he had selected at random only *one* sample (the situation in which he usually finds himself). The chances are two to one that the mean of this sample is no more than plus or minus one standard error from the true mean intelligence test score. Thus, if the psychologist had drawn only one sample at random, instead of the 200 random samples, he would have been able to assert that the chances were two to one that the mean of this one sample was within plus or minus one standard error of the true mean. To be more concrete, if the mean of the sample was 105, the psychologist would assert that the chances were two to one that 105 was within plus or minus one standard error of the true mean I.Q. In short, the psychologist is able to estimate (state the probability) that his statistic, the sample mean, will diverge a given distance from the parameter, the true mean.

Computing the standard error of the mean

In order to make a specific statement as to how often any given sample mean will differ from the true mean by any given distance, the value of the standard error of the mean must be computed. This is a straightforward matter, but it does involve one complication, which will be discussed below. The formula for computing the standard error of the mean is

$$\sigma_{\bar{x}} = \frac{\sigma}{\sqrt{n}}$$

The symbol $\sigma_{\bar{x}}$ stands for the standard deviation of the hypothetical distribution of sample means, but it is called the *standard error of the mean* so that it will not be confused with the standard deviation of the distribution of the basic data which appears in the numerator of the formula. The symbol n, of course, stands for the number of individuals in the sample.

The complication concerns the numerator, σ, in the above formula. Strictly speaking, the standard deviation in this formula must be the standard deviation of the *population* in question, and, of course, the value of the standard deviation in the population is seldom known to the investigator. However, the standard deviation of the *sample*, s, may be substituted for the unknown population standard deviation without much loss in accuracy if n is larger than 30. This point will be developed in more detail in the mathematical section of this chapter. For purposes of simplification, we shall merely substitute the standard deviation of the sample for the standard deviation of the population in the remainder of this section of the chapter.

Consider once again the psychologist who drew the sample of intelligence test scores which had a mean of 105. Suppose that this sample contained 100 individuals and that the standard deviation of the distribution of the individuals' test scores in the sample $s = 16$. Applying the formula $s_{\bar{x}} = \frac{s}{\sqrt{n}}$, we find that the standard deviation of the distribution of sample means (the standard error of the mean is $\frac{16}{\sqrt{100}}$ or $\frac{16}{10}$ or 1.6.

Thus it is possible to make a more specific statement than heretofore. On the basis of his knowledge of the form of random phenomena, the psychologist can assert that the chances are approximately two to one that the sample mean of 105 lies within plus or minus 1.6 units of the true mean intelligence test score in the population from which the sample was drawn (see Figure 32). In short, we now have a procedure for computing an interval (in the above example 103.4–106.6) which will—with greater or lesser relative frequency (probability)—include the true mean. Such intervals are computed very frequently and have been given the technical name of *confidence intervals*, because they denote the interval which the

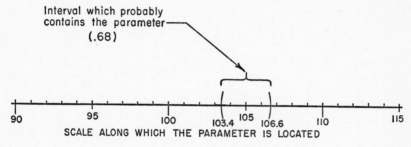

FIG. 32. Confidence interval 103.4 − 106.6.

investigator believes, with a specified amount of confidence, includes the true value. We now turn to a more detailed discussion of confidence intervals.

Confidence intervals

Whenever the scientist wishes to estimate a true value—say, the mean in a population—he draws a random sample and computes the mean and standard deviation of the sample. The sample mean and sample standard deviation are used as estimates of the corresponding population parameters (the true mean and standard deviation). The standard error of the mean is used to construct an interval which will include the true mean— with a degree of probability chosen by the investigator.

To continue with the above example, we have seen that the chances were approximately two to one that an interval extending one standard error (1.6 in the above case) above and below the sample mean included the true mean. Increasing the width of the interval would, of course, increase the relative frequency, and thus the probability (or, in other words, our confidence) that the interval would include the true mean.

Thus, if the interval were chosen to be 105 ± 1.96 standard errors. the probability would be nineteen to one that the interval 103.04–106.96 includes the true mean. In this case it is customary to assert that a probability of .95 is associated with the confidence interval 105 ± 3.14. The reason for this statement is that our knowledge of randomness provides us with the information that, indeed, 95 per cent of all sample means will lie within the interval between $+1.96s_{\bar{x}}$ and $-1.96s_{\bar{x}}$ units of the true mean. And it is for this reason that the interval with endpoints $\bar{X} \pm 1.96s_{\bar{x}}$ is referred to as a *95 per cent confidence interval*. (The endpoints $\bar{X} \pm 1.96s_{\bar{x}}$ are called *95 per cent confidence limits*.)

To increase the probability that the confidence interval will include the true mean, it is only necessary to increase the size of the interval, let us say, to 2.58 standard errors. Because $2.58 \times 1.6 = 4.13$, the probability is .99 that the interval 105 ± 4.13 includes the true mean. The student should note the remarkable fact that it is necessary to draw only *one* sample in order to obtain an estimate of the interval which includes the true value in the population. As will be shown later, the size of the interval and the degree of confidence associated with it also will depend on the sample size.

It has become conventional to employ confidence intervals such that the probability that the interval includes the parameter is .95 (or 95 per cent) or .99 (or 99 per cent.) This simply means that confidence intervals usually are the mean ± 1.96 or ± 2.58 times the standard error of the statistic involved.

Before leaving this point, the student must be reminded that s, the standard deviation of the sample, is only an estimate of σ, the standard deviation in the population (albeit a reasonably good estimate when n is large), and that when s is substituted for σ, the confidence limits calculated are not exactly what they would be if σ were known and used. Reduction of the error due to using s instead of σ is discussed in the mathematical section of this chapter.

Increasing precision

Examination of the formula for the standard error of the mean will show that it is possible to increase one's confidence of including the true mean within the interval based on $1.96s$ without increasing the confidence interval above $1.96s_{\bar{x}}$. Note that the right side of the formula

$$s_{\bar{x}} = \frac{s}{\sqrt{n}}$$ includes two parts, the standard deviation of the sample population (the numerator) and $\sqrt{n}$, the square root of the number of cases in the sample (the denominator). Of course, the standard deviation of the sample is produced by the data and cannot be made smaller or larger by

the investigator. But he *can* change *n;* that is, he can decide to have a smaller or larger number of cases in the sample which he draws. Note the effect of changing the value of *n*. If *n* is made larger, the standard error of the mean, $s_{\bar{x}}$, will become smaller, and, in turn, the estimate of the true mean will become more precise. In the example above, if the sample drawn included 500 cases, rather than 100, $s_{\bar{x}} = \dfrac{16}{\sqrt{500}} = .71$, rather than 1.6. The 95 per cent confidence interval would then be 105 ± 1.39 rather than 105 ± 3.14.

Increasing the precision of the inference concerning the value of the true mean by increasing the size of the sample is, of course, quite logical, since it is obvious that as a random sample grows increasingly larger, it becomes increasingly similar to the population. To take an extreme example, if the sample included only one individual less than the population, the chances of the sample mean being different from the population mean would be small indeed. The fact that precision is a direct function of the size of the sample is of considerable interest, for it indicates two consequences of importance for naturalistic studies. First, because precision can be gained only by increasing *n*, precision will cost money, time, and effort. It is a function of the cost of obtaining the data from each element

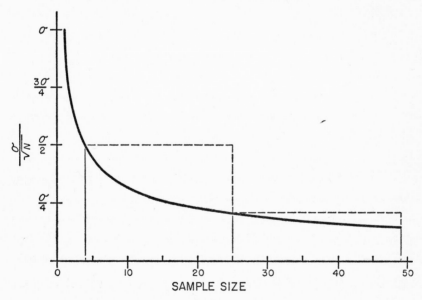

FIG. 33. The relation between the standard error of the mean ($\sqrt{N}$) and sample size.

of the population. Thus, increased precision may or may not be worth the cost. This is a factor every survey (and experiment) must take into account. Second, precision is related to the *square root* of *n*, which means that increasing the number of cases increases precision at a rate of diminishing returns (see Figure 33). For example, increasing *n* from 4 to 25 changes the value of $\sigma/\sqrt{n}$ from $\sigma/2$ to $\sigma/5$; adding twenty-one cases thus decreases $\sigma_{\bar{x}}$ to 40 per cent of its previous value. But increasing *n* from 25 to 49 causes a much smaller decrease in $\sigma/\sqrt{n}$. Thus, adding twenty-four cases when the sample is already large has much less effect on precision than adding twenty-one cases when the sample is very small. Increasing sample *n*'s to numbers over 500 has little effect on $\sigma_{\bar{x}}$, although there may be cases where the increase in precision is worth the cost of obtaining the larger number of cases. This point is discussed more fully in the next chapter.

Sampling distributions of proportions and correlation coefficients

It is of significance that the distribution of proportions in samples also fits the normal probability curve, and that proportions are also distributed approximately normally around the true proportion in the population. And the same reasoning is applied as in the case of sample means. Suppose a polltaker wishes to ascertain what proportion of the population owns automobiles. He draws a random sample, computes the proportion owning automobiles—say, $p = .80$—and then computes the standard error of the proportion by the formula $s_p = \sqrt{\dfrac{p(1-p)}{n}}$. If the sample contained 100 individuals, then $s_p = \sqrt{\dfrac{.80(.20)}{100}} = .04$. Thus, it may be said that the chances are approximately two to one that the proportion .80 is within $\pm.04$ of the true proportion. Note that the inference is made from those included in the study to those not included in the study.

The same holds true for correlation coefficients. The standard error of the product-moment correlation coefficient r_p is given by $\sigma_r = \dfrac{1 - \rho^2}{\sqrt{n-2}}$ where ρ is the population parameter. If σ_r is computed using a sample value *r* in place of ρ, the result is $s_r = \dfrac{1 - r^2}{\sqrt{n-2}}$. For an *r* of .50 and *n* of 102, s_r is .075. Thus, the probability is approximately .68 that .50 lies within .075 units of ρ. However, the sampling distributions of proportions and correlation coefficients both diverge from normality, and, as a result, the above statements must be taken as rough approximations. This matter is discussed in detail in the mathematical section.

By way of summary

Random sampling is the key to inductive inference. When samples are drawn at random, the statistics (means, proportions, and the like) computed from these samples will diverge from the parameters (the actual values in the population) in a random way. Put otherwise, the procedure of random sampling produces random rather than systematic errors. And the random sampling errors of some statistics (the mean, for example) have distributions in the form of the normal probability curve. Others, including the correlation coefficient, have non normal, but nevertheless manageable, random sampling distributions. This is a principle readily demonstrated in theory and in application. In short, the random sampling distributions of such statistics are known. As a consequence, it is possible to state the relative frequency with which random sampling errors of various size will occur.

Thus, given the statistic (mean, for example) of any sample drawn at random, it is possible to state how often a divergence from the true mean, a random sampling error, of any size will occur. In the case of the mean, the calculation of the probability of any error requires only a knowledge of the standard deviation of the population (or a reasonable estimate of it) and the number of cases in the sample. With this information, the standard error of the mean (the standard deviation of the random sampling distribution of the mean) may be calculated and the normal probability table consulted in order to discover the relative frequency of a sampling error of a given size. Thus, it is also possible to set forth confidence intervals— intervals which with a specified degree of probability contain the parameter in question.

Our discussion of the random sampling distribution of proportions and correlation coefficients followed the same logical pattern. Some qualifications remain to be made, but these will be set forth below, for it is not essential that the student grasp them at this point. What is essential is that the student perceive the similarity of the general reasoning, the logic of the method based on the normal probability model.

SAMPLING DISTRIBUTIONS AND EXPERIMENTS

The student is now prepared to understand the theory of a somewhat more complex random sampling distribution—the random sampling distribution of a *difference between two sample means*. As will be explained in detail below, scientists frequently plan their experiments so that they can compare one group of subjects with another. Consequently, they very frequently find themselves analyzing the difference between the mean performance of one group and that of another. In fact, one of the earliest and most pressing needs of the behavioral scientist was for a method which would permit a decision as to whether a difference between two means was a dependable one or not. Thus, for reasons of practical significance as well as intrinsic interest, the random-sampling distribution of a difference between two means is of importance. What is the logic behind it?

In order to understand the nature of a random-sampling distribution between two means, it will be best if the student begins by considering an entirely imaginary experiment.

An imaginary experiment and its use

In this imaginary experiment two groups of subjects are drawn at random from a population, and their reaction times are measured. In order to simplify matters, the two groups are treated exactly alike. Thus, we merely have two groups drawn at random, labeled A and B for convenience, and the records of the reaction times of all subjects. As a final condition, this experiment was performed not once but an endless number of times, there being an infinite number of A groups and B groups. What will the outcome of all these "experiments" be?

Because there was no difference in the treatment of the A groups and B groups, there should, *ideally*, be no difference between the mean reaction times of the A groups and the mean reaction times of the B groups. That is important, as we shall see later. But there *will* be differences—differences due to random sampling. For the fact that the A and B groups were treated exactly alike means only that the experiment set up conditions which eliminated all factors which could result in *systematic, regular*, differences between the groups. However, because the groups consisted of *samples drawn at random* from a population, differences between the groups *will* occur. Therefore, there will be differences between the means of the A's and the means of the B's even though A's and B's are treated exactly alike—such differences being random differences due to random sampling. Furthermore, the differences may be described in terms of a frequency distribution.

The fact that the differences between the means of the A groups and B groups must be random differences suggests, of course, that a model of randomness may be employed to describe the frequency distribution of these random differences between the means of the groups. And this is precisely the case. Models of randomness, such as the normal-probability model, can be employed to describe distributions of random differences between means; such models are called *random-sampling distributions of differences between means*. And these random-sampling distributions are similar to those described above for means.

The purpose of asking the student to consider the above imaginary experiment was to develop the point that in an endlessly repeated experiment in which two groups are treated exactly alike, with no intervention on the part of the experimenter, the resultant differences between the means of the two groups will form a random sampling distribution of differences between means. More concisely, differences between pairs of means drawn at random from the same population will be distributed normally (provided that the sample sizes are reasonably large).

We now consider two characteristics of this hypothetical distribution, its mean and standard error.

The mean and standard error of a random sampling distribution of differences between means

The Mean

The student will recall that it was pointed out in an earlier part of this chapter that certain statistics, such as the mean, when drawn at random, would be normally distributed around the true mean, the parameter, and, moreover, that the mean of the distribution of sample means would, ideally, coincide with the true mean. In other words, the distribution of sample means will be centered on the true mean. The same principle holds true in the case of the ideal distribution of differences between means: the mean of the distribution of differences will coincide with the true difference. What is the true difference in our imaginary experiment? The true difference is *zero*, for the groups were randomly drawn from the same population and were treated exactly alike. That is why we said above that *ideally* there should be no differences between the means of the A's and the B's; "no difference," of course, means "zero difference." In short, *the mean of the random-sampling distribution of differences between means of groups drawn from the same population is zero.*

The Standard Error

It now remains to calculate the standard error of this distribution, for once the value of the standard error is known, it is possible to calculate the relative frequency (probability of occurrence) of differences between means of various sizes. It is important to make such a calculation, as we shall see below. The standard error of the sampling distribution of differences between the means of independent random groups is calculated by means of the equation

$$\sigma_d = \sqrt{\sigma_{\bar{X}}^2 + \sigma_{\bar{Y}}^2}$$

the rationale of which is described in the following section.

All that is necessary, therefore, to calculate σ_d under the above conditions are the standard errors of the means which are to be compared. Thus, if the standard error of the mean of the A's was 3(i.e. $\sigma_{\bar{X}} = 3$) and the standard error of the mean of the B's was 4(i.e. $\sigma_{\bar{Y}} = 4$), then σ_d would be equal to $\sqrt{3^2 + 4^2} = 5$.

The standard error of the hypothetical distribution of differences is used in relation to the mean of the distribution of differences in much the same way as the standard error of the sampling distribution of means is used in relation to a parameter mean; that is, σ_d may be used to ascertain the relative frequency of occurrence of various values in the distribution. And in this case the values are differences between means.

A Note to the Student

It is of particular importance that the student see that the procedure for calculating the relative frequency of random occurrences of differences between means is exactly the same as that discussed in Chapter 5 in connection with calculating the relative frequency of random occurrences of various test scores, and the same as that discussed above in connection with the relative frequency of random occurrences of sample means and sample proportions. In each case the divergence of an event (a score, a sample mean, or the difference between two sample means) from the mean of the distribution, $X - \bar{X}$, or $\bar{X} - \mu_x$, or $(\bar{X}_1 - \bar{X}_2) - \mu_{\bar{X}_1 - \bar{X}_2}$, is expressed in terms of the standard deviation or standard error of the appropriate distribution—for example,

$$\frac{X - \mu_X}{\sigma_X}, \quad \frac{\bar{X} - \mu_x}{\sigma_{\bar{X}}}, \quad \frac{(\bar{X}_1 - \bar{X}_2) - \mu_{\bar{X}_1 - \bar{X}_1}}{\sigma_{\bar{X}_1 - \bar{X}_2}}.$$

In the next chapter we shall consider in detail why these differences are of such great importance in experimental research in the behavioral sciences. At this point we simply wish to indicate very briefly how the distribution of differences described above and its standard error may be used.

Suppose, for example, that two groups are drawn at random from the same population. One group (I) learns statistics by one method of instruction, and the other (II) learns by a second. Let us assume that on a final examination the mean for Group I was 84 and the mean for Group II was 92—the difference between the two means thus being 8.

Because the two groups are samples drawn from the same population, the question immediately arises as to whether the difference obtained is a dependable one or merely a random divergence from a true difference of 0. It is only natural to assume that the difference is a dependable one because the two groups were treated differently. That is the conjecture which comes most readily to mind. But there is "an ever present rival conjecture" whenever random samples are involved—that the difference obtained was due to *chance*, an error of random sampling, rather than to the treatment of the groups.

It is, however, possible to settle the issue. Because the characteristics of the random-sampling distribution of differences between means are known to us (as we have explained above), a difference between the means of groups randomly selected may be treated as was the mean. We compute the standard error of the random sampling distribution (in this case the random sampling distribution of means) and make a statement about confidence intervals. On the assumption that the standard error of the difference is 5, we may say that the interval 8 ± 1.96 (5) includes the true difference with a probability of .95. Since this interval extends from -1.80 to 17.80, it includes the value of 0. Therefore, the difference of 8 might well be a random, or chance, divergence from 0. If the true difference between the means were 0, then, of course, it would be concluded that there was no difference between the two methods used to teach the students. In short, the random sampling distribution of differences may be used to eliminate the conjecture as to whether an experimental variable did or did not have a dependable effect.

The important point to be grasped about a random sampling distribution of differences between means, then, is this: The relative frequency of occurrence of random differences between sample means may be ascertained by computing the standard error of the distribution of differences. In the next chapter we shall see how our knowledge about this random sampling distribution is put to work.

By way of summary

The purpose of this chapter is to demonstrate the key role of random sampling in the process of inductive inference. Without the concept of a random sample, of elements of a sample randomly drawn, it would be difficult, if not impossible, to conceive of the concept of random departures from true values. Once the concept of random errors is seen to be related to random samples, however, it becomes possible to employ models of randomness in order to state the relative frequency with which random errors of various sizes will occur. All this is fundamental.

The student must grasp the concept of a random sampling distribution of a statistic. Distributions of means, proportions, and even differences between pairs of means, when drawn at random from normally distributed variables (or otherwise if n's are large), have a stable and predictable form —the normal probability curve. And, of course, it is of great significance that the means of the random sampling distributions of means and proportions coincides with the population parameters. Given the facts of (1) stable and predictable form and (2) coincidence of the mean of the sampling distribution with the population parameter, it becomes possible to ascertain the relative frequency of various random departures from the mean (the parameter). This step requires only the calculation of the standard error of the random sampling distribution of the statistic in question. Once the standard error is calculated, the relative frequency of any random divergence from the mean may be ascertained from the normal probability model, because that is precisely what the normal probability model describes—the relative frequency of deviations from the mean in terms of the standard error.

This theoretical knowledge is applied successfully to various forms of the inductive problem—for example, (1) estimating the value of a population mean or proportion and (2) making decisions about the outcomes of experiments. The nature of that decision is discussed in the next chapter.

⟮ Mathematically . . .

In Part I our interest in various statistics, such as the mean, the standard deviation, and the correlation coefficient, was directed toward the fact that these statistics aid us in the analysis of the data from which they are computed. We now turn our attention in a different direction, for it is now our intention to investigate some of the mathematical characteristics, or properties, of these statistics themselves.

SAMPLING DISTRIBUTION OF THE MEAN

The Mean of Sample Means

Suppose, then, that a large number, t, of samples is drawn from an extensive population whose mean is μ and whose standard deviation is σ. Let all the samples be of size n, and let $X_{i,j}$ be the ith element of the jth sample; the symbol $X_{12,\,15}$ thus represents the twelfth element in the fifteenth sample. This notation allows every element of every sample to have a unique representation. Since each sample is to be of size n, the first subscript will always be some number from 1 to n inclusive. There are t samples taken from the population, and hence the second subscript will always be some number from 1 to t inclusive.

The mean of the jth sample is given by

$$(1) \qquad m_j = \frac{1}{n} \sum_{i=1}^{n} X_{i,j}$$

In reading this equation, think of j as fixed while i runs over the numbers 1, 2, . . . , n. Then $X_{i,j}$ runs over exactly those sample elements which belong in the jth sample. There are t such means, one for each of the t samples taken. The mean of all the sample means is then

$$(2) \qquad m = \frac{1}{t} \sum_{j=1}^{t} m_j$$

where the $m_j(j = 1, 2, \ldots, t)$ are defined by (1). Substituting from (1) into (2), it is found that

$$m = \frac{1}{t} \sum_{j=1}^{t} \left(\frac{1}{n} \sum_{i=1}^{n} X_{i,j} \right)$$

$$(3) \qquad = \frac{1}{tn} \sum_{j=1}^{t} \left(\sum_{i=1}^{n} X_{i,j} \right)$$

An examination of (3) shows that m is equal to $1/tn$ times the sum of all possible sample elements $X_{i,j}$. There are just tn such sample elements, and thus the *mean of all the means is precisely the mean of the very large sample obtained by combining all the smaller samples into one sample.* Since t may be taken as large as one pleases, it is possible to think of t as being so large that the t samples exhaust the entire population in such a way that no population element appears in more samples than any other population element. The value of m in (3) would then be the true population mean μ. *It is evident, then, that the true mean of the sample means is the same as the true mean of the population.*

An example of the above calculation for a population of as little as 100 elements would be very lengthy. For brevity, suppose that a population of six subjects yields the measurements 5, 7, 8, 12, 13, and 15. The population mean is $\mu = 10$. Now let every possible sample of size two be drawn. The results are given in Table 49, where S_j denotes the jth sample.

TABLE 49

Distribution of Samples of Size 2 from a Population of 6

j	S_j		$\sum_{i=1}^{2} X_{i,j}$	$m_j = \frac{1}{2}\sum_{i=1}^{2} X_{i,j}$	s_j^2
	$X_{1,j}$	$X_{2,j}$			
1	5	7	12	6.0	1.00
2	5	8	13	6.5	2.25
3	5	12	17	8.5	12.25
4	5	13	18	9.0	16.00
5	5	15	20	10.0	25.00
6	7	8	15	7.5	.25
7	7	12	19	9.5	6.25
8	7	13	20	10.0	9.00
9	7	15	22	11.0	16.00
10	8	12	20	10.0	4.00
11	8	13	21	10.5	6.25
12	8	15	23	11.5	12.25
13	12	13	25	12.5	.25
14	12	15	27	13.5	2.25
15	13	15	28	14.0	1.00

$$\sum_{j=1}^{15}\left(\sum_{i=1}^{2} X_{i,j}\right) = 300 \qquad \sum_{j=1}^{15} m_j = 150.0 \qquad \sum_{j=1}^{15} s_j^2 = 114.00$$

The double sum in this table is the sum of all the X's used in all fifteen samples. There are thus thirty contributions to the sum 300. The mean of the means m_j is clearly 10, as required by the theory.

The Variance of Sample Means

The next statistic whose mean value is to be sought is the square of the sample standard deviation. The square of the standard deviation is called the *variance*. If s_j denotes the standard deviation of the jth sample, then s_j^2 is the variance of the jth sample. The value of s_j^2 is given by

$$(4) \qquad s_j^2 = \frac{1}{n} \sum_{i=1}^{n} X_{i,j}^2 - m_j^2$$

where the $X_{i,j}^2 (i = 1, 2, \ldots, n)$ are the squares of the elements of the jth sample, and m_j is the mean of the jth sample. The formula used is that developed for rapid computation of the standard deviation. The square root sign is not used since s_j^2 is required instead of s_j. There being t samples, there are t values of s_j^2. The mean of all these values is

$$(5) \qquad \overline{s^2} = \frac{1}{t} \sum_{j=1}^{t} s_j^2$$

Substituting from (4) into (5) gives

$$(6) \qquad \overline{s^2} = \frac{1}{t} \sum_{j=1}^{t} \left(\frac{1}{n} \sum_{i=1}^{n} X_{i,j}^2 - m_j^2 \right)$$

Distributing the first $\sum$ symbol over the two terms of its general addend in (6) leads to

$$(7) \qquad \overline{s^2} = \frac{1}{tn} \sum_{j=1}^{t} \left(\sum_{i=1}^{n} X_{i,j}^2 \right) - \frac{1}{t} \sum_{j=1}^{t} m_j^2$$

$$(8) \qquad = \left[\frac{1}{tn} \sum_{j=1}^{t} \left(\sum_{i=1}^{n} X_{i,j}^2 \right) - \mu^2 \right] - \left[\frac{1}{t} \sum_{j=1}^{t} m_j^2 - \mu^2 \right]$$

The appearance of μ^2 in (8) is purely for convenience. It will be found that if the brackets are removed and the terms added, the two μ^2 terms will cancel each other out, leaving equation (7) as the result.

The reason for introducing μ^2 into the equation is that its presence makes it easy to evaluate the right member of (7). The expression

$$\sum_{j=1}^{t} \left(\sum_{i=1}^{n} X_{i,j}^2 \right)$$ is the sum of the squares of all the elements in all of the t

samples. If t is thought of as being sufficiently large, the mean of all these elements is μ. Then the first set of brackets in (8) encloses the variance, σ^2, of all these elements. Now μ not only is the mean of all the $X_{i,j}$ but is also the mean of all the sample means $m_j(j = 1, 2, \ldots, t)$ for sufficiently large t. Assuming t to be very large, the second set of brackets in (8) encloses the variance of the sample means. This quantity may be denoted by σ_m^2. With this interpretation of the terms of (8), the equation becomes

(9) $$\overline{s^2} = \sigma^2 - \sigma_m^2$$

when the number t of samples becomes sufficiently large to exhaust the population.

The variance of the numbers 5, 7, 8, 12, 13, and 15 used in Table 49 is 12.67, and the variance of the sample means m_j is $1576\frac{}{15} - 10^2 = 5.07$. According to the theory developed above, the mean value of all the sample variances should be $12.67 - 5.07 = 7.60$. These sample variances s_j^2 are shown in the last column of Table 49, their sum being 114. The mean sample variance is then $114\frac{}{15} = 7.60$ as expected.

The preceding development shows that if the variances (standard deviations squared) are computed for a very large number of samples, then the mean of the variances will be $\sigma^2 - \sigma_m^2$, where σ^2 is the variance of the whole population and σ_m^2 the variance of the distribution of sample means. It is clear from (9) that $\overline{s^2}$ is never exactly σ^2, since σ_m^2 can be 0 only if every sample mean is 0. The conclusion to be drawn from this is that a sample variance s^2 usually tends to be *less* than the population variance σ^2. This is to be expected, since no sample in practice spans the whole population.

Using methods too advanced for the present context, it has been found that if in the formula

$$s^2 = \frac{1}{n} \sum_{i=1}^{n} (X_i - \bar{X})^2$$

n is replaced by $n - 1$, the value of s^2 will be increased by the amount necessary to make the sample variances have a mean equal to the population variance σ^2. For large samples this change has a negligible effect, but for small samples it produces a value substantially larger than that of s^2. That this is true can be seen by considering the difference between the factors

$\dfrac{1}{n-1}$ and $\dfrac{1}{n}$:

$$\frac{1}{n-1} - \frac{1}{n} = \frac{1}{n(n-1)}$$

The value of the difference starts at $\frac{1}{2}$ for $n = 2$ and converges rapidly toward 0 as n becomes large. Because the mean of the sample variances s^2 becomes σ^2 when $n - 1$ is used instead of n, the expression

$$\frac{n}{n - 1}\left[\frac{1}{n}\sum_{i=1}^{n}(X_i - \bar{X})^2\right] = \frac{1}{n - 1}\sum_{i=1}^{n}(X_i - \bar{X})^2$$

is considered to be a better measure of the dispersion in the sample than the formula using n. If equation (9) is multiplied by $\dfrac{n}{n - 1}$ on both sides the result is

(9) $$\overline{s^2} = \sigma^2 - \sigma_m^2$$

(10) $$\frac{n}{n - 1}\overline{s^2} = \frac{n}{n - 1}\sigma^2 - \frac{n}{n - 1}\sigma_m^2$$

The term $\dfrac{n}{n - 1}\overline{s^2}$ is equal to σ^2, and, hence,

(11) $$\sigma^2 = \frac{n}{n - 1}\sigma^2 - \frac{n}{n - 1}\sigma_m^2$$

Solving this equation for σ_m^2 gives the very important result

(12) $$\sigma_m^2 = \frac{\sigma^2}{n}$$

or

$$\sigma_m = \frac{\sigma}{\sqrt{n}}$$

That is, the standard deviation of the distribution of sample means is $\sigma/\sqrt{n}$, where σ is the population standard deviation and n is the size of the sample. Because of the denominator, it is clear that the dispersion of the distribution of the means of all possible samples of a given size from a given population will be less for large samples than it will be for small ones.

Both the mean and standard deviation have now been found for the distribution of sample means. Each is expressed in terms of the corresponding statistic for the entire population. From formula (12) it is clear that, whatever the population we sample, σ_m can be made as close to 0 as desired by taking the sample size n large enough. For large samples the means, having a small standard deviation σ_m, will cluster closely about their mean μ, which is the mean of the population from which we imagine them to have been drawn. Each sample mean is then an estimate of the true mean μ. How close the estimate is depends on the value of σ_m, which thus becomes a measure of error in estimating the mean. It is called the *standard error of the mean* rather than the standard deviation of the sample means.

If the population in question is normally distributed, it can be proven that the sample means are also normally distributed. Since the mean and standard deviation are all that are required to describe a normal distribution, the distribution of sample means is fully known if the basic variable is normally distributed. *It is a remarkable fact that if the samples are sufficiently large, the sample means will be approximately normally distributed even though the population does not have a normal distribution.* The larger the samples used, the closer the approximation. This means that the methods developed for normal distributions may be used to make certain decisions concerning populations whose distributions are unknown. The normal or approximately normal distribution of sample means is one of the principle reasons for the emphasis placed upon normal distributions.

To see how a knowledge of the sampling distribution of means may be used, consider the following question: How large should samples drawn from a population with $\sigma = 4$ be if it is desired that 95 per cent of all such samples have a mean within 1.5 of the true population mean? This is a problem of considerable importance because it helps to answer the ever present question, how large should a sample be in order that it represent or mirror the population from which it is to be drawn? To find how large n must be in order that the sample will probably (.95) be within 1.5 of the true mean, let the true mean be μ. Then, since $\sigma = 4$, $\sigma_m = \dfrac{4}{\sqrt{n}}$, where n is the unknown sample size. From the theory of the normal curve (see pages 246–249) it is known that 95 per cent of all sample means will lie in the interval $\mu - 1.96\sigma_m$ to $\mu + 1.96\sigma_m$. With $\sigma_m = \dfrac{4}{\sqrt{n}}$, these limits become $\mu - \dfrac{7.84}{\sqrt{n}}$ to $\mu + \dfrac{7.84}{\sqrt{n}}$. The result is an interval of length $\dfrac{15.68}{\sqrt{n}}$ centered on μ. The requirements of the problem require this interval to extend 1.5 units to either side of μ, and, hence, $\dfrac{15.68}{\sqrt{n}} = 3.0$. Solving for n gives $n = 28$, which is the required sample size. If less accuracy were required, a smaller sample could be used. If, for example, it is required that the sample mean be within 2 rather than 1.5 of the true mean in 95 per cent of all samples, then the above technique gives $n = 16$. The sample size rises very rapidly as the degree of accuracy required increases.

CONFIDENCE INTERVALS

It is possible, by using the sample standard deviation s as an estimate for σ, to estimate quite accurately the mean of a population about which little is known. For example, suppose that a sample with $n = 100$ is taken from a population about which no prior information as to μ and σ is available. Suppose that $\bar{X} = 12$ and $s = 2.81$. Then $s_{\bar{X}} = \dfrac{s}{\sqrt{n}} = \dfrac{2.81}{\sqrt{100}} = .281$, which may be taken as a reasonably good estimate of the standard error of the mean. The interval from $12 - 1.96(.281)$ to $12 + 1.96(.281)$ will contain μ unless $\bar{X} = 12$ is either so large or so small that it differs from μ by more than $1.96\sigma_m$. Since the probability of this event is only .05, the probability is .95 that the interval 11.449 to 12.551 contains μ. Such an interval is called a *95 per cent confidence interval* for μ. (The accuracy of the figure 95 per cent depends on how accurately s represents σ. The larger the sample, the better the representation will be.)

If $2.58\sigma_m$ instead of $1.96\sigma_m$ is used in this example to form the confidence interval, then the interval would be from $12 - 2.58(.281)$ to $12 + 2.58(.281)$ or 11.275 to 12.725. In this case the confidence level for the interval would be 99 per cent, since 99 per cent of the distribution of sample means lies in the interval $\mu \pm 2.58\sigma_m$. Confidence limits corresponding to any degree of confidence (probability) may be formed by using the proper multiple of σ_m. The length of such intervals can be controlled by regulating the size of n, since $\sigma_m = \dfrac{\sigma}{\sqrt{n}}$ depends on n for its value.

SAMPLING DISTRIBUTION OF THE DIFFERENCE BETWEEN TWO MEANS

One of the most useful ways to compare two populations is to determine the difference between their means. To analyze the basis for such a comparison, let samples from two populations be considered. The data for the first sample will be represented by $X_1, X_2, \ldots, X_{n_x}$ and that of the second sample by $Y_1, Y_2, \ldots, Y_{n_y}$. Let the true means of the two populations be denoted by μ_x and μ_y, and the true standard deviations by σ_x and σ_y. If the two samples were completely "representative," then $\bar{X} = \mu_x$ and $\bar{Y} = \mu_y$ would be true and consequently $\bar{X} - \bar{Y} = \mu_x - \mu_y$ would be the true difference between the two population means. Perfect samples in this sense are, of course, not to be expected because of the ever present danger of sampling errors. If repeated pairs of means $\bar{X}$ and $\bar{Y}$ are obtained through repeated sampling, the resulting values of $d = \bar{X} - \bar{Y}$ can be studied in an effort to find out how they are distributed.

It has been found by advanced methods that the difference between two independent, normally distributed variables is a normally distributed variable. This result means that $d = \bar{X} - \bar{Y}$ is a normally distributed variable provided that the individual sample means $\bar{X}$ and $\bar{Y}$ are each normally distributed and provided that values of $\bar{X}$ and $\bar{Y}$ are uncorrelated. It is already known that $\bar{X}$ and $\bar{Y}$ are normally distributed if X and Y are normally distributed, and that $\bar{X}$ and $\bar{Y}$ are nearly normally distributed for sufficiently large n_x and n_y even though X and Y are not normally distributed. If the samples are chosen randomly, their means will be uncorrelated.

The sampling distribution of d will then be fully known if the quantities $\bar{d}$ and σ_d can be found; that is, the general form of the distribution of d is normal. Which particular normal distribution it is depends only on the mean $\bar{d}$ and the standard deviation σ_d. In discussing the several frequency distributions connected with this problem, it is well to keep in mind exactly what they are. The variables X and Y have frequency distributions which may or may not have the same means and standard deviations. The sample means $\bar{X}$ and $\bar{Y}$ have frequency distributions which depend on the frequency distributions of X and Y, respectively. And, finally, $d = \bar{X} - \bar{Y}$ has a frequency distribution which depends on the frequency distributions of $\bar{X}$ and $\bar{Y}$. If X and Y are normally or nearly normally distributed, then so also will be the variables $\bar{X}$, $\bar{Y}$, and d if random sampling is assumed. The mean and standard deviation of d will now be sought.

Suppose then that a large number, t, of pairs of samples have been taken, and that for each such pair a value of $d = \bar{X} - \bar{Y}$ has been found. Then,

$$\bar{d} = \frac{1}{t} \sum_{i=1}^{t} d_i$$

$$= \frac{1}{t} \sum_{i=1}^{t} (\bar{X}_i - \bar{Y}_i)$$

$$= \frac{1}{t} \sum_{i=1}^{t} \bar{X}_i - \frac{1}{t} \sum_{i=1}^{t} \bar{Y}_i$$

$$= \mu_x - \mu_y$$

provided that t is taken sufficiently large so that the t pairs of samples exhaust the entire basic populations. The last step above is a double application of the already established fact that the mean of the sample means is the mean of the basic population.

Having found $\bar{d}$, it is possible to find σ_d as follows. Using the familiar formula for the variance,

$$\sigma_d^2 = \frac{1}{t} \sum_{i=1}^{t} d_i^2 - \bar{d}^2$$

one has

$$\sigma_d^2 = \frac{1}{t} \sum_{i=1}^{t} (\bar{X}_i - \bar{Y}_i)^2 - (\mu_x - \mu_y)^2$$

and, upon expanding the squares,

$$\sigma_d^2 = \frac{1}{t} \sum_{i=1}^{t} (\bar{X}_i^2 - 2\bar{X}_i\bar{Y}_i + \bar{Y}_i^2) - (\mu_x^2 - 2\mu_x\mu_y + \mu_y^2)$$

Separating the sum into three sums gives

$$\sigma_d^2 = \frac{1}{t} \sum_{i=1}^{t} \bar{X}_i^2 - \frac{2}{t} \sum_{i=1}^{t} \bar{X}_i\bar{Y}_i + \frac{1}{t} \sum_{i=1}^{t} \bar{Y}_i^2 - \mu_x^2 + 2\mu_x\mu_y - \mu_y^2$$

Rearranging the terms of this expression results in

$$\sigma_d^2 = \left(\frac{1}{t} \sum_{i=1}^{t} \bar{X}_i^2 - \mu_x^2 \right) + \left(\frac{1}{t} \sum_{i=1}^{t} \bar{Y}_i^2 - \mu_y^2 \right) - 2\left(\frac{1}{t} \sum_{i=1}^{t} \bar{X}_i\bar{Y}_i - \mu_x\mu_y \right)$$

The first two terms are seen to be $\sigma_{\bar{X}}^2$ and $\sigma_{\bar{Y}}^2$. To evaluate the last term, let it be divided by $\sigma_{\bar{X}}\sigma_{\bar{Y}}$ and multiplied by the same quantity; the result is

$$-2\sigma_{\bar{X}}\sigma_{\bar{Y}} \left(\frac{\frac{1}{t} \sum_{i=1}^{t} \bar{X}_i\bar{Y}_i - \mu_x\mu_y}{\sigma_{\bar{X}}\sigma_{\bar{Y}}} \right) = -2\sigma_{\bar{X}}\sigma_{\bar{Y}} r_{\bar{X}\bar{Y}}$$

where $r_{\bar{X}\bar{Y}}$ is the correlation coefficient between the variables $\bar{X}_i$ and $\bar{Y}_i$. It follows that

(13) $$\sigma_d^2 = \sigma_{\bar{X}}^2 + \sigma_{\bar{Y}}^2 - 2\sigma_{\bar{X}}\sigma_{\bar{Y}}r_{\bar{X}\bar{Y}}$$

But if the samples are randomly (and thus independently) selected as has been assumed, then $r_{\bar{X}\bar{Y}}$ will be 0, and

(14) $$\sigma_d^2 = \sigma_{\bar{X}}^2 + \sigma_{\bar{Y}}^2$$

The conditions of randomness require that in each sample every datum have an equal chance of selection for the sample, and that the choices made in sampling one population have no effect on the choices made in sampling the other population. If these conditions are met with in sampling, it may be concluded that

$$\sigma_d = \sqrt{\sigma_{\bar{X}}^2 + \sigma_{\bar{Y}}^2}$$

Using the relations

$$\sigma_{\bar{X}} = \frac{\sigma_x}{\sqrt{n_x}} \text{ and } \sigma_{\bar{Y}} = \frac{\sigma_y}{\sqrt{n_y}}$$

this result can be written in the form

$$\sigma_d = \sqrt{\frac{\sigma_x^2}{n_x} + \frac{\sigma_y^2}{n_y}}$$

For randomly chosen samples from normal populations, the distribution of $d = \bar{X} - \bar{Y}$ has now been fully determined. The distribution is the normal distribution whose mean is $\mu_x - \mu_y$ and whose standard deviation is

$$\sqrt{\frac{\sigma_x^2}{n_x} + \frac{\sigma_y^2}{n_y}}$$

Some further facts concerning the structure and range of σ_d can be deduced from formulas (13) and (14). Notice that (14) has the form of the Pythagorean Theorem for right triangles; that is, if $\sigma_{\bar{X}}$ and $\sigma_{\bar{Y}}$ represent the lengths of the legs of a right triangle, then σ_d must be the hypotenuse. This geometric interpretation makes it clear that σ_d can never be as small as either $\sigma_{\bar{X}}$ or $\sigma_{\bar{Y}}$ and that it can never be as great as the sum $\sigma_{\bar{X}} + \sigma_{\bar{Y}}$ for randomly chosen samples. The implication of this result is that the dispersion of $d = \bar{X} - \bar{Y}$ is bounded both below and above by the dispersion of its constituent variables $\bar{X}$ and $\bar{Y}$.

The preceding analysis of the lower and upper bounds for σ_d shows that the size of σ_d is closely governed by the sizes of $\sigma_{\bar{X}}$ and $\sigma_{\bar{Y}}$. The sizes n_x and n_y of the samples also have an effect on σ_d. To see this, consider the special case in which σ_x and σ_y are equal. Using formula (14), and recalling that $\sigma_{\bar{X}} = \dfrac{\sigma_x}{\sqrt{n_x}}$ and $\sigma_{\bar{Y}} = \dfrac{\sigma_y}{\sqrt{n_y}}$, one has

$$\sigma_d^2 = \frac{\sigma_x^2}{n_x} + \frac{\sigma_y^2}{n_y}$$

Letting the common value of σ_x^2 and σ_y^2 be σ^2, the result is

$$\sigma_d^2 = \sigma^2\left(\frac{1}{n_x} + \frac{1}{n_y}\right)$$

and

$$\sigma_d = \sigma\sqrt{\frac{1}{n_x} + \frac{1}{n_y}}$$

If the sizes of the samples are equal—say, $n_x = n_y = n$—then the result becomes

$$\sigma_d = \sigma\sqrt{\frac{1}{n} + \frac{1}{n}}$$
$$= \sqrt{2}\left(\frac{\sigma}{n}\right)$$

This will be recognized as $\sqrt{2}$ times the standard error of the mean. The implication to be drawn here is that if two random samples of equal size are taken from populations having the same standard deviation, then their standard errors of the mean will be equal, and σ_d will be $\sqrt{2}$ times the common standard error of the mean for the two populations. The last equation shows that σ_d may be made as small as one desires by making n sufficiently large. In the case of unequal n_x and n_y the value of σ_d cannot be made arbitrarily small by increasing only one of the n's. Both must be increased to achieve very small values of σ_d.

The most useful application of the frequency distribution of $d =$

$\bar{X} - \bar{Y}$ is the testing of the hypothesis that the two means $\bar{X}$ and $\bar{Y}$ are from populations having identical means. This hypothesis is mathematically equivalent to assuming that $\mu_x = \mu_y$. If this assumption is true, then the variable $d = \bar{X} - \bar{Y}$ is normally or nearly normally distributed with $d = 0$ and $\sigma_d = \sqrt{\dfrac{\sigma_x^2}{n_x} + \dfrac{\sigma_y^2}{n_y}}$. Such tests will be treated in detail in the next chapter.

SAMPLING DISTRIBUTION OF PROPORTIONS

If a population consists of two parts one of which has some property while the other does not, it is of interest to estimate what proportion has the property in question. Examples are "What proportion of the voters are Independents?" "What proportion of the student body has I.Q. scores above 120?" and "What proportion of convicted felons are rehabilitated?" The answer to the problem of estimating such percentages lies in finding their sampling distribution—that is, the way in which the proportions observed in a great many samples are distributed. The binomial distribution will provide the basis for this information.

Let E be any event whose probability is p, and let E' be the nonoccurrence of E. Then E' is an event whose probability is $1 - p = q$. Let n trials of the event E be made, and suppose that E occurs t times out of the n. From the study of the binomial distribution, it is known that t is an approximately normally distributed variable with $\mu = np$ and $\sigma = \sqrt{npq}$ if n is as large as 30 and p is not too small; that is, if repeated sets of n trials of the event E are made, each set would produce a value of t. These values of t would be very nearly normally distributed with mean np and standard deviation $\sqrt{npq}$. It is not the distribution of t which is required here, however, but the distribution of the proportion t/n, the number of times E occurs divided by the number of trials.

It will be recalled that if each datum in a distribution is multiplied by a constant, the mean will be similarly affected as will also the standard deviation. Using these properties of the mean and standard deviation and letting the constant be $1/n$, the several values of t are converted into the proportions t/n. The mean, np, becomes

$$\frac{1}{n}(np) = p$$

and the standard deviation becomes

$$\frac{1}{n}\sqrt{npq} = \sqrt{\frac{npq}{n^2}} = \sqrt{\frac{pq}{n}}$$

Now multiplying every element of a numerical population by a constant does nothing to change the form of the distribution. A plot of the new frequency curve would differ from the former curve only in that the scale would be different. It follows then from the nearly normal distribution of t that the proportions t/n are also approximately normally distributed with mean p and standard deviation $\sqrt{pq/n}$, where p is the probability associated with E and n is the number of trials in the sample. Then p, being the probability associated with E, is also the proportion of events E expected in any sample.

The problem of finding the distribution of sample proportions is then completely solved. Sample proportions are approximately normally distributed, the mean being p and the standard deviation being $\sqrt{pq/n}$, where p is the true population proportion. (The Greek letter π is not used for the population proportion according to the convention mentioned earlier because of other meanings so closely associated with the symbol.)

For an application of this result, consider the following example. Since, of forty rats used in a maze learning experiment, six failed to reach a level of learning compatible with survival, the proportion $6/40 = .15$ may be taken as an estimate of the true proportion of all rats that would fail the test. How good an estimate it would be can be determined by finding confidence limits for the true proportion. The closer these limits are to .15, the more accurate (at the confidence level selected) the estimate will be. To form limits on the 95 per cent level of confidence, it is necessary to note from the normal probability table that 95 per cent of the area under the normal curve lies in the interval $\mu \pm 1.96\sigma$. Taking $\sqrt{pq/n} = \sqrt{(.15)(.85)/40} = .056$ as an estimate of σ, the 95 per cent confidence limits extend from $.15 - (1.96)(.056)$ to $.15 + (1.96)(.056)$, or, on completing the computations, from .04 to .26. This interval extending .11 on either side of the sample proportion probably (.95) contains the true population proportion. Had a higher level of confidence been desired, it would have been necessary to use more than 1.96σ in computing the interval, and it would have been longer as a consequence. Remember that .04 and .26 have been obtained using the normal approximation. The errors in the results are quite small, however. It will be observed that .15 could be considered a better estimate of the population proportion if the confidence limits were closer together. Since the confidence limits depend on n, the level of confidence selected, and the sample value of p, these limits may be narrowed in only two ways: the level of confidence may be lowered, or the size of the sample may be increased. If in this experiment 100 rats had been used instead of forty, the estimated value of σ would be reduced to $\sqrt{\dfrac{(.15)(.85)}{100}} = .036$. The 95 per cent confidence limits would then extend only .07 instead of .11 on either side of .15, giving .08 to .22 as the confidence interval.

An investigator who publishes an estimated proportion without giving confidence limits, or information from which such limits may be computed, conveys no real information to his readers. By giving confidence limits for his result, the experimenter has expressed himself in a form that is universally understood among scientists and that is independent of the details of the experiment. When the limits are widely separated, those viewing the result understand that the sample has been too small or that the variability of the data is too great for precise estimates.

All of the preceding has been based on samples of thirty or more. Samples of less than thirty are in most cases inadequate for estimating proportions. The limitations may be observed by examining the results for $n = 30$. Samples of a smaller size can only lead to wider confidence intervals. For $n = 30$ and a sample proportion of .10, the 95 per cent confidence limits are $-.007$ and .207; this means that the population proportion probably (.95) lies somewhere between 0 and .21—not a very good estimate. If the sample proportion is .5, the confidence limits are .322 and .678. Efforts to estimate proportions with samples of less than 30 are thus subject to quite large errors of estimate.

It has been pointed out that precision of estimate may be increased by increasing the sample size. The question of how much to increase the value of n in order to achieve a given level of precision arises. For proportions this problem is solved as follows. Suppose that p is not known and that an estimate accurate to within .08 is desired. Let 95 per cent confidence limits be set. Using the fact that sample proportions are normally distributed with standard deviation $\sqrt{pq/n}$, it is required that

$$1.96\sqrt{\frac{pq}{n}} = .08 \, ;$$

that is, 95 per cent confidence limits require that 1.96 standard errors of the proportion be not more than the error .08 allowed. Now let a trial sample be taken—say, twenty-five—to obtain a rough estimate of p. Suppose the event in question occurs eight times in the twenty-five trials. The rough estimate of p is then $\frac{8}{25} = .32$. Using $p = .32$ and $q = .68$ in the above equation gives

$$1.96\sqrt{\frac{(.32)(.68)}{n}} = .08$$

which must now be solved for n. If n turns out to be 25 or less, then an adequate number of trials will already have been made to establish the value of p under the conditions set. Dividing both sides by 1.96 and squaring both sides gives

$$\frac{.2176}{n} = .001666$$

from which $n = 131$. This indicates that, in order to establish the estimate $p = .32 \pm .08$ on the 95 per cent level of confidence, 131 trials would be necessary.

With 131 as an estimate for n, the experimenter increases the number of trials from twenty-five to 131. Suppose he then finds the event occurring thirty-nine times, giving a sample proportion of .30. Repeating the above process, he solves for n in

$$1.96\sqrt{\frac{(.30)(.70)}{n}} = .08 \text{ and } \frac{.2100}{n} = .001666$$

In this case n turns out to be 126, indicating that the 131 trials were more than enough to establish the estimate $p = .30$. It is now possible to say that, for this population, $p = .30 \pm .08$ with a probability of 95 per cent that the limits indicated will not be exceeded. Furthermore, 131 trials is established as a sufficient number (a lesser number down to 126 might also be sufficient) of trials necessary to insure an adequate sampling of this population within the confidence and error limits prescribed. Had the second determination of n yielded a value greater than 131, it would have been necessary to increase the number of trials and complete a third step in the process. In many cases two steps are sufficient, and rarely are more than three steps necessary.

A modification of this technique eliminates the first trial sample by assuming that $p = \frac{1}{2}$. If this is done, the first equation to be solved is

$$1.96\sqrt{\frac{(.5)(.5)}{n}} = .08$$

which gives $n = 150$; the first sample would then be one of 150 trials. This method will always give an adequate first sample, because pq is at its maximum possible value when $p = q = .5$. It is obviously more economical, however, to approach the correct sample size from below than from above.

Based on the normal or very nearly normal distribution of sample means and proportions, a method has been devised which reveals the unknown parameters of a population in such a way that (1) a predetermined degree of accuracy is obtained, (2) a method for minimizing the amount of sampling is available, and (3) the result can withstand criticism on as high a confidence level as may be desired. The values of n, p, and σ that are obtained, while still estimates, are far from blind guesses. Out of a knowledge of randomness and of probability theory, a method has been evolved for measuring the precision of estimates and of systematically improving estimates. The value of such methods to the empirical sciences is obviously very great. Much of statistics is devoted to refining and extending methods of precision control.

SAMPLING DISTRIBUTION OF THE PEARSON PRODUCT-MOMENT CORRELATION COEFFICIENT

Precision of estimate has been attained for the Pearson product-moment correlation coefficient by means similar to those used in the cases discussed above. The development is somewhat more difficult, because the sample correlation coefficients are not normally or even nearly normally distributed. As in the problems previously treated, it is expected that a correlation coefficient r obtained from a sample of size n will be an estimate of the true correlation coefficient ρ (rho as in rhododendron) of the whole population. How good an estimate it is will depend on how large n is and on how the sample values of r are distributed. The sampling distribution of r has been found, as previously stated, to be definitely non-normal. In spite of this, the normal distribution is still of great use in describing the sampling distribution of r. The reason for this is that the variable

$$Z = \frac{1}{2} \log \frac{1 + r}{1 - r}$$

is very nearly normally distributed. Every value of r from -1 to $+1$ produces a different Z; given any number, Z, the corresponding r can be calculated. The one-to-one correspondence between the numbers r and the numbers Z makes it possible to study the behavior of the correlation coefficient by using Z. The logarithms used above to compute Z are natural, not common, logarithms. If common logarithms are used, the fraction $\frac{1}{2}$ must be changed to 1.1513. It has been found that

$$\mu_Z = \frac{1}{2} \log \frac{1 + \rho}{1 - \rho}$$

and

$$\sigma_Z = \frac{1}{\sqrt{n - 3}}$$

can be taken as the mean and standard deviation of the nearly normal distribution of Z. The number ρ is the true population value of the correlation coefficient, and n is the size of the sample from which r, and in turn Z, may be computed.

Since the computations involved in changing from r to Z and from Z to r are quite laborious, tables for this purpose have been constructed. The sampling distribution of Z being very nearly normal, it is possible to estimate the precision of sample values of r. Suppose that a sample of 28 has yielded $r = .64$. Appendix Table B gives $Z = .7581$ corresponding to $r = .64$. Let the required level of confidence for the result be 99 per cent, which means that a confidence interval extending 2.58 standard deviations on either side of Z is to be used. The question is then, What margin e of error must be affixed to the sample value Z so that $Z \pm e$ will probably (.99) include the true mean, σ_Z, of the Z's. The error e is just $2.58 \sigma_Z = 2.58/\sqrt{28 - 3} = .516$. Then $Z \pm .516$ is an interval having a probability of .99 of containing μ_Z. If the 95 per cent level of confidence were sufficient, the error would be $e = 1.96\sigma_Z = .392$, and $Z \pm .392$ would probably (.95) contain μ_Z. It is clear that decreasing the level of confidence also shortens the confidence interval. It remains only to pass from the use of Z to the corresponding values of r. With $Z = .7581$ the values $.7582 - .516$ and $.7582 + .516$ are $.2421$ and 1.2741, respectively. According to Appendix Table B, the corresponding values of r are $r_1 = .24$ and $r_2 = .85$. Note that the sample value $r = .64$ does not lie midway between these two extremes. The notation $.64 \pm$ an error cannot therefore be used. The result may be stated as $P(.24 < \rho < .85) = .99$; this is read, of course, as "The probability that the interval (.24 to .85) contains the true correlation coefficient ρ is .99."

It is important to note that had a larger sample been used, more precision would have been obtained. If $n = 103$, then $\sigma_Z = 1/\sqrt{100} = .1$;

then $e = 2.58\sigma_Z = .258$, and the resulting interval would have been $Z \pm .258$ instead of $Z \pm .516$. It is worth noting that the size of the sample had to be increased by a factor of nearly 4 to double the precision of the result.

Since $\sigma_Z = 1/\sqrt{n-3}$ is a function of n only, it is quite easy to determine how large a sample should be to be representative of the population with a given degree of precision: it is only necessary to fix a level of confidence and the maximum error to be tolerated. Suppose that Z is required to be an estimate of μ_Z accurate to within .065 ninety per cent of the time. Then it is only necessary to set

$$1.64\sigma_Z = .065 \text{ and}$$

$$1.64 \frac{1}{\sqrt{n-3}} = .065$$

and solve for n; since $n - 3 = \left(\frac{1.64}{.065}\right)^2$, $n = 640$. Thus $n = 640$ is sufficiently large to obtain representative samples meeting the given requirements. If the confidence level is relaxed to a lower percentage, or if the tolerated error is increased, a lower value of n will be obtained.

Of course, the error to be tolerated in Z must be chosen with the corresponding effect on r in mind. If r is known to be near .50, then an error of .065 in Z corresponds to an error of about .05 in r. If r is near 90, the corresponding error in r is only about .01. The amount of error to be tolerated in Z must be chosen with at least the approximate value of r in mind.

To further illustrate the estimation of ρ by means of the distribution of Z, suppose that a sample of size 30 has produced an r of $-.82$. Then

$$Z = \frac{1}{2} \log \frac{1 + (-.82)}{1 - (-.82)}$$

$$= \frac{1}{2} \log \frac{1 - .82}{1 + .82}$$

$$= \frac{1}{2} \log \left(\frac{1 + .82}{1 - .82}\right)^{-1}$$

$$= -\frac{1}{2} \log \frac{1 + .82}{1 - .82}.$$

Hence the Z for $r = -.82$ is the negative of the Z for $r = +.82$. For this reason, Appendix Table B gives Z values only for positive values of r, and in this case the table gives $Z = -1.1569$. The sample standard deviation is $1/\sqrt{27} = .1925$. Using 95 per cent confidence limits, the confidence interval is then $-1.1569 \pm 1.96(.1925)$—that is, $-1.5342 \leq Z \leq -.7796$. Using the table to translate these Z's into r's, one finds $-.91 \leq \rho \leq -.65$. The probability that the interval between $-.65$ and $-.91$ will contain the true parameter ρ is .95.

Suggestions for Further Reading

The following books provide treatments of random sampling distributions which are about the same level of complexity as that presented here.

EDWARDS, A. 1954. *Statistical methods for the behavioral sciences.* New York: Rinehart.

WALKER, H., and LEV, J. 1953. *Statistical inference.* New York: Holt.

WALLIS, W., and ROBERTS, H. 1956. *Statistics: A new approach.* Glencoe: Free Press.

MOSTELLER, F., ROURKE, R., and THOMAS, G. 1961. *Probability and statistics.* Reading: Addison-Wesley.

   Especially Chapter 5.

More advanced treatments may be found in:

STEEL, R., and TORRIE, J. 1960. *Principles and procedures of statistics.* New York: McGraw-Hill.

   This book will be of special interest to students of biology.

TIPPETT, L. 1952. *The methods of statistics* (4th ed.). New York: Wiley.

PROBLEMS

1. If a large population is to be studied by choosing a sample from it, what are the two major requirements that must be met in selecting the sample? What kinds of useful conclusions depend for their justification on carefully satisfying these requirements?

2. It is obvious that few if any samples ever represent perfectly the populations from which they are drawn. How does the error in a random sample of adequate size differ from the error in a small and biased sample?

3. Explain in a short paragraph why the statistician considers random error more desirable than systematic error.

4. Devise a random selection procedure and use it to select two samples of five persons. Record their heights in inches, and denote these data by X's. Find $\sum X$, $\sum X^2$, and $\bar{X}$ for each of your two samples of size 5.

5. After sharing the data collected in problem 4 with all the other members of your class, compute the mean of all the heights in all the samples. Then compute the mean of the sample means and compare the results.

6. Compute the standard deviation of all the data collected by combining the results of problem 4. Compute the standard deviation of the sample means. Will you expect these two standard deviations to be equal or nearly equal?

7. What percentage of the sample means collected in problem 4 lie within one standard deviation (of the sample means) of the mean (of the sample means) as computed in problems 5 and 6?

8. Repeat problem 7 for .5 standard deviations, 1.5 standard deviations and 2 standard deviations. Are these percentages consistent with the assertion that the sample means are normally or very nearly normally distributed?

9-12. Repeat problems 4 to 8 inclusive using some non-normally distributed variable instead of height. Such a variable could be (a) amount of change carried by the subject, (b) the age of the subject in months, (c) number of hours per week spent in class, or (d) weight.

13. What number, z, of standard errors would be associated with (a) 80 per cent confidence limits, (b) 90 per cent confidence limits, and (c) 99 per cent confidence limits?

14. For what value of n is (a) $\dfrac{1}{\sqrt{n}} = \dfrac{1}{2}$, (b) $\dfrac{1}{\sqrt{n}} = \dfrac{1}{3}$, (c) $\dfrac{1}{\sqrt{n}} = \dfrac{1}{4}$, (d) $\dfrac{1}{\sqrt{n}} = \dfrac{1}{10}$.

15. In problem 4 each student was asked to accumulate data for two samples of size 5. Compute the difference $\bar{X}_2 - \bar{X}_1$ for the two samples. List the results obtained by the class. Compute the mean and standard deviation of the differences.

16. To see how nearly normal the distribution of differences in problem 15 is, compute the points $\bar{X} \pm zs$ for $z = .4$, .8, 1.2, 1.6, and 2.0. Compare the proportions of differences found between these points, $\bar{X} \pm zs$, with the expected proportions as found in the normal-probability table.

17. The next best thing to perfect accuracy is to know with a high degree

of probability what error exists. Explain in a paragraph how this is accomplished by using means of means and other statistics of statistics.

18. Compute the double sum $\sum_{a=1}^{7} \sum_{b=1}^{4} ab$ in the following three ways:

(a) $\sum_{a=1}^{7} \sum_{b=1}^{4} ab = \sum_{b=1}^{4} b + \sum_{b=1}^{4} 2b + \cdots + \sum_{b=1}^{4} 7b$

(b) $\sum_{a=1}^{7} \sum_{b=1}^{4} ab = \sum_{a=1}^{7} a + \sum_{a=1}^{7} 2a + \sum_{a=1}^{7} 3a + \sum_{a=1}^{7} 4a$

(c) $\sum_{a=1}^{7} \sum_{b=1}^{4} ab =$ the sum of all the 28 possible products ab where

$1 \le a \le 7$ and $1 \le b \le 4$

19. The "population" contributing the samples in Table 49 consists of the 6 numbers 5, 7, 8, 12, 13, and 15. List all of the twenty possible samples of size 3 that can be taken from these six numbers, and use Table 49 as a model for showing that the mean of the means is the mean of the population.

20. Compute the sample variances for the samples of problem 19. Check the relation $\bar{s}^2 = \sigma^2 - \sigma_m^2$ for these variances.

21. By how much will the standard deviation of a set of 5 data be increased if $n - 1$ instead of n is used in the formula for s?

22. Repeat problem 21 for sets of ten data, twenty data, and fifty data.

23. How large should samples drawn from a population with $\sigma = 5$ be if it is desired that 90 per cent of all such samples have a mean within 1.2 of the true population mean?

24. Repeat problem 23 for 95 per cent and for 99 per cent in place of 90 per cent.

25. Find 95 per cent confidence limits for the mean of a population if a sample of size 36 has a mean of 68 and a standard deviation of 10.

26. Repeat problem 25 with the sample size changed to (a) 64, (b) 100, and (c) 400.

27. Repeat problem 25 with 99 per cent in place of 95 per cent.

28. Repeat problem 26 with 99 per cent in place of 95 per cent.

29. How can the comparatively small effect due to the increase in n from 100 to 400 in problems 26 and 28 be explained?

30. What five different frequency distributions enter into a consideration of the distribution of the difference between two means?

31. Using $s_x = 5$ and $s_y = 8$ as estimates of σ_x and σ_y compute the standard deviation of the difference between pairs of sample means using (a) $n_x = 10$, $n_y = 15$, (b) $n_x = 30$, $n_y = 30$, (c) $n_x = 50$, $n_y = 10$.

32. From an analysis of the formula for σ_d, the standard deviation of the difference between two means, show that σ_d will always be greater than either $\sigma_{\bar{x}}$ or $\sigma_{\bar{y}}$ and will always be less than $\sigma_{\bar{x}} + \sigma_{\bar{y}}$ provided that the samples are chosen randomly.

33. If $\sigma_x = 8$, $\sigma_y = 12$, $n_x = 25$, and $n_y = 30$, find σ_d.

34. Show that no matter how large n_x is made in problem 33, σ_d can never be less than 2.19.

35. Suppose that a polltaker asks 200 persons the question, "Do you smoke?" If fifty-four replied "No," then what proportion of the sample were nonsmokers?

36. Shake a set of twenty-five pennies in a box and cast them on a table. Record the proportion of heads. Repeat this process until sixty casts have been made. Find the mean and standard deviation of the distribution of proportions you have recorded. How do your results compare with the theoretically expected values?

37. Cast six dice and record the proportions of dice showing (a) a three or a five, (b) an even number, and (c) a one. Repeat this process eighty times, and compute the means and standard deviations of the three sets of proportions recorded. Compare your results with the theoretically expected values.

38. In a sample of sixty students, nine were found to be working at least half time. Find 95 per cent confidence limits for the true proportion.

39. Suppose that the confidence limits obtained in problem 38 are considered to be too widely separated and that it is decided to enlarge the sample to 125 students. If twelve among the additional sixty-five students work at least half time, the sample proportion becomes $21/125 = .168$. Find the new 95 per cent limits for the true proportion.

40. It is necessary to estimate the proportion of trees infected with a virus in a certain forest. The estimate should be correct to within .12 with a probability of .95. If an initial sample of 25 trees leads to

a first rough estimate of .28 for p, to what number should the sample size be increased for the second estimate of p?

41. If in seeking the estimate referred to in problem 40, the sample size is increased to 54 trees and the sample proportion is .32, to what value should the sample size be increased for the third estimate of p?

42. Let it be given that a certain sample of size 28 has yielded a Pearson r of .78, and let it be required that 95 per cent confidence limits be fixed for the true value ρ of the population. The problem may be organized as follows:

    (a) Compute the standard deviation of the Z-distribution corresponding to samples of size 28.

    (b) Using Appendix Table B to record the value of Z corresponding to $r = .78$.

    (c) Set up a 95 per cent confidence interval based on the Z of part (b) and σ_Z.

    (d) Using Appendix Table B to convert the endpoints Z_1 and Z_2 of the confidence interval for Z into values r_1 and r_2. Then $r_1 \leq \rho \leq r_2$ will be the answer.

43. Suppose the confidence interval found in problem 42 is considered to be too long. The sample size is increased to 100 and the new correlation coefficient is found to be .77. What will the new 95 per cent confidence limits for ρ be?

44. Repeat problem 42 with r replaced by $r = -.65$.

45. Let the sample size in problem 44 be increased to 52 and compute new 95 per cent confidence limits for r. To what can the small change due to the increase in sample size be attributed?

"Quite true," said Parmenides; *"but I think you should go a step further, and consider not only the consequences which flow from a given hypothesis, but also the consequences which flow from denying the hypothesis; and that will be still better training for you."*

"What do you mean?" he [Socrates] said.

"That," said Parmenides, *"is a tremendous business . . ."*

PLATO *(Parmenides)*

CHAPTER

9

STATISTICAL DECISIONS

WE HAVE SEEN in earlier chapters, particularly in our discussion of estimation and confidence intervals (pages 292–299), that the statistical method permits a rigorous approach to the problem of *establishment* of fact—for example, what is the mean of this population? what is the correlation between this variable and that one?—despite the variability among the

BOX 2 8

Mute Facts

The following passage from Bronowski's *Science and human values* denies the notion that good science is a collection of uninterpreted facts:

"What is the insight with which the scientist tries to see into nature? Can it indeed be called either imaginative or creative? To the literary man the question may seem merely silly. He has been taught that science is a large collection of facts; and if this is true, then the only seeing which scientists need do is, he supposes, seeing the facts. He pictures them, the colorless professionals of science, going off to work in the morning into the universe in a neutral, unexposed state. They then expose themselves like a photographic plate. And then in the darkroom or laboratory they develop the image, so that suddenly and startlingly it appears, printed in capital letters, as a new formula for atomic energy.

"Men who have read Balzac and Zola are not deceived by the claims of these writers that they do no more than record the facts. The readers of Christopher Isherwood do not take him literally when he writes: 'I am a camera.' Yet the same readers solemnly carry with them from their school days this foolish picture of the scientist fixing by some mechanical process the facts of nature. I have had, of all people, a historian tell me that science is a collection of facts, and his voice had not even the irony of one filing cabinet reproving another.

"It seems impossible that this historian had ever studied the beginnings of a scientific discovery. The Scientific Revolution can be held to begin in the year 1543 when there was brought to Copernicus, perhaps on his deathbed, the first printed copy of the book he had written about a dozen years earlier. The thesis of this book is that the earth moves around the sun. When did Copernicus go out and record this fact with his camera? What appearance in nature prompted his outrageous guess? And in what odd sense is this guess to be called a neutral record of fact? . . . .

"The scientist looks for order in the appearances of nature . . . For order does not display itself of itself; if it can be said to be there at all, it is not there for the mere looking. There is no way of pointing a finger or a camera at it; order must be discovered and, in a deep sense, it must be created. What we see, as we see it, is mere disorder."

Reprinted by permission of Julian Messner, Inc. from *Science and human values* by J. Bronowski; Copyright © 1956 by J. Bronowski.

data. But equally pressing, if not more so, is the need for a method which will provide a clear, rigorous procedure for making *decisions* about these facts. If the facts could "speak for themselves" there would be no problem here. But facts always require interpretation. (See Box 28.) Thus, for example, when a scientist completes an experiment, he must interpret the results. Put in its simplest form, he must decide whether the results confirm or contradict the hypothesis his experiment was designed to test. The "bald" facts he has collected in the course of his experiment do not, in themselves, force one or another of these decisions. One of the most important functions of the statistical method is to provide a rigorous approach to the making of this decision. Thus, not only does the statistical method provide a procedure for the establishment of fact, but it also provides a procedure for deciding what the facts signify.

THE NEED FOR DECISION-MAKING

The need for logically rigorous decision-making procedures is rooted in the scientist's effort to make *all* of his procedures subject to analysis, criticism, and improvement. The most careful, painstaking efforts to design the most exact test of a scientific theory will be to no avail if the results of this test are to be interpreted on the sheer personal whim or preference of the experimenter.

REQUIREMENTS

The best method of making decisions, of course, is that method which is infallible—a method which *always* provides the correct decision. But in the situation with which we are concerned—inductive inference based on random sampling—no such method is known to man. Indeed, if there is variability among the subjects, and if inductive inference is based on random sampling, then not only will some of our decisions be wrong, but, in principle, some of our decisions *must* be wrong. Because under these conditions there are no infallible methods for making decisions about the results of experiments, we are brought face to face with a challenging problem: What are the requirements for a good method of decision-making when we know in advance that some of our decisions must be wrong?

There are at least three such requirements: (1) the risk of making an incorrect decision should be minimal, (2) the various kinds of risks should be specified, and (3) the procedure of arriving at decisions should be public—there should be no hidden or intuitive steps.

Minimizing risks

A primary requirement of any decision method is that the risk, or probability, of making an incorrect decision be minimal. Suppose we compared the probability of making an incorrect decision by the statistical method with the probability of making an incorrect decision by any other method. Will the statistical method involve a lower probability of error than any other method? This question has not been answered, and perhaps cannot be answered, but this much can be said. Given two fallible methods, the method which can specify in advance the probability of error has an advantage over one that cannot so specify. Obviously, if a method cannot specify the degree of risk it entails, then it will be impossible to compare it with any other method—in this respect at least. Thus, although it cannot be argued that statistical method of arriving at decisions will involve a lower risk than any other conceivable method, it can be argued that any method must specify (in advance) the risk it entails so that a comparison can be made. As we shall see, the statistical method meets this requirement.

Secondly, if we accept the fact that any decision procedure will occasionally lead us to make mistakes, and that a good procedure will specify the risk of an incorrect decision, then a good procedure should also specify the risks of various *kinds* of error the procedure will lead to.

Specifying kinds of risks

There are at least two major kinds of errors that the scientist can make with respect to the outcome of his research. On the one hand, he may decide that his hypothesis is confirmed when in fact it has not been. As a consequence, the investigator will be led into investing further time, effort, and money in a theory which is unfounded in fact. On the other hand, the investigator may decide that his results were negative when in fact his hypothesis has actually been confirmed. In this case he abandons a true theory when he should have stayed with it. How can one evaluate the cost of abandoning a true theory? Will the idea ever occur to anyone else? Who could say what the theory's impact might have been? In brief, *is it worse to follow a false theory or to reject a true theory?* There is no good, universal answer to this question. Statistical-decision procedures, however, make it possible in some cases for the experimenter to choose to increase or decrease the risk of making one error relative to the other. In short, by developing the logic of the decision problem, the statistical method increases the freedom of the investigator because it develops the possibility of a choice which was not available to him previously. In the final analysis, no guides to decision are completely value-free. There is always room for choice (See Box 29).

Furthermore, there are situations in applied scientific work where the differential consequences of various kinds of errors are immediately

---

B O X   2 9

Science, Decisions and Values

It is at the point where decision rules are formulated that the decision-maker's value system comes to the surface. And the more clear and explicit the reasoning which determines what the rule shall be, the more obvious becomes the value system. It is true that scientists are often thought of as the soul of objectivity, standing in their work as scientists, quite apart from value judgments. The following passage insists that decision rules rest on value judgments (and we agree).

"Since no scientific hypothesis is ever completely verified, in accepting a hypothesis on the basis of evidence, the scientist must make the decision that the evidence is *sufficiently* strong or that the probability is *sufficiently* high to warrant the acceptance of the hypothesis. Obviously, our decision with regard to the evidence and

how strong is 'strong enough' is going to be a function of the *importance,* in the typically ethical sense, of making a mistake in accepting or rejecting the hypothesis. . . . *How sure we must be before we accept a hypothesis depends on how serious a mistake would be. . . .*

"It would be interesting and instructive, for example, to know how high a degree of probability the Manhattan Project scientists demanded for the hypothesis that no uncontrollable pervasive chain reaction would occur before they proceeded with the first atomic bomb detonation or even first activated the Chicago pile above a critical level. It would be equally interesting and instructive to know how they decided that the chosen probability value (if one was chosen) was high

---

apparent. Suppose, for example, a drug which is highly useful for combatting a certain disease contains certain toxic elements which if present in sufficiently large quantities make the use of the drug fatal. Suppose further that the drug manufacturer must test batches of the drug after it is produced. This means that for such testing *samples* must be taken, for if the entire supply is tested, there will be none available for use. In this case, then, there are two errors which can be made by the sample-testing procedure: the drug may be determined to be safe when it actually is unsafe, or it may be determined to be unsafe when it is actually safe. The different consequences following these errors are obvious; one error is clearly far

enough rather than one that was higher; on the other hand, it is conceivable that the problem, in this form, was not brought to consciousness at all.

"In general, then, before we can accept any hypothesis, the value decision must be made in the light of the seriousness of a mistake, and the degree of probability must be *high enough* or the evidence must be *strong enough* to warrant its acceptance. . . .

"If the major point I have tried to establish is correct, then we are confronted with a first-order crisis in science and methodology. The positive horror with which most scientists and philosophers of science view the intrusion of value considerations into science is wholly understandable. Memories of the conflict, now abated but to a certain extent still continuing, between science and, for example, the dominant religions over the intrusion of religious value considerations into the domain of scientific inquiry are strong in many reflective scientists. The traditional search for objectivity exemplifies science's pursuit of one of its most precious ideals. For the scientist to close his eyes to the fact that scientific method *intrinsically* requires the making of value decisions, and for him to push out of his consciousness the fact that he does make them, can in no way bring him closer to the ideal of objectivity. To refuse to pay attention to the value decisions that *must* be made, to make them intuitively, unconsciously, and haphazardly, is to leave an essential aspect of scientific method scientifically out of control."

Rudner, R. 1954. Remarks on value judgments in scientific validation. *Scientific Monthly*, 79, 151–153. Reprinted from the *Scientific Monthly* by permission.

worse than the other: if the drug is declared unsafe and is destroyed when it is actually safe, all that is lost at the very worst is that batch or sample; on the other hand, if the drug is declared safe when it is actually unsafe, lives will be lost. As a result, the attempt will be made to develop a decision procedure which will minimize the likelihood of declaring the drug safe when it is not. As we shall see, statistical decision theory has a good deal to say about decisions of this sort (see Box 30).

Situations which entail differential consequences of various kinds of errors also arise in such fields of applied psychology as personnel selection. Because psychological tests perfectly free from error do not exist, every decision to employ or not to employ a given applicant involves the risk of an incorrect decision. And there are two different kinds of errors which can be made: the employer can either make the error of not hiring a suitable man, or he can make the error of hiring an unsuitable man. Sometimes he would rather run the risk of making the first kind of error, and sometimes of the second kind. If there are a large number of applicants, the employer will prefer risking the error of not hiring someone who is actually suitable, rather than risking the error of hiring someone who is actually unsuitable. Thus, when there are a large number of applicants, the employer will raise the requirements for employment. In this way he will maximize the chances of hiring suitable employees and minimize the chances of hiring unsuitable ones. On the other hand, if the applicants are few in number, his preference for the two risks will be reversed; that is, he will then prefer the risk of hiring an unsuitable person over the risk of losing a suitable one. *Preference for various risks depends upon the situation in which the decision-maker finds himself.*

Decisions publicly arrived at

And, finally, bearing in mind that no method of decision-making is infallible, a third requirement of a good method is that all the steps taken in reaching a decision should be public, perfectly clear, and open to inspection. Another way of putting this is to say that the procedure should be "retraceable"; that is, having arrived at a decision, it should be easy to retrace one's steps and perceive exactly how the decision was reached. There should be no mystery as to how or why any step in the procedure was taken. Openness to inspection entails openness to criticism. This is a clear advantage, because criticism makes it possible to improve the method. The use of mathematics will greatly aid in making clear the steps taken, and will make it much easier to retrace these steps. The fact that statistical decision theory is largely mathematical helps it to meet this requirement.

We turn now to the question of how well the statistical method of reaching decisions about the outcomes of experiments fits the needs and requirements of the behavioral scientist. Because this topic is a very

BOX 30

The Control of Quality

Statistical decision processes play an important role in industry as well as in science. This is particularly true in the field of quality control—controlling the quality of a product so that reasonable tolerance limits are assured in its manufacture. The following quotation is taken from an account of how the principles of the statistical method are now applied in factories.

"At each welding machine we establish a control station which will let us know immediately when the machine or any other element in the process falters. The operations at a control station are as follows. A sample of 10 units is selected from each hour's production. The welded contacts are torn from the springs, and the amount of force required in each instance is recorded. The results are plotted on a chart to provide a continuing record of two things: (1) the average strength of each 10-unit sample, and (2) the range from the strongest to the weakest unit. Statistical control limits also are put on the chart. The control limits are so calculated that if any average value falls outside them, it indicates that the margin between the average strength and the minimum required is too narrow. The control limits for range are so calculated that when units begin to fall outside these limits, this also

indicates that other-than-chance causes have intervened. Only when both the average and the range stay within their respective control limits is there adequate assurance that the welds made during the period in which the sample was taken are satisfactory. Whenever an average or range value of a sample falls outside the control limits, we know that we must stop the welding machine and look for the causes.

"At this stage of manufacture the spring plus welded contact has some cash value, but the value is very small in comparison with the cost of the completed relay. Therefore, the cost of maintaining a system of control at each welding machine represents a very small insurance payment against the much greater penalties that would be paid if defective parts were not detected and went on into the finished product. Moreover, so long as the samples are statistically satisfactory, we need not interrupt operation of the process or reset the welding machines, which means a saving in time, labor and the useful life of the machines.

"This example shows how statistical quality control can provide reliable warning signals on a production line."

Dalton, A. 1953. The practice of quality control. *Scientific American*, 188, 29–33.

broad and complex one, and one which is developing rapidly, it cannot be discussed in full detail in this book. We shall consider here only the situation in which statistical-decision theory is brought to bear on the experiment which is carried out under the rules of "classical design." When the student perceives how this is done, he will have a grasp of the

---

B O X   3 1

Classical Design of Experiments

"Classical design" refers to the procedure in which the effect of one variable is isolated and studied. There are many ways in which a single variable is isolated and studied, but the most frequent is to employ *experimental* and *control* groups. Comparison is the heart of the scientific method. Despite the variation in approach, the question to be answered is always the same: What is the effect of the experimental variable (the experimenter's intervention) on the experimental group relative to the control group? If there is a sufficient difference between experimental and control groups, the experimental variable is said to have had an effect. If the differ-

ence is not sufficient, it is concluded that the experimental variable (for example, the teaching method) did not have an effect.

The curious student will at this point immediately demand, "How do you know that it was the experimental variable and not some other variable which produced the result?" The answer to that is, except for the experimental variable, both groups received identical treatment. Let us make a closer examination of the procedure.

Suppose the attempt is made to discover the effect of a training method on motor performance. Clearly, an experimental group will have to be subjected to the training method;

---

general principles involved. (*Note:* the student who is unfamiliar with the general experimental procedure involving an experimental group and a control group should consult Box 31.)

THE RULES OF CLASSICAL DESIGN

One of the essential differences between a descriptive, or observational, study and an experiment lies in the fact that an experiment always involves some *intervention* on the part of the scientist. Instead of observing some phenomenon in its natural state, the scientist, when carrying out an experiment, does something to the materials he is studying and then observes the effect, if any, of his action. Of course, this is a very broad, highly general statement about experimentation; actually, the design and execution of experiments can be a highly technical matter. But this distinction will serve our purposes at this point: when carrying out an experiment, the

---

and, of course, in order to evaluate the performance of the subjects, their motor performance must be studied, or tested, before training as well as after, so that it may be discovered whether the method results in an increment in performance. Thus, the subjects will receive a pretest and a post-test. But mere practice on the pre-test may affect performance on the post-test. Or the mere fact of participating in an experimental situation may affect the subjects' performance. In order to be sure that only the training method accounts for any difference between pre- and post-test performance, a control group is given *exactly the same* treatment *except* for the fact that they are not given the training which was given to the experimental group. *The purpose of classical design is to control all variables except*

the one variable under study. If there is a difference in performance of the groups, then, it must be attributed to the *only* difference in their treatment—the experimental variable.

The student interested in historical origins will find the first formal statement of this procedure among J. S. Mill's "Canons of Induction." What we have here called classical design is Mill's "Method of Difference" and is stated as follows: "If an instance in which the phenomenon under investigation occurs, and an instance in which it does not occur, have every circumstance in common save one, that one occurring only in the former; the circumstance in which alone the two instances differ, is the effect, or the cause, or an indispensable part of the cause, of the phenomenon."

---

scientist arranges certain conditions and observes what happens as a result.

In a real experiment, then, in contrast with the imaginary one described on page 302, the experimenter does intervene—he *does* treat one group differently from the other. Thus, for example, the experimenter might have administered a drug to an experimental group and withheld it from a control group in order to observe its effect on reaction time. Moreover, the experimenter looks ahead: he anticipates the outcome of the experiment, and he does this in the simplest way possible. The number of outcomes, the possible conclusions, are reduced to two: either the drug had an effect or it did not. If the drug did have an effect, then, of course, the mean reaction time in a group which received the drug should be different from the mean reaction time in a group which did not receive the drug. And if the drug did not have an effect, the means of the two groups should not be different. More precisely, if the drug did not have an effect, the means of the two groups should differ only because of random sampling. (Remember that the two groups are *samples drawn at random* from the population to which the experimenter wishes to generalize his results.)

It is at this point that the random sampling distribution of differences between means serves a crucial purpose. Such a distribution indicates the relative frequency with which differences due to random sampling would occur *if the treatment had no effect*; in other words, the random sampling distribution provides a frequency distribution of results which would occur if the intervention (the drug in this case) had no effect. We shall call the random-sampling distribution of differences between means a *model of no effect*, because it describes a set of results to be expected from an endless series of repetitions of an experiment when the intervention (the treatment) has exactly no effect.

The hypothesis of no effect

In order to use the model of no effect, the scientist must make one assumption and one hypothesis. The *assumption* is a familiar one: that the experiment will be repeated an endless number of times. This is merely another way of saying that the scientist is again preparing the way for the employment of his statistical knowledge of a mathematical model of randomness. The hypothesis is that the treatment (in this case, the drug) will have no effect. We shall call this the *hypothesis of no effect*. It is good strategy to employ this hypothesis, for, together with the assumption of an infinite number of repetitions of the experiment, *the hypothesis of no effect makes the experiment performed perfectly analogous to the experiment imagined;* that is, if the experiment were endlessly repeated, and if the drug had no effect, then the only differences which would appear between the groups which received the drug and the groups which did not would be *random differences*. And, therefore, a model of randomness would provide a frequency distribution of results which would occur if the treatment had no effect. Thus, in order to make an inductive inference, a generalization from an experimental study, the scientist employs both his knowledge of the experimental method and the statistical method.

The scientist's knowledge of the experimental method leads him to arrange the conditions of the experiment so that all factors which could result in systematic, regular differences between the groups are eliminated —except for *one*. This factor consists of his intervention, his "treatment." It is this factor which the scientist is investigating. It is this factor which the scientist suspects will have an effect on the subjects.

His statistical knowledge in this case consists of knowing in advance the results of a hypothetical experiment (performed an endless number of times) in which two groups (randomly selected from the same population) are treated exactly alike. He knows that such an experiment would produce a frequency distribution of random differences between the means of the two groups and that this distribution corresponds to a model of randomness—usually the normal-probability curve. Under the hypothesis of no effect, the normal-probability curve is centered on 0; that is, the mean of the distribution is zero difference. Specifying a parameter of zero difference is the statistical manifestation of the hypothesis of no effect. At this point we turn to the question of how the hypothesis of no effect can be put to the test.

Testing the hypothesis of no effect

Now it is obvious that the hypothesis of no effect will not be overthrown simply because the means of the groups in the *actual experiment* are found to be different. Such differences are to be expected; according to the hypothesis of no effect, however, these are *random* differences. But there must be *some* differences between the two means, which would be incompatible with the hypothesis of no effect. The hypothesis of no effect cannot claim that *all* possible differences, no matter how large, are merely random departures from the parameter of zero difference. If this were so, there would be no point in conducting the experiment, because no imaginable result would be incompatible with the hypothesis. Thus, for example, if the actual difference between the means of the two groups was very large, and if the distributions of individual scores did not overlap, such a result would surely cast doubt on the truth of the hypothesis of no effect.

Having foreseen this possibility, it now remains for the scientist to decide which results would indeed be incompatible with the hypothesis of no effect, results which would force him to conclude that the experimenter's intervention *did* have an effect. Those results which he decides are incompatible with the hypothesis are those which are *improbable* under that hypothesis; those differences between the means of the two groups that are so large as to occur relatively *infrequently* (that is, that are improbable) are, under the hypothesis of no effect, the differences which cast doubt on the truth of the hypothesis, and lead the investigator to decide to reject it. (At this point the student should recall, or review, the discussion of confidence limits in Chapter 8, pages 297–299.) And if the hypothesis of no effect were rejected, the investigator would decide that the treatment did have an effect—and, moreover, that this effect was no mere random effect. In short, the investigator tests the hypothesis of no effect by confronting its statistical specification (zero difference) with the actual difference obtained in the experiment. If the obtained difference is one which is improbable if the true difference were 0, the hypothesis of no effect is rejected and the alternative—the hypothesis that the treatment, the intervention, did have an effect—is accepted. And, of course, that is precisely the point the investigator wished to settle.

By way of example

Suppose an investigator comes to believe that a certain type of training will lead to more rapid learning than a standard type of training currently in use, and he wants to discover whether his belief is correct. He could proceed according to the following steps:

STEP 1: Draw two samples at random from the population with which he is concerned.

STEP 2: Designate one sample, or group, as experimental subjects and the other group as control subjects.

STEP 3: Train the subjects in the experimental group according to the new system, and train the subjects in the control group according to the standard system.

STEP 4: Ascertain the difference in performance under the two training methods; that is, compute the mean number of trials necessary for the experimental subjects to reach a certain level of performance, and compute the mean number of trials necessary for the control subjects to reach the same level of performance. If, for example, the mean for the experimental group was twenty-seven trials ($\bar{X}_e = 27.00$) and the mean for the controls was 34.02 ($\bar{X}_c = 34.02$), the difference between these means would be 7.02.

STEP 5: Compute the standard error of the means for the two groups (see page 296); for example, $s_{\bar{X}e} = 2$ and $s_{\bar{X}c} = 3$.

STEP 6: Compute the standard error of the random sampling distribution of the difference between two means (see page 304); for example,

$$s_d = \sqrt{s_{\bar{x}_e}^2 + s_{\bar{x}_c}^2}$$
$$= \sqrt{2^2 + 3^2}$$
$$= 3.6$$

STEP 7: Calculate the probability that a difference between means as large as (or larger than) that obtained $(34.02 - 27.00 = 7.02)$ would occur through mere accident of random sampling.

In order to discover the probability of a difference as large as 7.02 in a distribution with a mean of zero difference and a standard error of 3.6, it is only necessary to employ the standard score form. Thus, $z = \dfrac{X - \bar{X}}{s} = \dfrac{7.02 - 0}{3.6} = 1.95$. By looking at Table A in the Appendix, we find that approximately 47 per cent of the area of the curve lies between zero and a z of 1.95. Therefore, differences as large (or larger than) 7.02 would occur in $50 - 47 = 3$ per cent of all trials in one direction, and $50 - 47 = 3$ per cent of all trials *in the other direction. Direction* refers to the fact that in 3 per cent of the random samples drawn the mean of the experimental group would exceed that of the control group by as much as 7.02 or more, and in 3 per cent of all random samples drawn the mean of the control group would exceed that of the experimental group by as much as 7.02 or more.

The result is that differences of less than 7.02 have a probability of occurrence of .94, and that differences of 7.02 or more occur in the model of no effect with a probability of .06 (or with a relative frequency of 6 per cent). The calculation of the latter probability was the ultimate aim of this procedure. The best way to grasp the meaning of this probability is to consider the conclusions which would be drawn from different values of it.

Suppose the probability were .35. This would mean that, if the true difference were indeed 0, and if the experiment were repeated endlessly, then differences as large as, or larger than, the one obtained would occur because of random sampling in 35 per cent of the repetitions of the experiment. This probability value, then, expresses the relative frequency of occurrence of a given set of differences due to random sampling. And in this example the set of differences (7.02 or larger) would occur randomly on about one third (.35) of the repetitions of the experiment—if, indeed, the true difference between the means were 0. Thus, a departure from 0 which would occur in as many as one third of all repetitions of the experiment would not be a surprising result of any one experiment. In short, if a probability value of .35 were associated with a given result, the experimenter ordinarily would not decide that the hypothesis of no effect was false. It would be too easy to explain the difference as a mere random departure from the mean of 0.

Suppose, however, the probability value was .10. This means that in 10 per cent of any very large number of repetitions of this experiment, differences as large as, or larger than, the one obtained would occur randomly if the true difference were 0. Such a result would be somewhat more difficult to account for as a mere *random* departure from 0, because it would occur less frequently as a result of random sampling. Under certain circumstances, to be discussed below, this probability value, or relative frequency of random occurrence, would lead the experimenter to reject the hypothesis of no effect.

Suppose the probability value was .001. This means that in only one-tenth of one per cent of all repetitions of this experiment would differences as large as, or larger than, the one obtained occur randomly if the true difference were 0. This result would ordinarily lead most experimenters to decide that the hypothesis of no effect was false, that the results were not compatible with the hypothesis of no effect, and, further, that the experimental treatment *did* have an effect. In other words, the result was so improbable (would occur so infrequently) if the hypothesis of no effect were true that the hypothesis is rejected.

At this point the student will see that the decision to accept or reject the hypothesis of no effect is affected by the various probability values associated with the results of the experiment. And that is crucial.

But the student will wonder why we have laid down no hard and fast rule as to how a decision should be reached. Probabilities as large as .35, we suggested, "ordinarily" would not lead the investigator to reject the hypothesis of no effect, but probabilities as small as .001 "ordinarily" would. But what about probabilities of .20, or .10, or .05? Where shall the line be drawn which determines which probability level leads to a rejection of the hypothesis of no effect?

There are two answers given to the matter of deciding what the probability value should be for rejecting the hypothesis of no effect. One answer suggests that the investigator need not bother to draw a line, that he merely report the probability and let the reader make his own decision. This appears to be an easy way out, but it really is not. For the investigator must in any event decide for himself what to conclude from his work, and he must be prepared to defend his decision. The other answer to this problem, then, starts from the premise that because the investigator must make a decision, the line *must* be drawn. Another way to put this is to say that a *decision rule* must be formulated. Moreover, the second position asserts that one must be prepared to say what the decision rule will be *prior* to the appearance of the results. For if one draws the line—that is, specifies at what probability level he will reject the hypothesis of no effect—*after* the results are in, he becomes vulnerable to the suspicion that the line was drawn—that is, that the rule was made—so as to produce the outcome most desired. In short, *the formulation of the proper decision rule involves the statement of the probability level at which the hypothesis of no effect should be rejected.* We turn now to a discussion of this problem.

Selecting the decision rule

Earlier we mentioned "decision rules," and we pointed out that the investigator must decide what the decision rule shall be. To be more specific, the investigator must set forth a rule which specifies under what conditions he will accept or reject the hypothesis of no effect. The general procedure is to determine, before the results are in, what the various outcomes of the study might be and to assign the appropriate decision to each outcome. In principle, a table is set up as follows:

Outcome A implies: decision 1
Outcome B implies: decision 2
Outcome C implies: decision 3
Outcome D implies: decision 4, etc.

In practice, however, by far the largest number of studies allow only two outcomes—one of which leads to the acceptance of the hypothesis of no effect, and one of which leads to its rejection. Thus, the table collapses to a simple one:

One set of outcomes, A, implies: *reject* hypothesis of no effect
One set of outcomes, B, implies: *accept* hypothesis of no effect

That is, of all the possible outcomes of the experiment, a division is made such that one set leads to one decision and one set leads to the other. The problem now becomes, how shall the division be made? Put otherwise, what shall the rule be by which we declare one set of outcomes to be A, and the other to be B? One answer which is commonly given is that the rule shall be: A set of outcomes which will occur in 5 per cent of all repetitions of the experiment by accidents of random sampling shall be labeled A, and the associated decision shall be to *reject* the hypothesis of no effect; the other 95 per cent of the outcomes shall be declared to be B, and the associated decision shall be to *accept* the hypothesis of no effect. The next step, then, is straightforward. The difference between the means is calculated, expressed in terms of the standard error of the distribution of differences, the probability value of the result is ascertained in Table A of the Appendix (see pages 342–344 for a detailed example of this procedure), and thus it may be determined whether the result falls in the set of outcomes A or the set B. Having determined the probability value, the decision to accept or reject the hypothesis of no effect is automatic, for the result must fall into one set of outcomes or the other.

We now turn to an examination of some of the factors which determine what this decision rule—or any other rule—shall be. These factors will, of course, involve the three requirements of a good decision procedure discussed above: minimizing the risk of an incorrect decision, specifying the risks of various kinds of error, and making the procedure a public one.

Minimizing the risk of an incorrect decision

When a decision rule is set forth, it specifies which set of outcomes will lead to an acceptance of the hypothesis of no effect and which set will lead to a rejection of it. The decision rule thus divides or partitions the model of randomness—in this case, the normal probability curve—into two areas, one of which is called the *area of acceptance* and the other the *area of rejection*. (Another term for the area of rejection is "critical region.") These areas are indicated in Figure 34 for the case in which the decision rule partitions the random sampling distribution of differences between means so that the area of rejection (see shaded area) includes 5 per cent of the distribution (2.5 per cent at one end of the distribution, and 2.5 per cent at the other.)

It is important to note that the size of the area of rejection, the critical region, has an important place with respect to specifying the probability with which a decision rule will provide the wrong decision. For if the hypothesis of no effect is true, and if the outcome falls in the critical region, then the decision rule leads to an erroneous decision. Why would a result fall in the critical region when the hypothesis of no effect is true? A result could fall in this critical region when the hypothesis of no effect is true by reason of accidents of random sampling. *How often* will a result fall in the critical region when the hypothesis of no effect is true? The size

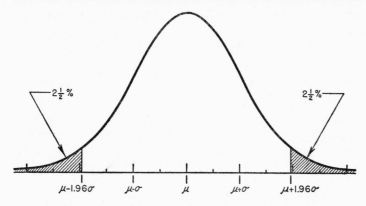

FIG. 34. An example of a normal probability distribution with the area of rejection (shaded) set beyond $\mu \pm 1.96\sigma$ and equal to 5% of the area of the curve.

of the area of rejection, the critical region, determines the answer to this question. If the critical region includes 5 per cent of the outcome space, then the outcome will fall in the critical region because of random sampling in 5 per cent of any large number of repetitions of this experiment; therefore, there is a probability of .05 that when rejecting the hypothesis of no effect as a result of following this rule, an error will be made. In short, *the size of the critical region specifies the relative frequency of error when the decision rule is followed.* Such an advance specification of the probability of error is, as we pointed out above, a good characteristic of a decision procedure when it is known in advance that at least some of the decisions will be wrong.

Now, of course, it is the aim of all investigators to keep the number of incorrect decisions to a minimum. One way to do this is to decrease the size of the critical region in such a way that the incorrect rejection of the hypothesis of no effect occurs less frequently. In the above example the frequency of incorrect decisions was set at 5 per cent. This percentage of incorrect decisions can be decreased to 1 per cent by reducing the size of the critical region in the way illustrated in Figure 35. There we see that a decision rule specifies that a difference between the experimental and control groups must be so large as to occur randomly in only 1 per cent of the repetitions of the experiment if the hypothesis of no effect were true. Thus, the percentage of incorrect decisions expected on the basis of this decision rule has been decreased by reducing the size of the critical region. (It should be pointed out that the size of the sample is also a factor here, but discussion of this matter is left to the mathematical section.)

At this point the student will want to know why the critical region should not be made infinitesimally small, for it is clear that the smaller the critical region, the less the risk of rejecting the hypothesis of no effect when it is true. This question brings us to the second requirement of a good decision procedure—specifying the risk of making errors of various kinds. Here we shall see that we shall have to deal with an incorrect decision of a

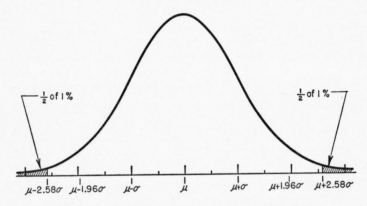

FIG. 35. An example of a normal probability distribution with the area of rejection (shaded) set beyond $\mu \pm 2.58\sigma$ and equal to 1% of the area of the curve.

second and different kind, that of accepting the hypothesis of no effect when it is *false* (in contrast to the error of rejecting it when it is true).

Specifying the risks of various kinds

As pointed out earlier, the experimenter is susceptible to at least two kinds of errors; he may reject the hypothesis of no effect when it is true (hereafter referred to as an *error of the first kind*, or as a *Type I error*), or he may accept the hypothesis of no effect when it is false (hereafter referred to as an *error of the second kind*, or as a *Type II error*).

Naturally, the investigator would like to avoid both these errors. Unfortunately, there is a difficulty here, not a totally insurmountable one but one which must be considered. If the critical region is made very small, the investigator minimizes the risk of rejecting the hypothesis of no effect when it is true (a risk he would like to minimize), but, by virtue of this very step, he increases the risk of accepting the hypothesis of no effect when it is false (a risk he would not like to increase). This dilemma is illustrated in a general way in the chart below.

	Critical region made very small	Critical region made very large
If hypothesis of no effect is *true*	leads to *correct* decision (decreases risk of Type I error)	leads to *incorrect* decision (increases risk of Type I error)
If hypothesis of no effect is *false*	leads to *incorrect* decision (increases risk of Type II error)	leads to *correct* decision (decreases risk of Type II error)

The explanation for this state of affairs must wait for the following section of this chapter. At this juncture we need only point out how the problem of selecting the appropriate size of the critical region is handled by behavioral scientists.

First of all, it must be noted that there is no perfectly defensible answer to this problem, because there is no direct or obvious criterion which will cover all cases. As a result, for better or worse, a *convention* to be adopted has been widely agreed upon.

In the context of basic research the convention has been established that the critical region shall be either the area beyond 1.96 standard errors, or the area beyond 2.58 standard errors. Thus, behavioral scientists ordinarily are willing to reject the hypothesis of no effect at a probability level of .05, or .01. In other words, it is conventional to reject the hypothesis of randomness when the chances are either nineteen to one against it or ninety-nine to one against it. Odd as it may seem, the question of whether the 5 per cent or 1 per cent significance level will be employed seems to be a matter of personal preference.

The student should note that the conventional critical region which consists of 5 per cent of the area of the normal probability model really involves *two* critical regions made up of 2.5 per cent at one end of the distribution and 2.5 per cent at the other, and that the critical region of 1 per cent includes 0.5 per cent at one end and 0.5 per cent at the other (see Figures 34 and 35). This arrangement, too, is a convention, but it is actually unsuitable in many instances; for this reason, the convention is occasionally dropped in favor of the selection of a critical region at one end of the distribution only. When the former rule is employed, the investigator may report that he is using a "two-tailed" (or "two-sided") test of the hypothesis of no effect; and when the convention is dropped, the investigator may report that he is using a "one-tailed" (or "one-sided") test.

It is important to remember that, despite conventions, if there are good, logical grounds for selecting a critical region of a different, unconventional size, the investigator should set forth his reasons and do so. After all, the only defense for the conventional critical regions is convention, which is not a formidable defense. On the other hand, when some form of action is to be taken in the context of applied research and the consequences of errors *can* be weighed in terms of some obvious cost, then the matter of setting significance levels (and confidence limits) can be discussed with more clarity and rules of thumb can be discarded.

BY WAY OF SUMMARY

A good decision procedure should specify in advance the probability that it will lead to the wrong decision. When working within the framework of classical design, the scientist employs the hypothesis of no effect as well as the assumption of the endless repetitions of the experiment. The size of the critical region of the random sampling distribution of differences between means specifies the probability that the decision rule will lead to a Type I error—the error of rejecting the hypothesis of no effect when it is in fact true. Therefore, the first requirement of a good decision procedure set forth on page 332 is met, for the risk of an incorrect decision is specified by this procedure. But there is more than one kind of error. And, although it is clear that reducing the size of the critical region will reduce the relative frequency of the Type I error, it becomes apparent that as we do so we increase the probability of a Type II error—that of accepting the hypothesis of no effect when it is in fact false.

This problem is ordinarily handled by a widely agreed upon convention to use either the 5 per cent or the 1 per cent level of significance except in connection with those problems in applied research in which the differential consequences of error can be more readily evaluated than in basic research.

But the question of quantifying the risk of the error of the second kind is also a requirement of a good decision procedure. This question is considered in detail in the next section. To what extent statistical decision procedures meet the requirement that the procedure must be public, that each step must be clearly visible and open to criticism, is a matter we shall leave for discussion until the student has read the mathematical aspects of the decision procedure, for it is these aspects which provide the necessary clarity.

❲ Mathematically . . .

In the previous section we gave most of our consideration to the logic involved in the rejection or acceptance of the hypothesis of no effect. We did not give full attention to the consequences of such rejection or acceptance with respect to the *alternative hypothesis*. However, now that the student has become acquainted with the general procedure involved in statistical decisions, he is ready to consider the matter of alternative hypotheses. This is a necessary step, for the framing of any hypothesis calls into being automatically at least one contradictory or alternative hypothesis. If one hypothesis is rejected, then the alternative hypothesis must be accepted. For this reason, it is essential that the two hypotheses encompass every possible outcome which may affect the decision. To illustrate this principle, consider the following hypotheses: H_0, sometimes called the *null hypothesis*, or the "hypothesis tested," and H_1, called the *alternative hypothesis*.

H_0: The mean I.Q. of population A is 120.

And the alternative,

H_1: The mean I.Q. of population A is greater or less than 120.

H_1 is the alternative of H_0 because it leaves no values uncovered by either H_0 or H_1. If H_0 and H_1 do not encompass the entire set of possibilities, then it is possible that neither H_0 or H_1 is true. Under such circumstances, a decision to reject H_0 does not necessarily imply the acceptance of H_1.

SPECIFIC VERSUS NONSPECIFIC ALTERNATIVE HYPOTHESES

It sometimes happens that H_0 has more than one alternative or that the alternative is difficult to express precisely. In such cases, it is frequently possible to resolve the difficulty by constructing H_1 to negate H_0; thus, H_1

would state that H_0 is false. In some cases it may be necessary to reframe H_0 in order to simplify the expression of its exact alternative. Alternative hypotheses are always easy to obtain if H_0 is put in the form "the treated and untreated groups are random samples drawn from the same population"—that is, if H_0 is the hypothesis of no effect. H_1 can then be stated simply as a contradiction of H_0; thus,

H_0: Differences between Group A and Group B are due to errors of random sampling.

H_1: Differences between Group A and Group B are not due to errors of random sampling.

But stating an *exact* alternative hypothesis is far more difficult; it depends in part upon the theoretical development of a given discipline. The behavioral sciences have not developed that degree of theoretical precision which is necessary to specify an *exact* value for the alternative hypothesis. The vast majority of all experiments in psychology (the most experimental of the behavioral sciences) employ alternative hypotheses which simply contradict H_0, as illustrated above. Therefore, we shall discuss first the situation in which the alternative hypothesis is nonspecific (merely the negation of H_0) and then provide one example of a test of a specific H_1 as a means of furthering the student's understanding of the general principles involved in testing hypotheses.

Nonspecific alternative hypotheses

In the earlier treatment of Type I and Type II errors and the critical region (see pages 333–336), the matter of assigning a probability to the Type I error was discussed, but not the question of assigning a probability to the Type II error. In order to discuss this point, we shall present the entire problem from a different point of view. First, we shall designate the probability that H_0 will be rejected when it is true as the *level of significance*, or the *size* of the critical region. This probability is denoted by α (alpha). Second, we shall designate the probability that H_0 will be accepted when it is false as the probability of a Type II error. This probability is denoted by β (beta). As indicated earlier, α is usually set at .05, or .01; for reasons which shall become apparent, there is no conventional value for β. It is obvious, however, that the smaller α and β can be made, the less the likelihood of an incorrect decision.

Unfortunately, as we have seen, with a given sample size, decreasing α means increasing β, and decreasing β means increasing α. Our next step is to make a closer examination of this problem, first in connection with estimating a single mean and then in connection with tests of hypotheses within the framework of classical design.

Alpha versus Beta in the estimation of a single mean

One of the first steps in testing hypotheses is to decide on a value for α *or* for β. If it is considered feasible to risk a 5 per cent (or one in twenty) chance of committing a Type I error, α is fixed at .05. The critical region then contains exactly 5 per cent of all possible random outcomes which may be expected *under the assumption that H_0 is true;* that is, if H_0 were true, 5 per cent of all the outcomes would lie in the critical region. If β rather than α were fixed—say, $\beta = .08$—then the critical region must contain ninety-two per cent of all outcomes *possible under the assumption that H_1 is true.* (In the ideal case, both α and β are specified; in most cases, however, only α is given.) Exactly which 5 per cent (or 92 per cent) of the outcomes go into the critical region depends on the form and content of both hypotheses and on the frequency distribution of the outcomes if it is known.

Consider the following example. Suppose H_0 asserts that the parameter $\mu = 80$. Suppose further that $s = 20$ and that 100 cases are included in the sample. In this case $s_{\bar{x}} = \dfrac{20}{\sqrt{100}} = 2$. Let us arbitrarily assume the critical region to be the left 5 per cent tail of this distribution; that is, a level of significance ($\alpha = .05$) is chosen. The table for the normal probability curve shows that 45 per cent of the distribution lies between the mean and a point $1.645s$ from it. Therefore, 5 per cent of the distribution lies beyond the mean minus $1.645s$, or, in our example,

$$80 - 1.645 s_{\bar{x}} = 80 - 1.645\,(2) = 76.7$$

(See Figure 36.) The shaded region in Figure 36 indicates the critical region for H_0. Therefore, the decision rule is, if the mean ($\bar{X}$) of the sample drawn falls in this region—that is, is less than 76.7—H_0 is rejected. Thus, if the sample mean were less than 76.7, the hypothesis that 80 is the parameter would be rejected. Note that if 80 were indeed the value of the parameter, the probability that it (H_0) would be rejected is α (that is, .05). Having set $\alpha = .05$, this is the risk of committing the Type I error, the error of rejecting H_0 when it is actually true.

But it will be seen that there is another risk, the risk of accepting H_0 when it is in fact false and an alternative is true. The probability of making

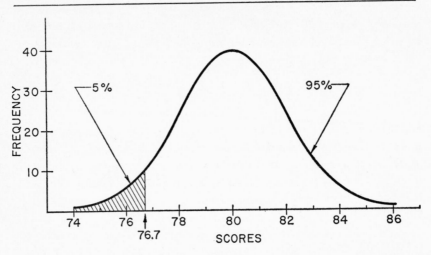

FIG. 36. Critical (shaded) and noncritical (unshaded) regions for $H_0 = 80$ and $a = .05$.

this error is β. In the above example we rejected H_0 when the sample mean was less than 76.7. Suppose now that the true value (μ) in the population is 78. What is the probability of accepting H_0 even though it is false? Under the decision rule given above, if the sample $\bar{X}$ is larger than 76.7 we shall accept H_0—that is, assert that the parameter is 80. But if the parameter is actually 78, then the distribution of sample means around $\mu = 78$ would appear as in Figure 37.

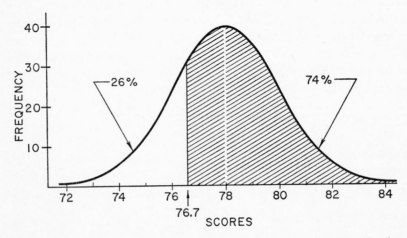

FIG. 37. Critical (shaded) and noncritical (unshaded) regions for $H_1 = 78$, when $H_0 = 80$ and $a = .05$.

Since H_0 ($\mu = 80$) is rejected only for values less than 76.7, it would be wrongly accepted for all values above 76.7 if indeed the true value is 78. If 78 is the true value of μ, then

$$z = \frac{X - \mu}{s} = \frac{76.7 - 78}{2} = \frac{-1.3}{2} = -.65$$

and the area to the right of the ordinate at μ–.65 is .74. This area is shaded in Figure 37 and represents the probability that $H_0(\mu = 80)$ will be accepted when in fact $\mu = 78$. In other words, with α set at .05, and with $n = 100$, the risk of rejecting H_0 when it is true is 5 per cent, and the risk (β) of accepting H_0 when it is false is 74 per cent, *if* the true value were $\mu = 78$. Note how large this risk is under these circumstances.

The main point to be observed here, however, is that the amount of the risk of the Type II error is unknown if H_1 is unspecified. This, of course, is a major disadvantage associated with the inability to state an exact alternative hypothesis. This problem is considered further in connection with classical design.

Alpha versus Beta in classical design

As an example, consider a teacher who decides to alter his teaching method in an effort to improve his students' grasp of the subject. He applies the usual method of teaching to a control group and the new method of teaching to an experimental class. Suppose that the control students had a mean score of 76 and a standard deviation of 5.6, there being thirty students in the sample, and let the mean and standard deviation for the experimental group of thirty-two students be 78 and 5.1, respectively. Now each of these means is an estimate of, or approximation to, the true means of the populations which produced them. Suppose these two true means are μ_X and μ_Y. The teacher may then hypothesize

$$H_0: \mu_X = \mu_Y$$
$$H_1: \mu_X \neq \mu_Y$$

The null hypothesis $\mu_X = \mu_Y$ is equivalent to $\mu_X - \mu_Y = 0$. Now the difference between *any* two sample means $\bar{X}$ and $\bar{Y}$ obtained from randomly selected samples is a normally or nearly normally distributed variable whose mean is $\mu_X - \mu_Y$ and whose standard deviation $(\sigma_{\bar{X}-\bar{Y}})$ is $\sqrt{\sigma_{\bar{X}}^2 + \sigma_{\bar{Y}}^2}$.

Therefore, the value of the difference $\bar{X} - \bar{Y} = 76 - 78 = -2$ in standard units is

$$z = \frac{-2 - (\mu_X - \mu_Y)}{\sigma_{\bar{X}-\bar{Y}}}$$

If H_0 is true, then $\mu_X - \mu_Y = 0$, and, approximating $\sigma_{\bar{X}-\bar{Y}}$ with $s_{\bar{X}-\bar{Y}}$,

(1)
$$z = \frac{-2}{\sqrt{\dfrac{5.6^2}{30} + \dfrac{5.1^2}{32}}}$$

Here z is the statistic whose value will determine whether or not H_0 is to be accepted. In order for this to happen, a critical region, R, must be selected. If z falls in R, H_0 is to be rejected. The teacher selects the following decision rule: He will risk a 5 per cent chance of rejecting H_0 or of committing a Type I error, and he will use a two-tailed test. By choosing a two-tailed test, he recognizes the possibility that his "treatment" of the experimental group may cause them to do *worse* than the control group and thus give a positive value to $\bar{X} - \bar{Y}$. He therefore selects the left 2.5 per cent tail and the right 2.5 per cent tail of the standard normal curve. The normal probability table shows that these tails start at the points $z = -1.96$ and $z = +1.96$.

The value of z in (1) is $-2/1.363 = -1.47$. H_0 is accepted, therefore, because the difference between the two means is too small to produce a z in either part of the critical region. The decision is that there is no difference between the two methods, or, more specifically, that the difference observed is due to random sampling. But what about the risk with respect to the alternative hypothesis? The lack of a specific alternative hypothesis makes the computation of β, the probability of the Type II error, more difficult.

TABLE 50

Probability of Type II Error (β) for Various Hypothetical Differences (θ) Between Two Means

θ	$z_1 = \dfrac{-1.96 - \theta}{1.363}$	$z_2 = \dfrac{1.96 - \theta}{1.363}$	β
-4	1.50	4.37	.0668
-3	.76	3.64	.2235
-2	.03	2.91	.4862
-1	$-.70$	2.17	.7430
0	-1.44	1.44	.8501
1	-2.17	.70	.7430
2	-2.91	$-.03$	.4862

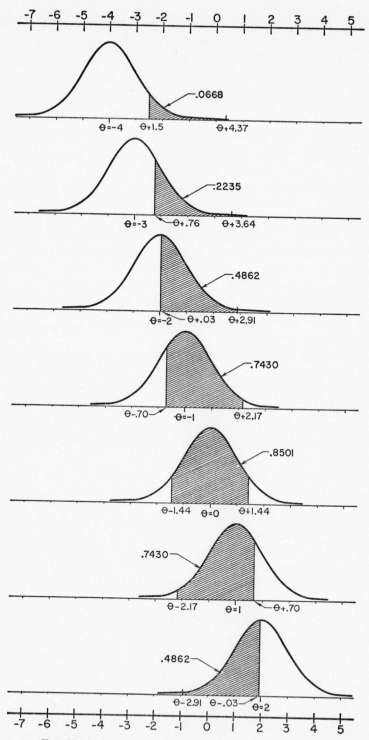

FIG. 38. A graphic representation of the noncritical regions computed for various values of Θ in Table 50.

To analyze β, suppose that H_1 is true and that $\mu_X - \mu_Y = \theta$ where $\theta \neq 0$. Then, under the assumption that H_1 is true, the mean of the sampling distribution of the difference between the means is θ.

The points -1.96 and $+1.96$ must be located with respect to the mean θ in terms of standard units. The distance between θ and -1.96 is $-1.96 - \theta$. Dividing by $s_{\bar{X} - \bar{Y}} = 1.363$ gives $\dfrac{-1.96 - \theta}{1.363}$ standard units.

The value $+1.96$ leads in the same manner to $\dfrac{1.96 - \theta}{1.363}$. The noncritical region of the test, interpreted under the assumption that $H_1: \mu_X - \mu_Y = \theta$ is true, starts at $(-1.96 - \theta)/1.363$ and ends at $(1.96 - \theta)/1.363$. By assigning various values to θ, various values are obtained for these two bounding values. Table 50 lists several such values, and Figure 38 diagrams their implications.

The β column in Table 50 is computed by using the normal probability table to find what proportion of the standard normal population lies between the various pairs, z_1 and z_2, which bound the noncritical regions corresponding to various values of $\theta = \mu_X - \mu_Y$.

Recalling the example of the teacher and his two groups of students, the difference between the sample means was -2, and the standard error of the difference between the sample means was 1.363. These differences are either normally or nearly normally distributed about their mean which is $\mu_X - \mu_Y$. Using -2 as an estimate for $\mu_X - \mu_Y = \theta$, the theory of the normal curve tells us that -2 lies within $1.96\,(1.363)$ of θ with a probability of .95. In symbols,

$$P[-2 - 1.96(1.363) < \theta < -2 + 1.96(1.363)] = .95$$
$$P[-4.67 < \theta < .67] = .95$$

The effect of this argument is that, although H_1, the hypothesis alternative to $H_0: \mu_X = \mu_Y$, is not exact, there is nevertheless some information as to its nature. It is hardly necessary to add that the interval $(-4.67, .67)$ in which $\mu_X - \mu_Y = \theta$ has been probably (.95) included can be made much smaller. To see the mathematical justification for this assertion, note that $s_{\bar{X} - \bar{Y}} = 1.363$ is used to fix the numbers -4.67 and $.67$. If a smaller $s_{\bar{X} - \bar{Y}}$ were used, the results would be closer together. To make $s_{\bar{X} - \bar{Y}}$ smaller, it is only necessary to increase the sample sizes (that is, use more students).

The preceding paragraphs have dealt with the problem of the inexact alternative hypothesis. This problem derives its importance from the fact that β, the probability of a Type II error, depends for its calculation on how exact H_1 is. The less exact H_1, the less accurately can β be determined. If H_1 is exact, β is known exactly also.

Although behavioral scientists seldom, if ever, employ specific alternative hypotheses, and therefore are seldom, if ever, in a position to calculate the risk of the Type II error, we present an example of this computation below so that the student will enhance his understanding of the logic involved. The example is taken from the field of genetics.

Specific alternative hypotheses

Consider the problem of a geneticist who is investigating the inheritance of a given characteristic in fruit flies. According to one theory, the proportion of viable descendants of certain mutated parent fruit flies should be $\frac{1}{4}$. But the geneticist has reason to believe that under certain circumstances which he has introduced, that proportion should drop to $\frac{1}{8}$. He must therefore choose between two values, one and only one of which is correct. The problem, therefore, is explicitly stated in terms of two hypotheses:

H_0: The true proportion is .25.
H_1: The true proportion is .125.

Some method is now required whereby a choice will be made between the two hypotheses. One method might well be to observe a large number— say, 100—of the descendents and to reject H_0 if the number of viable specimens is too much less than 25 per cent of the whole sample.

Now if H_0 is true, the distribution of outcomes is given by the binomial model with $n = 100$ and $p = .25$. The normal curve approximation for this distribution has a mean of $np = 100(.25) = 25$ and a standard deviation of $\sqrt{npq} = \sqrt{(100)(.25)(.75)} = 4.33$. The critical region is chosen to be the left 5 per cent tail of this distribution. Figure 39 shows the normal curve with its horizontal axis divided into two parts by the point $25 - 1.645(4.33) = 17.88$. (The factor 1.645 was used because the normal probability table shows that 45 per cent of the distribution lies between the mean and a point 1.645σ distant from it.) The shaded region of Figure 39 must then contain 5 per cent of the total area under the curve. This shaded region is the critical region for this test. The expression $B(100, .25)$ stands for the binomial distribution with $n = 100$ and $p = .25$.

If the number of viable specimens is 17 or less, then H_0 is to be rejected. Note that even if H_0: $p = .25$ is true, the probability that it will be re-

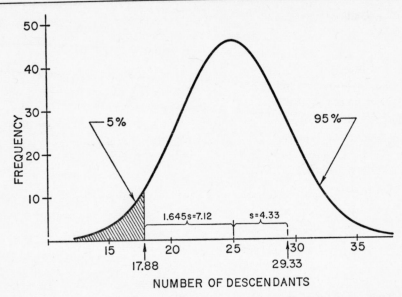

FIG. 39. Frequency of parents having various numbers of mutated descendants ($H_0 = 25$).

jected is .05. Having set $\alpha = .05$, this is the risk that is to be taken of committing a Type I error.

The critical region was selected at the lower end of the distribution because of the form of H_0 and H_1. It would not be reasonable to accept H_1: $p = .125$ if the result was considerably in excess of 25 per cent of the 100 specimens. If H_1 had the form $p \neq .25$, then it would be necesary to consider as critical, extreme excesses above 25 as well as extreme deficiencies below 25. The test would then be *two-tailed* with a part of the critical region at the far left and a part at the far right as in Figure 35. With $\alpha = .05$, each tail would ordinarily contain 2.5 per cent of the distribution.

A test of $H_0: p = .25$ and $H_1: p = .125$ has now been developed which will limit the probability of rejecting H_0 to .05 provided that H_0 is true. If, however, H_0 is actually false but, despite this, the outcome is 18 or more, H_0 will be accepted and a Type II error committed. The probability of this error is β, the value of which will now be sought. To compute β, it is necessary to assume that H_1 is true. In this case the outcomes have a binomial distribution with $n = 100$ and $p = .125$. The mean and standard deviation of the corresponding normal curve are, then, respec-

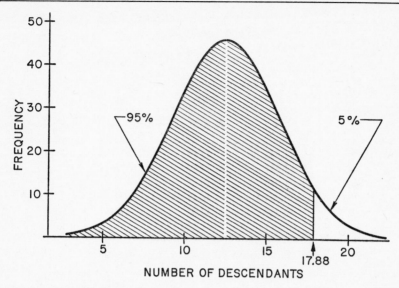

FIG. 40. Frequency of parents having various numbers of mutated descendants $(H_1 = 12.5)$.

tively $np = 12.5$ and $\sqrt{npq} = 3.31$. The distribution is shown in Figure 40 with the mean marked and the *previously computed critical region* shaded. In order to compute β, it is only necessary to compute the probability of an outcome exceeding 17.88 in this distribution; 17.88 is $\dfrac{17.88 - 12.5}{3.31} =$ 1.625 standard deviations to the right of the mean. Reference to the table of normal probabilities shows that $\beta = .0521$, the area of the unshaded, noncritical region. Hence if H_1 is true—if p is actually .125—there is a probability of .0521 that the outcome will be sufficiently large (18 or more), so that H_0 will be erroneously accepted.

It will be left as an exercise to show that β would have been larger if α had been reduced from .05 to .025. The solution of the problem involves only the replacement of the number 17.88 with a value appropriate to $\alpha = .025$ and computing this number in terms of the mean and standard deviation associated with Figure 36.

Sample Size and Precision

Any effort to *decrease* α, the size of the Type I error in the preceding example, is certain to *increase* β, the size of the Type II error, unless n is also increased by a sufficient amount. If, in the above example, n is held at 100 while α is given values less than .05, the corresponding increases in β will be as shown in Table 51.

TABLE 51

Variations in β Due to Changing α and Holding n Fixed

(1)	(2)	(3)	(4)	(5)
α	z	$R = 25 - 4.33z$	$= \dfrac{R - 12.5}{3.31}$	β
.05	1.645	17.88	1.625	.05
.04	1.751	17.42	1.486	.07
.03	1.880	16.86	1.317	.09
.02	2.054	16.11	1.091	.14
.01	2.327	14.92	.731	.23

This table gives the sequence of calculation needed to compute β. The first column is the chosen value of α. Column (2) is taken from the normal probability table and indicates the value of z which corresponds to the area $.5000 - \alpha$. Column (3) gives the point which separates the critical region from the noncritical region under the condition that H_0 is true. Column (4) gives the distance from 12.5 to the numbers of column (3) in terms of the standard deviation based on the truth of H_1. Note that 12.5 is the mean if H_1 is true. Column (5) is taken from the normal probability table and corresponds to the values of z' in column (4). The relation between α and β for fixed $n(= 100)$ is apparent here.

Now let n vary and notice the effect on β. Table 52 shows how β for the previously discussed test varies if n is increased to various values. The value of α is chosen in advance to be .05 and is held at this value. Some of the numbers needed in Table 52 are developed in Table 53. There μ_0 and σ_0 are, respectively, the mean and standard deviation based on the truth of H_0: $p = \frac{1}{4}$. Similarly, μ_1 and σ_1 are the mean and standard deviation if H_1: $p = \frac{1}{8}$ is true.

TABLE 52

Variations in β Due to Changing n and Holding α Fixed

n	$R = \mu_0 - 1.645\sigma_0$	$z = \dfrac{R - \mu_1}{\sigma_1}$	β
100	17.88	1.625	.05
120	22.20	1.989	.02
140	26.58	2.322	.01
160	30.99	2.629	.004

TABLE 53

μ and σ for Various Binomial Distributions

$H_0: p = \frac{1}{4}$ $H_1: p = \frac{1}{8}$

n	$\mu_0 = n/4$	$\sigma_0 = \sqrt{n(\frac{1}{4})(\frac{3}{4})}$	$\mu_1 = n/8$	$\sigma_1 = \sqrt{n(\frac{1}{8})(\frac{7}{8})}$
100	25	4.33	12.5	3.31
120	30	4.74	15.0	3.62
140	35	5.12	17.5	3.91
160	40	5.48	20.0	4.18
180	45	5.81	22.5	4.44
200	50	6.12	25.0	4.68

In Table 52, R is the point separating the critical region from the noncritical region, and z is the distance R is from μ_1 in terms of σ_1. β is taken from the normal probability table.

It is clear from this discussion that increasing the sample size will decrease β. It is possible to decrease α (which increases β) and to increase n (which decreases β) so that the net effect is a decrease in both α and β. Increasing the sample size will then make possible an increase in precision in the decision rule with respect to both types of errors.

By way of summary

The geneticist's problem discussed above has these major features. The investigator knows that he can count the viable specimens in a large sample and that the number obtained will be distributed according to one of two binomial distributions. One distribution corresponds to $H_0: p = .25$, and one corresponds to $H_1: p = .125$. He fixes α at .05 and computes the boundaries of the critical region in terms of numbers of viable specimens. Then, to compute β, he expresses these boundaries in terms of the mean and standard deviation of the binomial distribution corresponding to H_1. The proportion of this distribution spanned by the noncritical region (under H_0) is then determined from the normal probability table to be $\beta = .0520$. The geneticist has a probability of .05 of rejecting H_0 if it is true and a probability of .0520 of accepting H_0 if it is false.

It is important to note that, although the possibility of error has not been eliminated by this procedure, two important things have been accomplished. A quantitative measure has been placed on the various kinds of risks associated with the decision. Moreover the decision has been made according to a process which can be refined to any practical level of precision. That is, both α and β can be made very small if the sample size is increased sufficiently. It is in this way that the second requirement of good decision procedure is met by the statistical method.

If the alternative hypothesis is not exact, as is very often the case, β cannot be accurately computed. This will not be serious if the investigator is concerned mainly with the danger of rejecting a true hypothesis. The probability of this error can be controlled. If β is important, the alternative hypothesis can be made more exact by using larger samples to narrow confidence limits for the population parameters in question.

NONPARAMETRIC TESTS

The examples given above have been concerned with the question of the similarity or difference between certain statistics associated with the populations under study. In both cases the frequency distribution of some statistical quantity was known and used in constructing the test to be used. It frequently happens that no such frequency distribution is known for the problem at hand, or that samples must necessarily be too small to yield sufficient precision in the results. A special class of tests has been designed for use in such situations. Since their use requires no knowledge of, or assumptions about, the specific distribution being studied, these tests are called "distribution-free," or "nonparametric," tests; that is, no knowledge of the form of the distribution, or of means, standard deviations, or other statistical measures associated with the variable being studied, is required. As an elementary typical example of such tests, the *sign test* will be discussed here.

The sign test

The sign test is useful whenever the experiment in question can be construed as a series of events with a binomial distribution. This is a very general requirement, as will be shown by the quite different examples below.

A true-false examination of forty statements including twenty that are false is easily seen to be a series of binomial trials with $n = 40$ and $p = \frac{1}{2}$. It is known that some subjects have a "response set" which favors true above false or vice versa on such tests; that is, some subjects when given a true-false test tend to mark more items "true" than "false," while other subjects tend to mark more items "false" than "true." In order to test for a subject's "response set," let the hypothesis be

$$H_0: P(+) = P(-)$$
$$H_1: H_0 \text{ is false}$$

where P $(+)$ denotes the probability of an answer of *true* and P $(-)$ is the probability of an answer of *false*. (Note the nonspecific nature of H_1). $B(40, \frac{1}{2})$ has $\mu = 40(\frac{1}{2}) = 20$ and $\sigma = \sqrt{40(\frac{1}{2})(\frac{1}{2})} = 3.16$. Let $\alpha = .05$ and let a two-tailed critical region be used, since the subject may show a response set in either direction. The critical region may then be taken as the two 2.5 per cent tails of the normal distribution with $\mu = 20$ and $\sigma = 3.16$. This means that the noncritical region extends from $20 - 2(3.16)$ to $20 + 2(3.16)$. This gives the interval 13.68 to 26.32 as the noncritical region. Hence, H_0 will be accepted if the number of *true* responses is from fourteen to twenty-six inclusive and will be rejected otherwise. The acceptance of H_0 is equivalent to denying a response set in the subject. A result of twenty-seven or more "true" responses out of forty would lead to the acceptance of H_1 with a response set of *true* implied. A response set of false would be implied by a result less than fourteen.

As a second example, consider a teacher who wishes to compare the performance of a class of forty students on an examination for which the median score in the past is 72. Let each score equal to or in excess of 72 be called a plus and let each score below 72 be called a minus (that is, one of two different "signs" is attached to each score). Again, there is a series of forty binomial trials with $p = \frac{1}{2}$. The hypotheses will be just those used above. If $\alpha = .05$ again, then the test is identical with that for response set. The number of scores above the former median (pluses) must be below fourteen or above twenty-six to cause H_0 to be rejected.

In each of the examples above, the size of the sample was taken to be forty and H_0 involved equal relative frequencies of plus and minus. It is, of course, possible to use samples of any size. The relative frequencies or probabilities of pluses and minuses may or may not be equal to $\frac{1}{2}$, according to the demands of the particular problem. Such changes merely give a different mean np and a different standard deviation, $\sqrt{npq}$. If n is less than 30, the normal curve approximation should not be used.

Cumulative probability

For $n < 30$ the relevant terms of the binomial expansion should be computed or taken from available tables and summed. An example using a smaller sample and unequal relative frequencies for plus and minus is the following. In conducting a public opinion poll on a college campus where males constitute 65 per cent of the enrollment, it is desired to apportion the interviews with men and women in the ratio sixty-five to thirty-five. Since the interviewers are to approach subjects at random, some check is necessary to insure that random selections between the sexes are being made. A supervisor wishing to check on whether or not an interviewer has a tendency to favor one of the sexes in his choices could proceed by selecting a sequence of twelve subjects and recording a plus for each man and a minus for each woman in the sample. If the interviewer is choosing randomly, his series of plus and minus signs constitutes a set of twelve binomial trials with $p = .65$; $n = 12$ is too small to justify the normal approximation method. The binomial expansion of $(.65 + .35)^{12}$ must be expanded and used to compile the list of *cumulative probabilities*, as shown in Table 54.

TABLE 54

Table of Probabilities for the Sign Test ($n < 12$)

k	$P(k)$	Probability of at least k plus signs
12	.0057	.0057
11	.0368	.0425
10	.1088	.1513
9	.1954	.3467
8	.2367	.5834
7	.2039	.7873
6	.1281	.9154
5	.0591	.9745
4	.0199	.9944
3	.0048	.9992
2	.0008	1.0000
1	.0001	1.0000
0	.0000	1.0000

In Table 54 the first column lists the various numbers of plus signs that are possible. The second column gives the value of the corresponding term of $(.65 + .35)^{12}$. The third column is the cumulative sum of the entries in the second. A two-tailed critical region corresponding to $\alpha = .05$ is chosen. This means that, with 2.5 per cent marked off at each end of the distribution, the noncritical region will extend from five pluses to eleven pluses, inclusive. As many as eleven pluses and as few as five pluses ($5 \leq k \leq 11$) are to be expected under H_0 because of possible sampling errors by the supervisor in selecting his sample of twelve interviews. If H_0 is true, the expected number of pluses is the mean of $B(12, .65)$, which is $12(.65) = 7.8$. Note that this value is not at the center of the noncritical region of the test. This is because the distribution is skewed or asymmetrical about its mean. This will always occur for $p \neq q$ and n that is small. As n becomes large, the asymmetry caused by $p \neq q$ becomes negligible and the distribution tends to fit the perfectly symmetrical normal curve.

The chi-square (χ^2) test

The sign test is based on a division or conversion of the data into two exhaustive, mutually exclusive subsets. One subset is characterized by pluses and the other by minuses. Implicit in the method is the assumption that each plus or minus is the result of an independent random choice in selecting the sample, and that the probability of a plus remains the same for every such choice. The binomial distribution then fully determines the relative frequency associated with each possible number of pluses.

The chi-square test is an extension or generalization of the sign test. Instead of using two categories as in the sign test, the chi-square test allows a separation of the data into as many categories as desired. When the number of categories exceeds two, the binomial distribution is no longer adequate, and a different frequency distribution is required. This need is met by the chi-square distribution, the derivation of which is reserved for advanced texts.

Just as in the sign test, it is necessary to compute, on the assumption of randomness, what expected number of data will lie in each category. After this is done for each category, a measure of the difference between the observed and expected values in each category is computed.

The problem of expected frequencies will be discussed first, after which the measure of difference between observed and expected values will be treated. Suppose that a psychologist is studying the effect of education on personality adjustment. He obtains a random sample of 500 subjects and, by testing, rates each one on a scale of 1, 2, 3, 4, and 5, with 1 representing very poor adjustment and 5 representing excellent adjustment. He also rates each subject according to the amount of formal education received. Displaying his data in a two-way classification, he obtains Table 55.

TABLE 55

A Two Way Classification of 500 Subjects on Two Measures

Years of Education	Adjustment Level					
	1	2	3	4	5	
0–8	8	15	50	12	7	100
9–12	15	34	170	40	8	275
13 or more	7	21	80	28	7	125
	30	70	300	80	20	500

The 500 data have been classified into fifteen categories. The numbers at the right and at the bottom are row and column totals, respectively. The fifteen cells contain the observed distribution of the data. Since 100 out of 500 are in the first row, the probability that a randomly selected person will be classified into one of the first row cells is $^{100}\!/_{500} = \frac{1}{5}$. Similarly, the probability of such a selection being classified into row 2 is $^{275}\!/_{500} = ^{11}\!/_{20}$, and for the last row the probability is $^{125}\!/_{500} = \frac{1}{4}$. Note that $\frac{1}{5} + ^{11}\!/_{20} + \frac{1}{4} = 1$. A probability is thus associated with each row. In a similar manner, a probability is associated with each column of the classification. In this case, the probabilities will be $^{30}\!/_{500}$, $^{70}\!/_{500}$, $^{300}\!/_{500}$, $^{80}\!/_{500}$, and $^{20}\!/_{500}$ for Columns (1), (2), (3), (4), and (5), respectively. These fractions reduce to $^{3}\!/_{50}$, $^{7}\!/_{50}$, $\frac{3}{5}$, $^{4}\!/_{25}$, and $^{1}\!/_{25}$. The problem of expected frequencies can now be solved by use of the multiplicative theorem on probabilities. The assumption that there is no relationship between the two classification criteria can be put in the form

H_0: Education and personality adjustment are independent variables.
H_1: H_0 is false.

If H_0 is true, then the probability that a randomly chosen subject will be classified to row one is $\frac{1}{5}$ and that he will be classified to column one is $^{3}\!/_{50}$. According to the multiplicative theorem on probabilities, the probability that these two independent events will occur is $(\frac{1}{5})(\frac{3}{50}) = \frac{3}{250}$. Now $\frac{3}{250}(500) = 6$, and 6 is then the expected number in that cell which is in the first row and the first column. The probability associated with the cell in the second row and third column is $(\frac{11}{20})(\frac{3}{5}) = \frac{33}{100}$. The expected value for the cell is then $\frac{33}{100}(500) = 165$. When each of the fifteen cells has been treated thus, the result is as in Table 56 where expected values are shown in italics along with the corresponding observed values.

The problem of expected frequencies is thus solved by using the row and column totals and the sample size to compute probabilities for each row and column. If H_0 is true, then the row and column classifications of any subject are independent events, the joint occurrence of which is the product of their individual probabilities. It will be noted in Table 56 that the row and column totals for the expected frequencies are exactly those of the observed frequencies. This provides a convenient check for accuracy in computing expected values. It is a consequence of the fact that the sum of the row probabilities is 1, and the sum of the column probabilities is 1. The result is that 500 data have been partitioned into fifteen cells or categories in two ways. One of the partitions is the result of observation, and

TABLE 56

*Observed and Expected Frequencies for a
Two-way Classification of 500 Subjects on Two Measures*

Years of Education	Adjustment Level					
	1	2	3	4	5	
0–8	*6* 8	*14* 15	*60* 50	*16* 12	*4* 7	100
9–12	*16.5* 15	*38.5* 34	*165* 170	*44* 40	*11* 8	275
13 or more	*7.5* 7	*17.5* 21	*75* 80	*20* 28	*5* 7	125
	30	70	300	80	20	500

the other is the result of the assumption of randomness. The problem of testing H_0 against H_1 reduces to a consideration of how much difference there is between the two distributions and whether or not such a difference is significantly large.

If the difference between the observed and expected frequencies in each cell is computed, it will be found that some are positive and some are negative. In order not to have differences of opposite sign cancel one another, each difference is squared. Since squares are never negative, the sum of these squares will contain a contribution of 0 or more from each cell. The size of the frequencies in any cell must also be taken into account in computing their measure of difference. For example, in the row 1, column 1, cell of Table 56, the difference is $8 - 6 = 2$, and, in the row 3, column 3, cell, the difference is $80 - 75 = 5$. On the other hand, 6 is only 75 per cent of 8, whereas 75 is 94 per cent of 80. Some means is necessary whereby the difference $8 - 6 = 2$ will be given more weight than the difference $80 - 75 = 5$. This is accomplished by dividing the squared difference in each cell by the expected value in that cell. The two cells being discussed then produce contributions of $\dfrac{(8-6)^2}{6} = \dfrac{2}{3}$ and $\dfrac{(80-75)^2}{75} = \dfrac{1}{3}$.

The contribution of each cell to the total difference between the two distributions is then $\dfrac{(o-e)^2}{e}$, where o stands for observed frequency and e

stands for expected or theoretical frequency. The sum of all these contributions, one for each cell, constitutes chi-square; that is,

$$\chi^2 = \sum_{i=1}^{k} \frac{(o_i - e_i)^2}{e_i}$$

where k is the number of cells being used. Note that expected frequencies are never negative and squares are never negative. Hence no term of chi-square can be negative. Chi-square is therefore always a positive number unless every cell has o and e equal, in which case $\chi^2 = 0$.

Degrees of freedom

Now, quite clearly, the size of the chi-square depends on how many cells were used in computing it. If the number of cells is small, the contributions to the value of chi-square will be few in number. There are, for this reason, many different chi-square distributions. The one to be used in any specific case depends on the number of cells used.

To see the nature of this dependence, observe that in Table 55 the expected frequencies in the last column are fully determined as soon as those in the first four columns are known. This is because the row totals must equal those for the observed frequencies. Similarly, the expected frequencies in the third row are fully determined as soon as those in the first two rows are known. Put another way, there is no freedom of choice for expected frequencies in the last row and the last column; all are determined by what happens in the upper left two-by-four rectangle of cells. These eight cells each contribute one *degree of freedom* to the computation of chi-square. The chi-square distribution with eight degrees of freedom must then be used. In general, the number of degrees of freedom is $(r - 1)$ $(c - 1)$ where r is the number of rows and c is the number of columns. An exception to this rule occurs when there is just one row. Then $c - 1$ is used.

Table C in the Appendix has thirty lines, one each for thirty different chi-square distributions. The row corresponding to eight degrees of freedom shows that the probability that chi-square will be *as large as* or larger than 2.088 due to random sampling errors is .99. The probability that chi-square will be as large as 15.507 is only .05. The other entries in the row correspond to other probabilities as listed across the top of the table. If, in the example being discussed, a one-tailed critical region of size .05 is chosen, $\chi^2 = 15.507$ is the value which separates the critical and non-critical regions into which the total range of chi-square is divided. The computations required to obtain chi-square for Table 56 are shown in Table 57.

TABLE 57

Computation of Chi-square for Data of Table 56

$$\frac{(8 - 6)^2}{6} = .6667 \qquad \frac{(170 - 165)^2}{165} = .1515$$

$$\frac{(15 - 14)^2}{14} = .0714 \qquad \frac{(40 - 44)^2}{44} = .3636$$

$$\frac{(50 - 60)^2}{60} = 1.6667 \qquad \frac{(8 - 11)^2}{11} = .8182$$

$$\frac{(12 - 16)^2}{16} = 1.0000 \qquad \frac{(7 - 7.5)^2}{7.5} = .0333$$

$$\frac{(7 - 4)^2}{4} = 2.2500 \qquad \frac{(21 - 17.5)^2}{17.5} = .7000$$

$$\frac{(15 - 16.5)^2}{16.5} = .1364 \qquad \frac{(80 - 75)^2}{75} = .3333$$

$$\frac{(34 - 38.5)^2}{38.5} = .5260 \qquad \frac{(28 - 20)^2}{20} = 3.2000$$

$$\frac{(7 - 5)^2}{5} = .8000$$

$$\overline{12.717 = \chi^2}$$

According to the chi-square distribution with eight degrees of freedom, χ^2 can be expected to be as large as 12.717 between 10 and 20 per cent of the time due to random sampling errors alone. Chi-square is not sufficiently large to fall into the critical region beyond 15.507, and H_0 is therefore accepted. An inspection of the several contributions shows that the cells at row 1, column 5, and row 3, column 4, are the largest. It is in these cells that the most substantial random sampling errors occurred, assuming that the correct decision (to accept H_0) has been made.

A shorter formula

The method of computation used to obtain chi-square can be shortened by an algebraic manipulation of the formula

$$\chi^2 = \sum_{i=1}^{k} \frac{(o_i - e_i)^2}{e_i}$$

The first step is to expand $(o_i - e_i)^2$ into $o_i^2 - 2o_ie_i + e_i^2$ and then to separate the whole sum into three different sums. The result is

$$\chi^2 = \sum_{i=1}^{k} \frac{o_i^2}{e_i} - 2\sum_{i=1}^{k} \frac{o_ie_i}{e_i} + \sum_{i=1}^{k} \frac{e_i^2}{e_i}$$

Canceling an e_i from numerator and denominator in both the second and third sums gives

$$\chi^2 = \sum_{i=1}^{k} \frac{o_i^2}{e_i} - 2\sum_{i=1}^{k} o_i + \sum_{i=1}^{k} e_i$$

Since the sum of the expected frequencies is the same as the sum of the observed frequencies, the formula reduces to

$$\chi^2 = \sum_{i=1}^{k} \frac{o_i^2}{e_i} - n$$

where n is the sample size. All subtractions are thus combined into one subtraction. Another advantage exists in that all the numbers to be squared are whole numbers. This formula will be used in the next example of the use of the chi-square test.

The expression "grading on the curve" refers to a method of distributing grades under the assumption that performance is normally distributed in the class being graded. A professor with a large lecture class of 200 students has given an examination and classified the results into 12 categories. The results are shown in columns (1) and (2) of Table 58. Before using the normal curve as a basis for grading, he decides to test the hypotheses

H$_0$: Performance on this test is normally distributed.
H$_1$: H$_0$: is false.

If H$_0$ is true, the actual normal distribution can be found by determining the mean and standard deviation of the data, since every normal curve depends only on these two parameters. This normal distribution will then give the expected number of students in each classification interval under the assumption that H$_0$ is true. The mean and standard deviation of the 200

TABLE 58

Illustrative Computation of Expected Normal Frequencies

(1)	(2)	(3)		(4)	(5)
NO. OF CORRECT RESPONSES	NO. OF STUDENTS	COLUMN (1) EXPRESSED IN STANDARD UNITS		SIZE OF THE INTERVALS IN COLUMN (3)	EXPECTED NO. OF STUDENTS
13.5–16.5	6	−2.22	−1.82	.02117	4.23
16.5–19.5	9	−1.82	−1.42	.04342	8.68
19.5–22.5	12	−1.42	−1.02	.07606	15.21
22.5–25.5	15	−1.02	−.62	.11377	22.75
25.5–28.5	25	−.62	−.22	.14531	29.06
28.5–31.5	36	−.22	−.18	.15848	31.70
31.5–34.5	40	−.18	−.58	.14762	29.52
34.5–37.5	21	−.58	−.98	.11742	23.48
37.5–40.5	11	−.98	−1.38	.07975	15.95
40.5–43.5	13	−1.38	−1.78	.04625	9.25
43.5–46.5	8	−1.78	−2.18	.02291	4.58
46.5–49.5	4	−2.18	−2.58	.00969	1.94
	200				

observed data are 30.125 and 7.472. In order to get the expected number of students in each classification interval, it is necessary to express these classification intervals in terms of standard units. The interval 13.5–16.5 is replaced by the interval from $\dfrac{13.5 - 30.125}{7.472}$ to $\dfrac{16.5 - 30.125}{7.472}$ inclusive. If this computation is completed for each of the classification intervals, column (3) of Table 58 is obtained. Note that the values in column (3) increase by equal amounts just as do those in column (1). The difference between successive values is the length of the classification interval divided by $s = 7.472$.

The normal probability table is now used to determine what part of the expected normal distribution lies in each of the intervals given in column (3). For the first interval the result is $.48679 - .46562 = .02117$. Column (4) lists this computation and those for each of the other intervals. The expected number of students is then found by multiplying column (4) by 200, the size of the sample. The results are shown in column (5).

Columns (2) and (5) then constitute a set of twelve pairs of observed and expected values. The chi-square to be obtained from these will have nine degrees of freedom. This value results from having a one-by-twelve table and from having estimated two parameters, μ and σ. Each such estimation further reduces the number of degrees of freedom by one.

$$\chi^2 = \sum_{i=1}^{12} \frac{o_i^2}{e_i} - n$$

gives the following computation: $\dfrac{36}{4.23} + \dfrac{81}{8.68} + \dfrac{144}{15.21} + \dfrac{225}{22.75} + \dfrac{625}{29.06} +$

$\dfrac{1296}{31.70} + \dfrac{1600}{29.52} + \dfrac{441}{23.48} + \dfrac{121}{15.95} + \dfrac{169}{9.25} + \dfrac{64}{4.58} + \dfrac{16}{1.94} - 200 = 19.42.$

The chi-square distribution for nine degrees of freedom, Appendix Table C, shows that the probability of a chi-square as large as 19.42 is between .05 and .02. If α was chosen to be .05, the hypotheses of normal distribution will be rejected. If α was chosen smaller—say, $\alpha = .02$ or $\alpha = .01$—then H_0 will be accepted. By comparing the histograms of the two distributions, the disparities which contribute to the high value of chi-square may be observed graphically.

Appendix Table C gives the chi-square distribution only for degrees of freedom up to thirty. The reason for this is that for more than thirty degrees of freedom, the distribution of $\sqrt{\chi^2}$ is very nearly normal. For n' degrees of freedom ($n' > 30$), the quantity $\sqrt{2\chi^2} - \sqrt{2n' - 1}$ is used instead of chi-square. This quantity is normally distributed with mean 0 and standard deviation 1. As an example of this usage, suppose that a chi-square of 101.32 with 85 degrees of freedom is found. Then

$$\begin{aligned} \sqrt{2\chi^2} - \sqrt{2(85) - 1} &= \sqrt{202.64} - \sqrt{169} \\ &= 14.23 - 13.00 \\ &= 1.23. \end{aligned}$$

Since 1.23 standard deviations lies well short of the usual critical regions in the right tail of the standard normal curve, the result does not fall in the critical region and H_0 would be accepted. The left tail is not used as a critical region in this case, because a negative value of $\sqrt{2\chi^2} - \sqrt{2n' - 1}$ corresponds to a quite low chi-square for the number of degrees of freedom. The chi-square test is a more sensitive test than the sign test because it leads to a decision based on a more detailed comparison of the observed and expected frequency distributions.

PARAMETRIC AND NONPARAMETRIC PROCEDURES COMPARED

At this point it will be well to point out to the reader the similarities between the two kinds of tests discussed here. The parametric tests depend on a knowledge of some population statistic (a parameter). The knowledge referred to here is knowledge about the random sampling distribution of the parameter in question. Very often it is the sampling distribution of means or the sampling distribution of differences of means. Sample values are then compared with the theoretically deduced values and a decision is made. The difference between the parametric test and the nonparametric test is that for the latter no knowledge of the sampling distributions associated with the given population is required. A random sampling distribution is required for the nonparametric procedure, but it is one that is imposed by the form or technique of the experiment rather than by the population being studied. The binomial distribution is the most common distribution arising in this way, although it is not the only one.

The rule for making a decision is formed in the same way whether the sampling distribution arises from the population being studied or from outside it. The selection of a critical region, the risks to be taken on various errors, and the framing of hypotheses are all carried out in the same way once a frequency distribution has been found as a basis.

It will be observed that nonparametric tests are substantially simpler to perform, if only for the reason that less knowledge of the population is required for their operation. Since simplicity is nearly always a virtue, the reader may well ask if the nonparametric procedure is not always preferable to the parametric one; the answer is, No. For, although the nonparametric procedure is simpler, it is *less powerful* than the parametric procedure. To say a procedure is less powerful is to say that it is more likely to lead to acceptance of the null hypothesis (H_0) when the alternative is true than is a more powerful test. Thus, nonparametric procedures are more likely to accept the null hypothesis when the alternative is true than are parametric procedures. And, therefore, the choice of one procedure over the other involves more than the matter of simplicity of procedure.

It should be pointed out, however, that virtually all statistical procedures increase their precision when the size of the sample is increased. Therefore, should it be impossible to meet the requirements of the parametric procedures, one need only to increase the sample size in order to have the nonparametric procedure match the power of a parametric procedure. Indeed, the power of various nonparametric procedures may be expressed in terms of the number of cases which are needed in order to match the power of parametric procedures. This point is discussed in detail in more advanced texts.

BY WAY OF SUMMARY

Earlier we pointed out that a good decision procedure developed in the face of the fact that some decisions must be wrong should (1) make the risk of an incorrect decision minimal, (2) specify the risks of making various kinds of errors, and (3) be a public procedure, open to criticism. How well do statistical decision procedures meet these requirements?

1. The risk of an incorrect decision should be minimal

Although the use of the statistical method cannot in itself make the risk of an incorrect decision minimal, the statistical method does possess the advantage of quantifying the risk of an incorrect decision under given circumstances. Furthermore, the statistical method indicates what steps must be taken in order to make such a risk smaller (or larger).

2. The risks of errors of various kinds should be specified

The mathematical section of this chapter concerned the problems involved in the quantification of two types of errors. The logic and methods of computing the risk associated with each type of error were explained, as well as the conditions which affect these computations. Thus, for example, it was demonstrated that the more precisely the alternative hypothesis is stated, the more precisely may the error of the second kind be computed. In short, the manner in which the statistical method meets the second requirement of a good decision procedure was set forth.

3. The steps of the decision procedure should be public

The student should now be able to see the public nature of statistical decision procedures. They are public rather than private in the sense that they rest on objective criteria known to all and not on the subjective judgment of the investigator. It is not necessary to know the philosophical bias of an investigator if his statistical methods are described; it will be possible to replicate his experiment *and his decision-making process* and to subject both to scholarly criticism.

Having reached this point, the student may well agree with Parmenides when he urged Socrates to "consider not only the consequences which flow from a given hypothesis, but also the consequences which flow from denying the hypothesis," and sympathize with his remark that Socrates would find such a consideration not only good training, but "a tremendous business."

A NOTE ON THE DISCREPANCY BETWEEN THEORY AND PRACTICE AND A SUGGESTION AS TO HOW THIS DISCREPANCY MIGHT BE REDUCED

Research in the behavioral sciences requires both a knowledge of experimental design and observational methods, as well as knowledge of the statistical method. For simplicity's sake, let us call the former two "data-producing" procedures, and the latter a "data-analyzing" procedure.

Now data production is, so-to-speak, the stock in trade of the scientist. He invents, changes, and discards procedures for data production; indeed he is expert in this regard. Procedures for data analysis, however, are not his in the sense that data-producing procedures are. Ultimately, data-analyzing procedures belong to the mathematical statistician; he is the inventor, the critic, the expert in this field. And this makes a difference—an important one—in the way in which statistical decision theory is applied to research problems. The mathematician, it must be remembered works in a world of symbols, the scientist in a world of things. The world of symbols, the world of idealized forms, is, if nothing else, tidier—the issues are drawn more sharply, logical steps become more apparent, and decisions follow more directly—than in the world of things.

In the scientist's world of things, sharply drawn issues and clear thinking are, of course, also primary aims, but they are not easily achieved because the problems the scientist deals with cannot always be put in symbolic form. This difference may be illustrated by a brief consideration of how statistical decision procedures are frequently—in fact, more often than not—employed by scientists.

Suppose a scientist sets about investigating a certain hypothesis, and suppose he sets the level of risk of the Type I error at .05. (For the sake of convenience, as well as faithfulness to usual circumstances, we shall ignore the matter of the alternative hypothesis.) Now suppose that a result is obtained, and the scientist finds that H_0 should be accepted, according to his decision rule, because the probability value associated with the result is .06—just barely outside the critical region of .05. A mathematician looking over the shoulder of the scientist might well say, "Well, that's that. H_0 is to be accepted, eh?" But the scientist will not be so quick to say "that's that," or to follow his own decision rule. He is more likely to say something like, "Say! that was close, wasn't it? I'll bet that if I had done a better job on the apparatus, or making those observations, my hypothesis would have been supported!" In short, the scientist is likely to ignore his own decision rule (and at this point he is likely to become keenly aware of the fact that his decision rule was determined by *convention*), and he will probably pursue the research with a great deal of faith in his ideas. And he will do this because he will have invested a great deal of time, money, effort, and, most important, his own hopes in the problem. It will be easy for the mathematician to point out that, after all, it makes little sense to form decision rules if one has no intention of abiding by them. The world of symbols is tidy. But the world of things involves people's aims, hopes, and fears—and one's research career may be heavily dependent upon the outcome of an experiment. But of greatest importance is the fact that one becomes a devotee of his own ideas: they are not easily come by, and they are not easily given up. And, therefore, a result which appears to be "close" will invite an after-the-fact revision of the decision rule.

Yes—no—maybe

Now there need be nothing intrinsically wrong with a revision of a decision rule after the results are in—*provided a new experiment is conducted.* After all, the probability level obtained in one experiment concerns only the matter of endless repetitions of that experiment. A new experiment will involve new computations. But the entire procedure might be clarified somewhat if, instead of a "yes-no" decision rule, a "yes-no-maybe" rule was formulated. We make this suggestion only because it seems more in keeping with the actual working habits of the scientist. For in practice the scientist seems to face not merely two alternatives "accept or reject," but at least three alternatives. Let us take a closer look at these.

Two of these alternatives are the extreme actions—a clear, unequivocal acceptance or rejection of H_0. A third alternative, however, might be called "maybe," or better, "pursuit"; that is, when the probability associated with a given result falls near the critical region but not in it, the investigator may decide to pursue the hypothesis further either by a different analysis of the data, or by a different experiment. And the nearer and dearer the hypothesis is to his general theory, the more he is likely to pursue the hypothesis.

Should the "pursuit" of the hypothesis lead to a new and different analysis of the data, however, and should the new analysis indicate that H_0 should be rejected rather than accepted (under the original decision rule), *the investigator is obliged to repeat the experiment and data analysis with new subjects.* If this is not done, the possibility always remains that the second analysis of the data was carried out with an eye to the specific arrangement of the data obtained. This is analogous to forming the decision rule to fit the data so as to insure a given result. In this case the use of a statistical procedure would be meaningless, because it would be employed merely to provide the decision desired. Should the hypothesis be pursued by employing a new *experiment*, rather than simply by a new analysis of the data, the caution mentioned above is automatically observed.

In view of the actual practices of research investigators, then, it seems to us that the conventional "accept-reject" rule should be supplanted by an "accept-pursue-reject" rule. Three specific regions of the sampling distribution in question ought to be specified, and the appropriate decision should be associated with each. For example, R, the region of rejection of H_0, might be retained as the .05 region in, say, one tail of the distribution. But the region from .05 to .15 might well be associated with a decision to "pursue," while the remaining region of size .80 might be associated with a decision to accept H_0. (As a matter of fact, there are good grounds for suspecting that in many cases the region actually associated with "pursuit" now approximates .05 to .25.)

This form of a decision rule would doubtless complicate matters in those cases where a specific alternative hypothesis is employed and β calculated, but such cases are so few that such complications would seldom arise. The main point, however, is that the investigator could set forth a decision rule which reflected his practice, or what he would like to practice, and a rule, therefore, which he would not want to revise after the data are analyzed.

Suggestions for Further Reading

ACKOFF, R. 1953. *The design of social research.* Chicago: University of Chicago Press.

A thorough discussion of the application of statistical logic and experimental design to problems of social research.

COOMBS, C., DAVIS, R., and THRALL, R. (eds.). 1954. *Decision processes.* New York: Wiley.

A general introduction to decision theory.

WALLIS, W., and ROBERTS, H. 1956. *Statistics: a new approach.* Glencoe: Free Press.

See especially Chapter 12.

PROBLEMS

1. When "facts speak for themselves," what may generally be said of the result?

2. A jury hearing a murder trial is working through the evidence toward a decision centered on the hypothesis: The defendant is not guilty. What two errors are possible in the decision, and which is the most serious?

3. It is sometimes said that scientific questions cannot be settled by taking a vote. Why does such an excellent decision-making process fail when applied to questions of fact?

4. (a) What is meant by "the critical region" of a test?
   (b) The fixing of a critical region of a frequency distribution automatically calls into being a "noncritical region." What can be said of the outcomes which lie in such a region.

5. (a) What is the nature of a type I error?
   (b) What is the nature of a type II error?
   (c) In arriving at a decision concerning the following hypotheses which type of error would be most serious?

   H_0: The brakes on my car are too poor to be safe.
   H_1: The brakes are safe.

   (d) Repeat part (c) for the following hypotheses.

   H_0: Teenagers should be trusted with guns.
   H_1: H_0 is false.

6. A psychologist studying the effect of color on students in a classroom arranged filters to subtly change the illumination for one of the two classes chosen for the experiment. Which class constitutes the control group? What treatment or intervention is involved? Frame a hypothesis of no effect for the experiment.

7. Supposing the classes in problem 6 to be in social studies, how might the hypothesis of no effect be tested for acceptance or rejection?

8. In a medical experiment designed to test a new analgesic drug, the experimental group of subjects was given the drug and placebos were given to a control group. The results showed that 65 per cent of the experimental group and 20 per cent of the control group reported substantial relief of pain.

(a) Did the presence of a control group in the experiment make the results more, less, or equally as decisive as would have been the case had it not been used?

(b) What aspect of the investigator's problem is emphasized by the control group results?

(c) What action must the investigator take in designing this experiment to make it conform to the "classical design"?

9. (a) Frame suitable null and alternative hypotheses for the experiment described in problem 8.

(b) Why is it always necessary to frame the basic question in the form of such hypotheses?

10. What are the reasons for the almost universal use of critical regions of sizes .05 and .01? Would any of these reasons be valid arguments against the use of regions of size .03, .07, or .20?

11. What is wrong with choosing a critical region for a test after the experimental results are known?

12. A student, weighing the advantages and disadvantages of showing up for a statistics test, decides to roll a die and to cut the class if either a one or a two results. Using the outcomes one and two as a critical region, frame his dilemma in proper hypotheses and compute the size of his type I error.

13. In the experiment of the geneticist, the number of viable descendents turned out to be fifteen.

(a) Which of his hypotheses did he accept?

(b) If H_0 was actually true, what type of error, if any, did he commit?

14. In the example of the geneticist, let all parts of the problem be the same except that $\alpha = .025$ instead of .05. Compute the boundaries of the critical region and find β.

15. In the example of the geneticist, let all parts of the problem be the same except that the size of the sample is increased from 100 to 400. Compute the boundaries of the noncritical region and find β.

16. In the teaching methods example, let the data be changed to $\bar{X} = 75$ and $\sigma_X = 5.4$ for the control group and $\bar{Y} = 79$ and $\sigma_Y = 5.1$ for the experimental group. Then, using $\alpha = .05$ as in the example, decide whether to accept or reject H_0: $\mu_X = \mu_Y$.

17. In the teaching methods example, let all features of the problem remain the same except that the sample sizes be increased from 30 and 32 to 90 and 94, respectively. Does $\bar{X}$ differ significantly from $\bar{Y}$?

18. By means of the theorems on the Σ symbol, show that the formula

$$\chi^2 = \sum_{i=1}^{n} \frac{(o_i - e_i)^2}{e_i} \text{ is equivalent to the easier computational forms}$$

$$\chi^2 = \sum_{i=1}^{n} \frac{o_i^2}{e_i} - \sum_{i=1}^{n} e_i \quad \text{and}$$

$$\chi^2 = \sum_{i=1}^{n} \frac{o_i^2}{e_i} - \sum_{i=1}^{n} \theta_i$$

19. A teacher with 135 students estimates on the basis of past experience that twenty students will earn an A, twenty-five a B, forty-nine a C, twenty-five a D, and sixteen an F. The grades given at the end of the term included fifteen A's, twenty-one B's, forty-two C's, thirty-one D's, and twenty-six F's.
    (a) Frame suitable null and alternative hypotheses which may be tested using the χ^2 test with $\alpha = .05$.
    (b) Find χ^2 and the number of degrees of freedom.
    (c) What conclusions or decisions can be made concerning the method of estimating grades and the class to which the method was applied?

20. There being some question as to whether or not a die is truly fashioned, it is decided to roll it 300 times to test it. The hypotheses

$$H_0\text{: There is no bias in the die}$$
$$H_1\text{: The die is biased}$$

   are set up.
    (a) Choose a value α for the type I error that is consistent with a considerable reluctance to play with a biased die.
    (b) The expected values for a χ^2 test are those to be expected under the assumption that H_0 is true. What are the expected frequencies of rolls of 1, 2, 3, 4, 5, and 6 under this assumption?
    (c) Suppose that the results of the experiment are:

Outcome	1	2	3	4	5	6
Frequency	46	52	51	45	54	52

   Find χ^2 and the number of degrees of freedom.
    (d) What is your decision concerning the die?

21. A public opinion poll taken two months ago in a certain locality showed that 38 per cent of the voting public would vote for a bond issue, 32 per cent would vote against it, and 30 per cent were undecided. A poll just completed gives the current percentages as 45 per cent, 35 per cent, and 20 per cent, respectively.

    (a) Assume that 100 persons were polled in each case and compute χ^2 using the first poll for expected values.

    (b) Assume that 1,000 persons were polled in each case and compute χ^2 using the first poll for expected values.

    (c) On the basis of the results in (a) and (b), what can be concluded about the comparison of percentages when the sample sizes are not known? What conclusions can be drawn concerning the frequently published poll results intended to demonstrate trends of opinion?

22. In analyzing some data involving $n = 41$ degrees of freedom, χ^2 was found to be 60.5. Using $\sqrt{2\chi^2} - \sqrt{2n - 1}$ as a standard normal variable, find the probability that as large a value of χ^2 as 60.5 would occur due to chance.

23. Assuming twenty-three degrees of freedom, give the value of χ^2 which separates the critical region from the noncritical region in tests for which (a) $\alpha = .01$, (b) $\alpha = .05$, (c) $\alpha = .075$.

24. A sign test using samples of size 12 is to be designed to test the hypotheses

    H_0: There is no difference between the observed distribution and the binomial distribution with $n = 12$ and $P(+) = .4$.
    H_1: H_0 is false.

    (a) Make a table of cumulative binomial probabilities for the test. [*Note:* Recall that the term following $C(n, r)p^{n-r}q^r$ can be obtained by multiplying this term by $\dfrac{(n - r)q}{(r + 1)p}$.]

    (b) If a two-tailed test using $\alpha = .30$ is used, what will be the noncritical numbers of pluses?

    (c) If high numbers of plus signs are to be placed in a one-tailed critical region of size .30, what will the critical numbers of pluses be?

Epilogue

An Index of Formulas and Symbols

Answers to Problems

Appendix Tables

Indexes

EPILOGUE

THE STUDENT must not lose sight of the fact that all of the knowledge of the statistical method he has so far acquired has now brought him to the point of grasping the logic and procedures of inductive inference employed by the behavioral scientist. Understanding the needs and methods for organizing the data into frequency distributions and describing these distributions in terms of central tendency and variability were fundamental and necessary steps preliminary to the direct attack on the problem of induction. Equally fundamental was the understanding of the importance of the concept of randomness, models of randomness, and the fact that the random sampling distributions of certain statistics take the form of the normal probability curve. Understanding of all these ideas is prerequisite to understanding how it is possible to generalize, to make an inductive inference from those individuals observed in the sample to those not observed in the population from which the sample was drawn, despite the variability among the subjects.

It may now be seen, for example, that the concept of the arithmetic mean and the standard deviation have implications far beyond those outlined in Part I—and, indeed, far beyond any imagined by the layman. The fact that the random sampling distributions of the mean and proportion and other statistics are known, and that some of these statistics are normally or nearly normally distributed around the true value in the population, is of fundamental importance because it thus becomes possible to apply all our knowledge of randomness and the normal probability model to the occurrence of sample statistics. Such knowledge also makes it possible to state what the probability is of any sample statistic approximating the parameter within a given distance. This, of course, is the achievement we have been aiming for.

The student may well say: "Enough of this guesswork. I'm not interested in the fact that the probability is .95 that the sample proportion is within $\pm 1.96\sigma_p$ of the true proportion. I want to know what the true proportion really is!" The answer to that is—the guesswork is here to stay. It is true, of course, that the statistical method merely provides us with a statement that begins "the probability is . . . ," but that is all that can be done. And, in principle, *that is all that ever will be done.* So long as the inductive inference is based on random sampling procedures, it will always involve probability, and, therefore, inductive inferences will begin with "the probability is . . . ." But, as Krech and Crutchfield put it, "The scientist is a gambling man. He has no choice."

This, of course, is a serious matter. The search for certainty should never be lightly given up, and the student is urged to examine critically all sides of this matter. Let the student ask himself why we must forego certainty in our inductive inferences, and let him weigh carefully these replies. The statisticians' reply is to the effect that certainty can be obtained only at the cost of examining *all* instances. And the behavioral scientist's reply is that it is impossible to examine *all* instances. Sampling is absolutely necessary and unavoidable, and sampling will involve error.

If this were the end of the story, it could hardly be termed a happy ending. But it is not the end. Sampling does involve error, of course, but *random* sampling involves only *random* error, and, as we have seen, there is at hand considerable knowledge about the behavior of random phenomena. It is this knowledge which permits the calculation of the relative frequencies of random errors of various sizes. And this is what we need to make our guesses—guesses, it is true, but very special ones. These guesses are rigorously derived and they are *quantified.* Thus, when the hypothesis of no effect is rejected at the 5 per cent level of significance, the risk in rejecting it is quantified. The point is that we *know* what the risk is. And, because of the necessity for sampling, no more can be done—at least until a new method of making inductive inferences is discovered. The probability of this occurring seems small indeed.

AN INDEX OF FORMULAS
AND SYMBOLS

FORMULAS AND SYMBOLS	DESCRIPTIVE AND EXPLANATORY NOTES	CHAPTER AND PAGES WHERE DEFINITION OR DERIVATION IS FOUND
$\dfrac{1}{n}\sum(X+c)=\bar{X}+c$	The addition of a fixed constant to each datum changes the mean by the same additive constant	3; 91–2
$\dfrac{1}{n}\sum kX=k\bar{X}$	The multiplication of each datum by a fixed constant changes the mean by the same fixed factor	3; 92
$\bar{X}=C_e+\dfrac{I}{n}\sum_{i=1}^{h}\dfrac{(C_i-C_e)f_i}{I}$	The mean for grouped data: C_e is the class interval estimated to contain the mean; the C_i are the several class interval midpoints; the f_i are the class frequencies; I is the class interval length; h is the number of class intervals	3; 95
$m=\dfrac{n_1\bar{X}_1+n_2\bar{X}_2}{n_1+n_2}$	The combining of the means of two samples to form the mean of the combined sample	3; 95
$\bar{X}=\dfrac{\sum n_i\bar{X}_i}{\sum n_i}$	The combining of the means of k samples to form the mean of the combined sample	3; 96
$\mu=np$	The mean of the binomial distribution of n trials and probability p	7; 279
$\sum(X_i-\bar{X})=0$	The sum of the mean deviations is always 0	3; 97
$\sum(X_i-\bar{X})^2$ as a minimum	No other number in place of $\bar{X}$ in this sum will produce as low a sum	3; 98
$R=X_{max}-X_{min}$	The range is the largest datum less the least datum	4; 114

FORMULAS AND SYMBOLS	DESCRIPTIVE AND EXPLANATORY NOTES	CHAPTER AND PAGES WHERE DEFINITION OR DERIVATION IS FOUND

Mean deviation

$$MD = \frac{1}{n}\sum|X_i - \bar{X}|$$

The mean deviation is the mean of the absolute values of the deviations of the data from the mean   4; 116

$$\frac{2(Mn - R)}{R(n - 2)}$$

A formula for comparing a mean deviation with the extremities of its range: R is the range of the data, and M is the mean deviation   4; Box 15

Standard deviation

$$s = \sqrt{\frac{1}{n}\sum(X_i - \bar{X})^2}$$

The sample standard deviation   4; 120

$$s = \sqrt{\frac{1}{n}\sum X^2 - \bar{X}^2}$$

A simplified form of the sample standard deviation   4; 123–4

$$s = \frac{1}{n}\sqrt{n\sum X^2 - (\sum X)^2}$$

A computational form of the sample standard deviation   4; 125

$$s = \frac{1}{n}\sqrt{n\sum_{i=1}^{h}f_i d_i^2 - \left(\sum_{i=1}^{h}f_i d_i\right)^2}$$

A computational form of the sample standard deviation for grouped data: h is the number of class intervals, the f_i are the class interval frequencies, and the d_i are the class interval midpoints   4; 128

$$s = \sqrt{\frac{n^2 - 1}{12}}$$

The standard deviation of the first n consecutive integers   6; 213

$$s_{X+k} = s_X$$

Adding a fixed constant to each datum does not change the standard deviation   4; 126

FORMULAS AND SYMBOLS	DESCRIPTIVE AND EXPLANATORY NOTES	CHAPTER AND PAGES WHERE DEFINITION OR DERIVATION IS FOUND
$s_{kX} = ks_X$	Multiplying each datum by a fixed constant has the same effect on the standard deviation	4; 126
$\dfrac{R}{\sqrt{2n}} \le s \le \dfrac{R}{2}$	Bounds in terms of the range R exist for the standard deviation	4; 130
$s^2 = \dfrac{1}{n}\Sigma(X - \bar{X})$	The variance is the square of the standard deviation	4; 123
$s_e = s_Y\sqrt{1 - r^2}$	The standard error of estimate: r is the Pearson product moment correlation coefficient	6; 222
$s_p = \sqrt{\dfrac{pq}{n}}$	The standard error of a proportion: p is the probability that a given trial will fall into the proportion of interest	8; 319
$\sigma_m = \dfrac{\sigma}{\sqrt{n}}$	The standard error of the mean	8; 311
$s_X = \dfrac{s}{\sqrt{n}}$	The sample standard error of the mean	8; 313
$\sigma_d = \sqrt{\sigma_{\bar{X}}^2 + \sigma_{\bar{Y}}^2}$	The standard error of the difference between two means: d denotes $\bar{X} - \bar{Y}$	8; 316
$\sigma_d = \sqrt{\dfrac{\sigma_X^2}{n_X} + \dfrac{\sigma_Y^2}{n_Y}}$	An alternative form of the standard error of the difference between two means: d denotes $\bar{X} - \bar{Y}$	8; 316
$\sigma_d = \dfrac{\sqrt{2\sigma}}{\sqrt{n}}$	The special case of the standard error of the difference between two means taken from samples of equal size and equal standard deviations	8; 317
$\sigma = \sqrt{npq}$	The standard deviation of a binomial distribution of n trials and probability p	7; 279

		CHAPTER
		AND PAGES
		WHERE
		DEFINITION
		OR
	DESCRIPTIVE AND	DERIVATION
FORMULAS AND SYMBOLS	EXPLANATORY NOTES	IS FOUND

$$r = \frac{\sum X_i Y_i - n\bar{X}\bar{Y}}{n s_X s_Y}$$

A computational form of the Pearson product moment correlation coefficient 6; 208

$$r = \frac{n\sum X_i Y_i - (\sum X_i)(\sum Y_i)}{\sqrt{[n\sum X_i^2 - (\sum X_i)^2][n\sum Y_i^2 - (\sum Y_i)^2]}}$$

A computational form of the Pearson product moment correlation coefficient 6; 209

$$r = \frac{\sqrt{s_Y^2 - s_e^2}}{s_Y}$$

The Pearson product moment correlation coefficient in terms of the variance of Y and the standard error of estimate 6; 225

$$r = 1 - \frac{6\sum d^2}{n(n^2 - 1)}$$

The rank-order correlation coefficient in terms of the rank differences d 6; 183, 186,214

$$r = \frac{12\sum X_i Y_i}{n(n^2 - 1)} - \frac{3(n + 1)}{n - 1}$$

The rank-order correlation coefficient in terms of the basic data 6; 213

$$Y' = r\frac{s_Y}{s_X}(X - \bar{X}) + \bar{Y}$$

The regression equation of Y on X in terms of the basic data 6; 219

$$Y' = r \cdot \frac{s_Y}{s_X}x$$

The regression equation of Y on X in terms of the deviations x from the mean 6; 219

$$\text{Tan } \theta = \frac{1 - r^2}{r} \cdot \frac{s_X s_Y}{s_X^2 + s_Y^2}$$

The tangent of the angle between the two regression lines of a distribution 6; 221

$$\bar{e} = 0$$

The mean of the estimates obtained with the regression equation is 0 6; 223

FORMULAS AND SYMBOLS	DESCRIPTIVE AND EXPLANATORY NOTES	CHAPTER AND PAGES WHERE DEFINITION OR DERIVATION IS FOUND
$A \cap B$	The intersection of two sets	7; 253
$m(A \cup B) = m(A) + m(B) - m(A \cap B)$	The measure of the union of two sets	7; 255
$m(A \cup B \cup C) = m(A) + m(B)$ $+ m(C) - m(A \cap B) - m(A \cap C) -$ $m(B \cap C) + m(A \cap B \cap C)$	The measure of the union of three sets	7; 255
$P(E) = \dfrac{m(E)}{m(I)}$	The probability of the event E in terms of its measure	7; 258
$P(E \cup F) = P(E) + P(F) - P(E \cap F)$	The probability of the event E or F	7; 260
$P(E \cup F) = P(E) + P(F)$	The probability of the event E or F when E and F are disjoint	7; 260
$P(E \cup F) = P(E) + P(F) - P(E)\,P(F|E)$	The probability of the event E or F in terms of the conditional probability of F	7; 263
$P(E \cap F) = P(E)P(F|E)$	The probability that both E and F will occur	7; 262–3

ANSWERS TO PROBLEMS

ANSWERS, hints, and references to aid in the solution of problems. Numbers in parentheses refer to some, but not necessarily all, of the pages on which relevant material is found.

CHAPTER 1

1. "The sun rises in the east" is a generalization about facts—the many observed sunrises. Ohm's Law (Voltage equals current times resistance: $E = IR$) is a generalization about relations between electromotive force, current, and resistance.
2. (5)
3. (6)
4. (5–9)
5. The observations support his conjecture. Consider the simpler conjecture, "All blondes in this class are married," which may be tested either by recording the marital status of every blonde or by recording the hair color of every unmarried student.
6. (8–9)
7. (a) Test the statement with $n = 1, 2, 3, 4, 5$, and 6.
   (b) The formula does produce a prime for $n = 0, 1, 2, \ldots, 79$, but for $n = 80$, the result is $1681 = 41^2$. The statement is thus false.
8. (10–14)
9. (15–16)
10. (a) 23   (b) 11   (c) 0   (17)
11. (a) b may be any number if c is positive and a is a positive fraction less than one.
    (b) b and c may be any numbers if $a = 1$.
    (c) b may be any number if c is positive and a exceeds 1   (18).
12. (a) 54   (b) 62   (18)

13. $\sqrt{(-6)^2} = \sqrt{36} = 6$. Note that $\sqrt{n}$ means the principle (positive) square root of n (19).

14. If $a = 2$ and $b = 1$, the numerical equivalents for the 5 members shown are -6, -6, -6, 0, and 0. Hence the error is in the third line (21).

15. Squares never end in numbers such as 26 or 75 which when divided by 4 leave remainders of 2 or 3. No square can end in 2 or 8. Thus 5476 is the only one not eliminated. If 5476 is a square, it must be the square of a number between 70 and 80 and it must end in 4 or 6 (21).

16. The apparently smaller increment leads to an income of $50 per year more than the other.

17. (a) 8 (b) -16 (c) 19 (d) 9.2 (e) -6 (21–2)

18. (a) 53 (b) 74 (c) 169 (22–3)

19. 119 (23–6)

20. 119 (23–6)

21. 119 (23–6)

22. (23–6)

24. 277

25. 184

26. (a) $3\frac{7}{3}$ (b) $4\frac{1}{18}$

27. 173 (24)

28. 13 (24)

29. 288 (24)

30. (a) 94 (b) 526 (c) 71

31. All three expressions are identical for all integers $n \geq 1$.

32. 320, $\frac{4}{5}$ or .8 (27–8)

33. 400 (28)

34. (28)

36. $5 (28)

37. An increase from $16\frac{2}{3}$ per cent of the present value 30 (28).

38. (a) $\frac{1}{4}$ (b) $\frac{1}{13}$ (c) $\frac{3}{13}$ (d) $\frac{5}{26}$ (e) $\frac{5}{26}$ (28)

39. $\frac{4}{15}$ (28)

CHAPTER 2

1. Nominal, Ordinal, Interval, Ratio (35–40).

2. Ratio.

3. The minimum (0) and maximum (20) scores could not be used for

comparison purposes if an interval scale is used (40). The relative differences between scores may not be used except to establish rank order if an ordinal scale is used (37). Scores may be used only to categorize as "pass" or "fail," or as "good," "fair," or "poor" if a nominal scale is used (35–6).

4. Which runners placed better than fourth? Who won?
5. The time for each contestant would permit the use of a ratio scale.
6. It is an ordinal scale.
7. (a) Ratio scale—there is an absolute zero.
   (b) Interval scale—no absolute zero exists.
   (c) Interval scale.
8. (a) It could be an ordinal, interval, or ratio scale according to the use to which the grades are put. The ordinal scale has the best justification for use here.
   (b) Ordinal scale.
   (c) (37–9)
9. (a) Consider the values of monetary units in 1932 and 1952 (39).
   (b) Ratio scale.
   (c) Ratio scales may be used if a standard (constant value) monetary unit is used.
10. An interval scale replaces an ordinal scale (39).
11. (43–4)
12. (44–5)
13. The formula has no meaning if L or W are negative (45–7).
14. If L is "cost per item" and W is "number of items," then A is "total cost." Let L denote "principal" and W denote "rate of interest" (46).
15. (47–9)
16. (49–55)
17. The second and eighth are discrete; the others are continuous (51–4).
18. Find the height of the midpoint of the segment joining the tops of the bars for B and C (54–6).
19. (a) If the first interval is 99–95, then the 16 class frequencies are 1, 2, 5, 2, 2, 7, 6, 6, 5, 5, 4, 4, 3, 1, 1, 1.
    If the first interval is 98–94, then the 16 class frequencies are 1, 2, 6, 3, 3, 8, 5, 6, 3, 5, 4, 5, 2, 1, 1, 1.
    If the first interval is 97–93, then the 16 class frequencies are 2, 2, 5, 3, 4, 8, 7, 4, 2, 5, 5, 5, 1, 1, 1, 1.
    If the first interval is 96–92, then the 16 class frequencies are 3, 3, 4, 3, 4, 8, 7, 3, 2, 6, 6, 3, 1, 2, 0, 1.

    (b) The first interval must be 96–90. The 11 class frequencies are 3, 6, 4, 10, 9, 5, 5, 7, 4, 2, 1.

    (c) If the first interval is 99–96, then the 20 class frequencies are 1, 2, 1, 5, 2, 2, 4, 7, 4, 4, 5, 0, 5, 4, 4, 2, 1, 1, 1, 1.

        If the first interval is 98–95, then the 20 class frequencies are 1, 2, 3, 3, 3, 1, 7, 5, 6, 3, 3, 3, 3, 4, 4, 2, 1, 1, 0, 1.

        If the first interval is 97–94, then the 20 class frequencies are 1, 2, 3, 4, 2, 3, 5, 6, 6, 3, 2, 5, 1, 6, 3, 1, 1, 1, 0, 1.

        If the first interval is 96–93, then the 20 class frequencies are 2, 1, 5, 2, 3, 3, 7, 3, 6, 3, 2, 5, 4, 3, 3, 1, 1, 1, 0, 1.

20. If the first interval is 56.5–52.5, then the 13 class frequencies are 2, 3, 4, 4, 5, 6, 8, 5, 3, 3, 2, 2, 1.

    If the first interval is 55.5–51.5, then the 13 class frequencies are 2, 4, 4, 5, 4, 7, 7, 5, 2, 4, 1, 2, 1.

    If the first interval is 54.5–50.5, then the 13 class frequencies are 4, 4, 2, 6, 6, 5, 7, 4, 4, 2, 2, 1, 1.

21. (a) The frequencies are identical with those of problem 20 if the intervals used are those of problem 20 with each interval endpoint divided by 10.

    (b) The first interval is 5.4–4.9 and the class frequencies are 5, 4, 6, 7, 8, 7, 3, 4, 2, 2   (58).

22. (59–62)

23. (62–3)

CHAPTER 3

1. Note that the mean of 15, 18, and 20 is $17\frac{2}{3}$ which is also the mean of 1, 3, and 49   (82–83).

2. (73–4, 86–7)

3. (72–4, 83)

4. (72, 75, 83)

5. Construct examples similar to the one given here to assist in the formulation of your answer (79–83).

    (a) 1, 2, 50, 51, 56   (b) 10, 30, 60, 90, 110   (c) 1, 3, 6, 10, 100

6. (a) Mean and median are equal to 2.

    (b) Mean is 6.76; median is 6   (77).

7. 2, 4, 6, 8, 10 is symmetric with respect to the mean and median, 6. Change 10 to 8 and 4 to 6, and check the new mean and median. Other examples may be constructed.

8. The examples constructed for problem 5 should be of help here (83).
9. Two ones added to the set 2, 5, 6, 9, 13, and 19 gives a set of 8 numbers whose mean is 7. Twelve sixes instead of 2 ones are needed. The reduction is impossible using sevens.
10. (85)
11. 51, 63. No single mode exists when two data have the maximal frequency. Such distributions are *bimodal*.
12. C (87)
13. 32.64 (88)
14. .6
15. $\frac{3}{13}$
16. The groups are analogous to class intervals.
17. If 1–9 and 1–11 provide an insufficient basis for a conjecture, try also 1–13 inclusive, 1–15 inclusive, and so on until the pattern of results becomes obvious.
18. 1–14 inclusive, 1–16 inclusive, and so on provide further information on which to base a conjecture.
19. 62.29
20. If the first interval is 56.5–52.5, then $p_1 = 54.5$, and $f_1 = 2$. The subscript i will assume 12 additional values.
21. f_i is the ith class frequency and p_i is the ith class mark or interval midpoint.
22. If the first class interval is 56.5–52.5, the mean is 32.75.
    If the first class interval is 55.5–51.5, the mean is 32.58.
    If the first class interval is 54.5–50.5, the mean is 32.67.
23. (a) 3.28, 3.26, or 3.27 according to whether the first class interval is 5.65–5.25, 5.55–5.15, or 5.45–5.05.
    (b) 32.33
24. (91)
25. (90)
26. If actual ages are not conveniently available, invent a set of ages.
27. $\frac{3}{4}$
28. 60
29. (92–3)
30. 32.75, 32.58, or 32.67 according to whether the first class interval is 56.5–52.5, 55.5–51.5, or 54.5–50.5.
31. (a) 3.28, 3.26, or 3.27 according to whether the first class interval is 5.65–5.25, 5.55–5.15, or 5.45–5.05.
    (b) 32.33

32. 9.03
33. Greater by .196   (95–7).
34. Equal—each is 28.75   (95–7).
35. Less by .196 (95–7).
36. $\bar{X} = 8.$ $8 - (-8) = 16$ is the deviation of -8 from the mean.
37. 675   (97–9)
38. 675   (97–9)
39. 670   (97–9)
40. The first two steps are
$$\{(2 - A)^2 + (5 - A)^2 + (6 - A)^2\}$$
$$= \{(4 - 4A + A^2) + (25 - 10A + A^2) + (36 - 12A + A^2)\}$$
$$= \{(4 + 25 + 36) + (-4A - 10A - 12A) + (A^2 + A^2 + A^2)\}$$

CHAPTER 4

1. 3, 6, 9, 11, 16. There are endless other ways to accomplish the result.
2. 3, 6, 10, 12, 14. See No. 1.
3. 4, 7, 10, 13, 16 is one solution. 3, 10, 11, 12, 15 is another among many possible solutions.
4. 2, 4, 6, 7, 14 is one solution. -2, 1, 4, 7, 10 is another among many possible solutions.
5. -100, -50, -20, 110, 260 and 1, 2, 3, 4, 190 are two out of many possible answers.
6. 38, 39, 40, 41, 42 and 38.5, 39.7, 40.1, 40.3, 41.4 are two out of many possible answers.
7. There are many such schedules. For example, 6 salary levels 7, 8, 9, 10, 11, and 12 thousand dollars may be used with 4, 8, 11, 50, 15, and 12 employees respectively. Another such schedule has 3 salary levels: 7,500, 10,000, and 12,500 dollars with 1, 98, and 1 employees respectively. Each of these has a $10,000 mean and a range of $5,000. If one man receives $100,000 and each of 450 employees receives $2,000, the mean is $10,000 and the range is $92,000. Another example is 4, 8, 11, 50, 15, and 12 people working for $100,000, $10,000, $8,000, $7,260, $3,000, and $2,000, respectively (109).
8. Contrast these with $4.02 and $1,505 and consider the ranges that are relevant here.
9. The answer here lies in the nature of absolute values and principal square roots.
10. (113–14)

11. 0
12. 8.32
13. 13.12 (114–17)
14. Columns similar to 6 and 7 in Table 22 must be added to Table 16 to complete the computation 12.86 (118–20).
15. All are doubled.
16. All are multiplied by k.
17. $\sqrt{.1\sum(8.8 - X)^2} = \sqrt{109.56} = 10.47$
18. $\sqrt{8.25} = 2.87$
19. Try 3 and 4; 7 and 8; 105 and 106. Make a conjecture.
20. (109–10, 120–2)
21. (122)
22. The standard deviation is never more than half the range (26). For data between 80 and 100 the standard deviation cannot be more than 10.
23. (123)
24. $14\frac{4}{9}$ for both lines.
25. $\sqrt{.025\sum X^2 - 40.1^2} = 10.57$
26. $.025\sqrt{40\sum X^2 - (\sum X)^2} = \frac{1}{40}\sqrt{178624} = 10.57$
27. (125)
28. $s = 3.16.$ $c = -50$ is a good choice.
29. $s = 15.80.$ $c = \frac{1}{5}$ is a good choice.
30. $s = 15.07.$ Multiplying by $\frac{1}{4}$ and adding -5 is a good choice.
31. (126)
32. 5.74 (126–7)
33. A seventh column (column 4 times column 6) is required in Table 16 to complete the computation (127–9). $s = .06\sqrt{76900 - 81} = 16.63.$
34. The first interval is 69–71 and the frequencies are 4, 4, 6, 9, 8, 10, 10, 9, 5, 5, 3, 3, 2, 1, 0, 0, 1. $\sum f_i p_i = 49$ and $\sum f_i p_i^2 = 899.$ $s = 9.89$ (127–9).
35. (126–7)
36. Use Theorem 1 (126).
37. First apply Theorem 2 and then Theorem 1 (126–7).
38. Use problem 35.
39. Similar to problem 37.
40. (a) 2.5, 25 (b) 20, 100 (c) $\frac{\sqrt{2}}{2}, \frac{\sqrt{n}}{2}$ (130–1)
41. The differences are $.112R$, $.035R$, and $.001R$, respectively.
42. For the first set, $4.24 \le s \le 30$; and for the second set, $3.95 \le s \le$

25. The first s is 15 out of a possible 25.76 points from its maximum. The second s is 15 points out of a possible 21.05 points from its maximum. Hence the first s is highest in its range of variability.

43. .3989, 3.989, .0399

44. Some examples are $y = \dfrac{1}{x^2}, y = \dfrac{1}{x^3}, y = \dfrac{8}{x^2 + 4}$.

45. .13 if interpolation is not used. Interpolating for more accuracy gives .126.

46. .25, .39, .52, .67, .84, 1.04, 1.28, 1.65 without interpolation, and .253, .385, .524, .674, .841, 1.037, 1.282, 1.645 with interpolation.

47. 5.10, 7.32, 8.76, 9.96, 10.98, 11.88, 12.66, 13.50, 14.22, 15.78, 16.50, 17.34, 18.12, 19.02, 20.04, 21.24, 22.68, and 24.90 if interpolation was not used to get the z's.

48. 38.3 per cent or 57.45 of the numbers should lie in the interval. Actually, the 59 numbers from 76 to 118 inclusive lie in this range (132–6).

49. The expected values are 23.79, 46.62, 67.74, 86.43, 102.39, 115.47, 125.76, 133.56, and 141.39 while the actual values are 24, 46, 68, 86, 101, 111, 121, 130, and 141 respectively (132–6).

50. The indices of dispersion in January and May were respectively .9875 and .8667. Hence more variability was present in January (136–42).

51. .9875 for January and .7428 in May, and hence more variability in January (136–42).

52. A — .93, B — .99, C — .75   (136–42)

CHAPTER 5

1. (148–50)

2. (a) An absolute zero would exist for altitude if it were measured from the center of the earth but not otherwise.

   (b) No absolute zero exists for velocity since velocity may be negative with no known bound.

   (c) and (d) have absolute zeros while (e) does not.

3. (161)

4. (a) is false and (b) is true (150–4).

5. (a) Consider the numbers 1, 2, 3, 4, 5, 6, 7, 8, 9, 17, 18, 19, 20, and 21. Use the formula for p_k to compute p_{60} and p_{61}. Then compute the mean and compare.

   (b) (162)

     (c) Make your point by constructing an example similar to that used in part (a).

     (d) Yes, always (162).

6. Use the example in the answer to 5(a) to suggest the kind of distributions needed.

7. Consider which test allows the best chance for high rank.

8. A zero score could be in the 90th percentile if a sufficient number of other scores are negative.

9. (159–60)

10. (a) 76th percentile.

     (b) The values of the mean and standard deviation are not needed.

11. (166–7)

12. (a) $.08X_{21} + .92X_{22} = 41.76$ (b) 40.26   (c) 40.5

13. (a) 13   (b) 32   (c) 87   (d) 93   (160–1)

14. $p_{10} = X_{8.5} = 74.5$. The second to ninth decile points are in order 78.5, 81, 84, 86, 88, 91, 95, 99.5   (160–1).

15. $\dfrac{38 - 71.99}{15.72} = -2.16$ is the first one (164–5).

16. (a) English   (b) .25, .70, and $-.48$, respectively.

17. $\dfrac{25}{15.72}(51 - 71.99) + 50 = 16.62$ is the first one (168–9).

18. $\bar{X} = 54.56$, $s = 7.47$. $Y = \dfrac{10}{7.47}(X - 54.56) + 70$. The series of standard scores begins with 47.83 and ends with 83.98.

19. $X = 50.72$, $s = 6.11$. Hence it is necessary to solve the equations

$$\frac{s}{6.11}(38 - 50.72) + m = 50$$

$$\frac{s}{6.11}(59 - 50.72) + m = 99$$

for s and m in order to answer the question.

20. $m = 29.68$, $s = 14.26$

CHAPTER 6

1. (226, 7)

2. (226, 7)

3. Consider the correlation between 1, 2, 3, 4, 5, and 4, 3, 2, 1, 5, respectively.

4. The ordinal scale (first, second, third, . . .) is such a scale. The ce-

phalic index (100 times the ratio of head width to length) is without units. Most index numbers are designed to have this property.

5. (179–82)

6. 24 rankings are possible. $\sum d^2$ starts at 0 for 1 2 3 4 and takes on all even values up to 20 (some repeated). The ranking 4 3 2 1 has the maximum (20).

7. r appears to decrease with increasing n due to the factor $\dfrac{1}{n^2 - 1}$. This is false, however, since the mean of the squared differences increases with N, and the two variations offset one another.

8. 1, 2.5, 2.5, 4, 5 (214)

9. 1, 2.5, 2.5, 5, 5, 5, 7, 8, 9.5, 9.5   (214)

10. -89

11. The z-scores for 2, 5, and 10 are -1.11, $-.20$, and 1.31. The z-scores for 3, 5, and 8 are -1.14, $-.16$, and 1.30. The various values of r are 1.00, .70, .27, $-.47$, $-.53$, and $-.97$ (189, 207).

12. (200)

13. Consider whether or not a causal relationship may exist where $r_p = 0$. If experimental variables are well controlled, the question of causation is more easily handled.

14. (201, 203)

15. $\bar{X} = 8$, $\bar{Y} = 6$ (201–4)

16. $s_X = 2.76$, $s_Y = 1.90$ (201–7)

17. (206, 207)

18. $r = .23$

19. Multiply the factors of the general term and apply the three properties of the $\sum$ symbol. A good form to aim for is that of problem 20.

20. $r = .23$

21. $r = .23$

22. Use the sums given in the text.

24. .38

25. This interchange raises $\sum d^2$ from 424 to 736. Then $r = -.08$.

26. (215)

27. $r_{RJ} = .1$, $r_{RT} = .1$, $r_{JT} = -.7$

28. (202)

29. Consider the results of problems 27 and 28.

30. $Y = \frac{5}{4}x - 2$ or $5x - 4y = 8$ (216–18)

31. $30x + 10y = 53$ (216–18)

32. Use the calculations in Table 37 to get $Y' = .567X + 46.296$.

33. $X' = .496Y + 50.567$
34. (219–20)
35. The problem is equivalent to setting $\sqrt{1 - r^2} = \frac{1}{3}$ and solving for r.
    $$r = \frac{2\sqrt{2}}{3} = .94$$
36. $\pm.5$
37. Let N increase and consider the effect on r and s_y upon which s_e depends for its value.
38. Substitute x and y for $(X - \bar{X})$ and $(Y - \bar{Y})$ respectively throughout the derivation (224).
39. (200, 225–6)

CHAPTER 7

1. The question may be answered by analyzing the procedure to determine whether or not any digit or digits are favored over others. It may also be answered empirically by producing two or three hundred digits and comparing their frequencies. This data will be useful in problem 2.
2. (238)
3. (a) $f(\frac{1}{2}) = \frac{11}{16}$ (b) $f(\frac{1}{6}) = \frac{19}{144}$ (c) $f(\frac{1}{3}) = \frac{11}{27}$
5. (a) The first interval in terms of standard deviations from the mean is -3 to -2. Appendix Table A gives the answer. .0214 (b) .1360 (c) .3413 (d) .3413 (e) .1360 (f) .0214 (246–8)
6. (246)
7. Larger than $40 + 1.28(10) = 52.8$.
8. If S, M, and P represent, respectively, the sets of sculptors, musicians, and finger painters, then the best answer is $S \cup M \cup P$ (255).
9. $\{7, 8, 10, 11, 13, 14\}$ (252)
10. $A \cup B = \{2, 4, 6, 7, 8, 10, 11, 12, 13, 14, 16\}$, $A \cap B = \{8, 10, 14\}$ (252–3)
11. ϕ (252–3)
12. (a) 10, (b) 16, (c) 0, (d) 6 (252–3)
13. (a) 1, 2, 3, 4, 5, 6 (b) 2, 5 (c) 1, 2, 3, 4, 5, 6, 7 (d) 1, 2, 3, 4, 5, 6, 7 (e) 5 (f) 5 (g) 1, 2, 4, 5, 6 (h) 2, 4, 5 (253–4)
14. 12 (255)
15. 21 (255)
16. Let R, A, and H denote the 3 sets of students referred to in the prob-

lem and consider the measures of these sets, their unions, and their intersections. The result is 10.

17. (252)

18. After $m([A \cup B] \cup C)$ has been expanded according to the theorem, it will be necessary to apply the theorem again to the expression $m[A \cup B]$.

19. (a) Assign a weight of 1 to each ticket holder.
    (b) Assign a weight equal to the number of tickets held.
    (c) Assign a weight of 1 for each $\frac{1}{3}$ share of a ticket.

20. (a) HHT and THH are different elements of the outcome space (256).
    (b) $E = \{HHT, HTH, THH\}, m(E) = 3$ (257–8)
    (c) $E = \{HHH, HHT, HTH, THH\}, m(E) = 4$ (257–8)
    (d) $E = \{HHT, HTH, THH, TTH, THT, HTT, TTT\}, m(E) = 7$ (257–8)
    (e) The measure of the outcome space in part (a) is 8. Hence the measures of the complements are obtained by subtracting each measure from 8.

21. (b) $\frac{3}{8}$ (c) $\frac{1}{2}$ (d) $\frac{7}{8}$ (258–9)

22. Note that $m(E') = m(I) - m(E)$ and that E' is the set of all elements in the outcome space I which are not in the set E.

23. (a) Jack, queen, and king of spades. (b) All the spades and all the face cards. (c) $P(S \cap F) = \frac{3}{52}$ (d) $P(S \cup F) = \frac{11}{26}$ (259–64)

24. $\frac{5}{13}$

25. (a) $(\frac{1}{5})(\frac{28}{59}) = \frac{28}{295} = .095$ (b) $(\frac{7}{15})(\frac{12}{59}) = .095$ (c) (264)

26. (a) .12   (b) $(1 - .3)(1 - .4) = .42$ (c) $.3(1 - .4) = .18$ (d) .28 (259, 265)

27. (a) $P(R \cup F) = .088$ (260)   (b) $P(R \cap F) = .002$ (263)

28. .40

29. (a) $S_b = \{bacd, badc, bcad, bcda, bdac, bdca\}$. The other sets are similarly constructed.
    (b) $S_{bd} = \{bdac, bdca\}$
    (c) $S_{bdc} = \{bdca\}$ (268–9)

30. (a) $n - r + 1 = 8$
    (b) The smallest factor is 17   (269).

31. (a) $6! = 120$
    (b) Think of two of the books as being tied together to form "one book." Then the result is $5! = 120$ for each of the two ways the two books can be tied together. Hence 240   (269–70).

32. $C(9, 4) = 126$ (271)

33. 210 (271–2)
35. (273)
36. The coefficient of $p^{14}q^{11}$ in $(p + q)^{25}$ is required (273).
37. (274)
38. Note that r is the summation variable here and runs over 10 values.
39. (a) $P(4$ or less$) = \frac{2}{3}$ and $P(5$ or more$) = \frac{1}{3}$. The result is given by the term $C(10, 3)(\frac{2}{3})^3(\frac{1}{3})^7$
    (b) $\frac{896}{6561} = .137$
    (c) .120
40. (a) $\dfrac{64 - 68}{2.5} = -1.6$ (b) 2.4 (c) .4452 (d) .4918 (e) .9370 (279–80)
41. Taller than 72.90 inches.
42. (a) 68.26 per cent, (b) 38.30 per cent, (c) 53.28 per cent, (d) 53.28 per cent, (e) 91.04 per cent, (f) 49.51 per cent, (g) 95.00 per cent, (h) 95.44 per cent

CHAPTER 8

1. (287–9)
2. (289–91)
3. (287–92)
4. If actual data are not available, invent fictitious data.
5. (294, 307–8)
6. (311–12)
7. Use the results of problems 5 and 6.
8. Compare your results here and in problem 7 with the percentages obtained from Appendix Table A.
13. (a) 1.28 (b) 1.65 (c) 2.58
14. (a) 4 (b) 9 (c) 16 (d) 100
17. (297–9, 313–14, 319–20)
18. (a) $10 + 20 + \ldots + 70 = 280$
    (b) $28 + 56 + 84 + 112 = 280$
    (c) $4 + 8 + \ldots + 28 + 3 + 6 + \ldots + 21 + 2 + 4 + \ldots$
    $+ 14 + 1 + 2 + \ldots + 7 = 280$
19. Note that there are $C(6, 3) = 20$ samples of size 3 possible. The 20 samples have means ranging from $\frac{20}{3}$ to $\frac{40}{3}$. The mean of the means is 10.
20. The sample variance for the sample $\{5, 7, 8\}$ is
    $$s^2 = \frac{1}{3}(25 + 49 + 64) - [\frac{1}{3}(5 + 7 + 8)]^2 = \frac{14}{9}; \quad \sigma^2 = \frac{38}{3}$$

and σ_m^2 is the variance of the 20 means considered in problem 19 and is $38\frac{8}{15}$ (307–10).

21.   By a factor of $\frac{1}{4}$ (310).

22.   By factors of $\frac{1}{9}$, $\frac{1}{19}$, and $\frac{1}{49}$, respectively (310).

23.   The interval $\mu \pm 1.65\sigma_m$ contains 90 per cent of all sample means for samples of size n. Hence solve for n in $1.65\sigma_m = 1.65\dfrac{\sigma}{\sqrt{n}} = 1.2$. The result is 48   (312–13).

24. $n = 67$ for 95 per cent and $n = 116$ for 99 per cent (312–13).

25. $P(64.73 < \mu < 71.27) = .95$ (313)

26.   (a) $P(65.55 < \mu < 70.45) = .95$ (b) $P(66.04 < \mu < 69.96)$
      (c) $P(67.02 < \mu < 68.98) = .95$ (313)

27. $P(63.7 < \mu < 72.3) = .99$ (313)

28.   (a) $P(64.78 < \mu < 71.23) = .99$ (b) $P(65.42 < \mu < 70.58) = .99$
      (c) $P(66.71 < \mu < 69.29) = .99$

29.   (312–13)

30.   (314)

31.   (a) 2.60, (b) 1.72, (c) 2.63

32.   Consider what happens to the value of $\sqrt{a^2 + b^2}$ as a or b tends toward zero. The relation $(a + b)^2 = a^2 + 2ab + b^2$ should be helpful.

33.   2.71

34.   (317)

35.   .27

36.   The proportion of heads in a cast will be .04 times the number of heads appearing. The mean and standard deviation of the 60 proportions observed should be quite close to .5 and .1, the theoretically expected values (319).

37.   (a) $p = \frac{1}{3}$ and $\sigma_p = .053$ are to be expected.
      (b) The expected values are $p = \frac{1}{2}$ and $\sigma_p = .056$.
      (c) $p = \frac{1}{6}$ and $\sigma_p = .042$ are expected (319).

38. $.15 \pm .09$ (319–20)

39. $.168 \pm .033$ (319–20)

40.   54   (320–2)

41.   59   (320–2)

42.   (a) $\sigma_z = \frac{1}{5}$ (b) 1.0454 (c) $1.0454 \pm .3920$ (d) $P(.57 \le \rho \le .89) = .95$ (322–4)

43. $P(.68 \le \rho \le .84) = .95$ (322–4)

44. (a) .2 (b) $-.7753$ (c) $-.7753 \pm .3920$ (d) $P(-.82 \le \rho \le -.37)$
45. $P(-.78 \le \rho \le -.46)$. Note how n enters into the formula for the standard deviation of Z.

CHAPTER 9

1. (330–2)
2. (333–6)
3. (336)
4. (346–9, 353–5)
5. (333–6, 348–9)
6. (338–41)
7. (341–4)
8. If no placebos are given, there is an assumption that all of the effect on the treated group is due to the treatment. Consider how such subjects should be chosen.
9. (340–2)
10. (349–50)
11. See problem 1.
12. If H_0 is "cutting class will not affect his grade," then $\alpha = \frac{2}{3}$ (351–2).
13. $p = .125, I$ (359–61).
14. $(0 - 16.51)$ is the critical region. $\beta = .1131$ (359–61).
15. $(0 - 85.75)$ is the critical region. If H_1 is true, the result would have to be above 5.4σ beyond the mean 50 in order for a Type II error to occur. Hence β is practically 0.
16. H_0 is rejected. A significant difference (at the 5 per cent level) in the means is recognized.
17. Yes, the difference -2 is equivalent to a z of 2.53.
18. Expand $(\theta_i - e_i)^2$, distribute the summation symbol and simplify (371–2).
19. (a) The hypotheses may be framed in terms of a comparison between observed and expected values.
    (b) $\chi^2 = 10.58$ with 4 degrees of freedom.
    (c) The χ^2 table gives 9.488 as the random expectation for $\alpha = .05$. Hence reject the hypothesis that no difference exists between observed and expected values.
20. (a) A Type II error here is most damaging; hence a small β should be sought. An α of .50 would not be too high.
    (b) All are 50.

(c) $\chi^2 = 1.32$ with 5 degrees of freedom.

(d) H_0 will be accepted for α up to .93.

21. (a) 4.9041   (b) 49.041

22. .0228

23. (a) 41.638   (b) 35.172   (c) 33.590

24. (a) .00002 12; .00032 11; .00281 10; .01527 9; .05731 8; .15821 7; .33479 6; .56182 5; .77466 4; .91656 3; .98041 2; .99782 1; 1.00000 0

(b) 4 to 9 inclusive   (c) 4 to 7

TABLE A

Areas and Ordinates of the Standard Normal Curve

z	Area	Ordinate	z	Area	Ordinate	z	Area	Ordinate
00	.0000	.3989	.50	.1915	.3521	1.00	.3413	.2420
.01	.0040	.3989	.51	.1950	.3503	1.01	.3438	.2396
.02	.0080	.3989	.52	.1985	.3485	1.02	.3461	.2371
.03	.0120	.3988	.53	.2019	.3467	1.03	.3485	.2347
.04	.0160	.3986	.54	.2054	.3448	1.04	.3508	.2323
.05	.0199	.3984	.55	.2088	.3429	1.05	.3531	.2299
.06	.0239	.3982	.56	.2123	.3410	1.06	.3554	.2275
.07	.0279	.3980	.57	.2157	.3391	1.07	.3577	.2251
.08	.0319	.3977	.58	.2190	.3372	1.08	.3599	.2227
.09	.0359	.3973	.59	.2224	.3352	1.09	.3621	.2203
.10	.0398	.3970	.60	.2257	.3332	1.10	.3643	.2179
.11	.0438	.3965	.61	.2291	.3312	1.11	.3665	.2155
.12	.0478	.3961	.62	.2324	.3292	1.12	.3686	.2131
.13	.0517	.3956	.63	.2357	.3271	1.13	.3708	.2107
.14	.0557	.3951	.64	.2389	.3251	1.14	.3729	.2083
.15	.0596	.3945	.65	.2422	.3230	1.15	.3749	.2059
.16	.0636	.3939	.66	.2454	.3209	1.16	.3770	.2036
.17	.0675	.3932	.67	.2486	.3187	1.17	.3790	.2012
.18	.0714	.3925	.68	.2517	.3166	1.18	.3810	.1989
.19	.0753	.3918	.69	.2549	.3144	1.19	.3830	.1965
.20	.0793	.3910	.70	.2580	.3123	1.20	.3849	.1942
.21	.0832	.3902	.71	.2611	.3101	1.21	.3869	.1919
.22	.0871	.3894	.72	.2642	.3079	1.22	.3888	.1895
.23	.0910	.3885	.73	.2673	.3056	1.23	.3907	.1872
.24	.0948	.3876	.74	.2703	.3034	1.24	.3925	.1849
.25	.0987	.3867	.75	.2734	.3011	1.25	.3944	.1826
.26	.1026	.3857	.76	.2764	.2989	1.26	.3962	.1804
.27	.1064	.3847	.77	.2794	.2966	1.27	.3980	.1781
.28	.1103	.3836	.78	.2823	.2943	1.28	.3997	.1758
.29	.1141	.3825	.79	.2852	.2920	1.29	.4015	.1736
.30	.1179	.3814	.80	.2881	.2897	1.30	.4032	.1714
.31	.1217	.3802	.81	.2910	.2874	1.31	.4049	.1691
.32	.1255	.3790	.82	.2939	.2850	1.32	.4066	.1669
.33	.1293	.3778	.83	.2967	.2827	1.33	.4082	.1647
.34	.1331	.3765	.84	.2995	.2803	1.34	.4099	.1626
.35	.1368	.3752	.85	.3023	.2780	1.35	.4115	.1604
.36	.1406	.3739	.86	.3051	.2756	1.36	.4131	.1582
.37	.1443	.3725	.87	.3078	.2732	1.37	.4147	.1561
.38	.1480	.3712	.88	.3106	.2709	1.38	.4162	.1539
.39	.1517	.3697	.89	.3133	.2685	1.39	.4177	.1518
.40	.1554	.3683	.90	.3159	.2661	1.40	.4192	.1497
.41	.1591	.3668	.91	.3186	.2637	1.41	.4207	.1476
.42	.1628	.3653	.92	.3212	.2613	1.42	.4222	.1456
.43	.1664	.3637	.93	.3238	.2589	1.43	.4236	.1435
.44	.1700	.3621	.94	.3264	.2565	1.44	.4251	.1415
.45	.1736	.3605	.95	.3289	.2541	1.45	.4265	.1394
.46	.1772	.3589	.96	.3315	.2516	1.46	.4279	.1374
.47	.1808	.3572	.97	.3340	.2492	1.47	.4292	.1354
.48	.1844	.3555	.98	.3365	.2468	1.48	.4306	.1334
.49	.1879	.3538	.99	.3389	.2444	1.49	.4319	.1315
.50	.1915	.3521	1.00	.3413	.2420	1.50	.4332	.1295

TABLE A
Areas and Ordinates of the Standard Normal Curve. Continued

z	Area	Ordinate	z	Area	Ordinate	z	Area	Ordinate
1.50	.4332	.1295	2.00	.4772	.0540	2.50	.4938	.0175
1.51	.4345	.1276	2.01	.4778	.0529	2.51	.4940	.0171
1.52	.4357	.1257	2.02	.4783	.0519	2.52	.4941	.0167
1.53	.4370	.1238	2.03	.4788	.0508	2.53	.4943	.0163
1.54	.4382	.1219	2.04	.4793	.0498	2.54	.4945	.0158
1.55	.4394	.1200	2.05	.4798	.0488	2.55	.4946	.0154
1.56	.4406	.1182	2.06	.4803	.0478	2.56	.4948	.0151
1.57	.4418	.1163	2.07	.4808	.0468	2.57	.4949	.0147
1.58	.4429	.1145	2.08	.4812	.0459	2.58	.4951	.0143
1.59	.4441	.1127	2.09	.4817	.0449	2.59	.4952	.0139
1.60	.4452	.1109	2.10	.4821	.0440	2.60	.4953	.0136
1.61	.4463	.1092	2.11	.4826	.0431	2.61	.4955	.0132
1.62	.4474	.1074	2.12	.4830	.0422	2.62	.4956	.0129
1.63	.4484	.1057	2.13	.4834	.0413	2.63	.4957	.0126
1.64	.4495	.1040	2.14	.4838	.0404	2.64	.4959	.0122
1.65	.4505	.1023	2.15	.4842	.0395	2.65	.4960	.0119
1.66	.4515	.1006	2.16	.4846	.0387	2.66	.4961	.0116
1.67	.4525	.0989	2.17	.4850	.0379	2.67	.4962	.0113
1.68	.4535	.0973	2.18	.4854	.0371	2.68	.4963	.0110
1.69	.4545	.0957	2.19	.4857	.0363	2.69	.4964	.0107
1.70	.4554	.0940	2.20	.4861	.0355	2.70	.4965	.0104
1.71	.4564	.0925	2.21	.4864	.0347	2.71	.4966	.0101
1.72	.4573	.0909	2.22	.4868	.0339	2.72	.4967	.0099
1.73	.4582	.0893	2.23	.4871	.0332	2.73	.4968	.0096
1.74	.4591	.0878	2.24	.4875	.0325	2.74	.4969	.0093
1.75	.4599	.0863	2.25	.4878	.0317	2.75	.4970	.0091
1.76	.4608	.0848	2.26	.4881	.0310	2.76	.4971	.0088
1.77	.4616	.0833	2.27	.4884	.0303	2.77	.4972	.0086
1.78	.4625	.0818	2.28	.4887	.0297	2.78	.4973	.0084
1.79	.4633	.0804	2.29	.4890	.0290	2.79	.4974	.0081
1.80	.4641	.0790	2.30	.4893	.0283	2.80	.4974	.0079
1.81	.4649	.0775	2.31	.4896	.0277	2.81	.4975	.0077
1.82	.4656	.0761	2.32	.4898	.0270	2.82	.4976	.0075
1.83	.4664	.0748	2.33	.4901	.0264	2.83	.4977	.0073
1.84	.4671	.0734	2.34	.4904	.0258	2.84	.4977	.0071
1.85	.4678	.0721	2.35	.4906	.0252	2.85	.4978	.0069
1.86	.4686	.0707	2.36	.4909	.0246	2.86	.4979	.0067
1.87	.4693	.0694	2.37	.4911	.0241	2.87	.4979	.0065
1.88	.4699	.0681	2.38	.4913	.0235	2.88	.4980	.0063
1.89	.4706	.0669	2.39	.4916	.0229	2.89	.4981	.0061
1.90	.4713	.0656	2.40	.4918	.0224	2.90	.4981	.0060
1.91	.4719	.0644	2.41	.4920	.0219	2.91	.4982	.0058
1.92	.4726	.0632	2.42	.4922	.0213	2.92	.4982	.0056
1.93	.4732	.0620	2.43	.4925	.0208	2.93	.4983	.0055
1.94	.4738	.0608	2.44	.4927	.0203	2.94	.4984	.0053
1.95	.4744	.0596	2.45	.4929	.0198	2.95	.4984	.0051
1.96	.4750	.0584	2.46	.4931	.0194	2.96	.4985	.0050
1.97	.4756	.0573	2.47	.4932	.0189	2.97	.4985	.0048
1.98	.4761	.0562	2.48	.4934	.0184	2.98	.4986	.0047
1.99	.4767	.0551	2.49	.4936	.0180	2.99	.4986	.0046
2.00	.4772	.0540	2.50	.4938	.0175	3.00	.4987	.0044

TABLE B *

Values for Transforming r into $z = \frac{1}{2} \text{Log}_e \frac{1+r}{1-r}$

	.00	.01	.02	.03	.04	.05	.06	.07	.08	.09
.0	.0000	.0100	.0200	.0300	.0400	.0500	.0599	.0699	.0798	.0898
.1	.0997	.1096	.1194	.1293	.1391	.1489	.1587	.1684	.1781	.1878
.2	.1974	.2070	.2165	.2260	.2355	.2449	.2543	.2636	.2729	.2821
.3	.2913	.3004	.3095	.3185	.3275	.3364	.3452	.3540	.3627	.3714
.4	.3800	.3885	.3969	.4053	.4136	.4219	.4301	.4382	.4462	.4542
.5	.4621	.4700	.4777	.4854	.4930	.5005	.5080	.5154	.5227	.5299
.6	.5370	.5441	.5511	.5581	.5649	.5717	.5784	.5850	.5915	.5980
.7	.6044	.6107	.6169	.6231	.6291	.6352	.6411	.6469	.6527	.6584
.8	.6640	.6696	.6751	.6805	.6858	.6911	.6963	.7014	.7064	.7114
.9	.7163	.7211	.7259	.7306	.7352	.7398	.7443	.7487	.7531	.7574
1.0	.7616	.7658	.7699	.7739	.7779	.7818	.7857	.7895	.7932	.7969
1.1	.8005	.8041	.8076	.8110	.8144	.8178	.8210	.8243	.8275	.8306
1.2	.8337	.8367	.8397	.8426	.8455	.8483	.8511	.8538	.8565	.8591
1.3	.8617	.8643	.8668	.8693	.8717	.8741	.8764	.8787	.8810	.8832
1.4	.8854	.8875	.8896	.8917	.8937	.8957	.8977	.8996	.9015	.9033
1.5	.9052	.9069	.9087	.9104	.9121	.9138	.9154	.9170	.9186	.9202
1.6	.9217	.9232	.9246	.9261	.9275	.9289	.9302	.9316	.9329	.9342
1.7	.9354	.9367	.9379	.9391	.9402	.9414	.9425	.9436	.9447	.9458
1.8	.9468	.9478	.9488	.9498	.9508	.9518	.9527	.9536	.9545	.9554
1.9	.9562	.9571	.9579	.9587	.9595	.9603	.9611	.9619	.9626	.9633
2.0	.9640	.9647	.9654	.9661	.9668	.9674	.9680	.9687	.9693	.9699
2.1	.9705	.9710	.9716	.9722	.9727	.9732	.9738	.9743	.9748	.9753
2.2	.9757	.9762	.9767	.9771	.9776	.9780	.9785	.9789	.9793	.9797
2.3	.9801	.9805	.9809	.9812	.9816	.9820	.9823	.9827	.9830	.9834
2.4	.9837	.9840	.9843	.9846	.9849	.9852	.9855	.9858	.9861	.9863
2.5	.9866	.9869	.9871	.9874	.9876	.9879	.9881	.9884	.9886	.9888
2.6	.9890	.9892	.9895	.9897	.9899	.9901	.9903	.9905	.9906	.9908
2.7	.9910	.9912	.9914	.9915	.9917	.9919	.9920	.9922	.9923	.9925
2.8	.9926	.9928	.9929	.9931	.9932	.9933	.9935	.9936	.9937	.9938
2.9	.9940	.9941	.9942	.9943	.9944	.9945	.9946	.9947	.9949	.9950
3.0	.9951									
4.0	.9993									
5.0	.9999									

* Table B is abridged from Fisher and Yates: *Statistical Tables*. Edinburgh and London: Oliver and Boyd. Reprinted by permission of the authors and publishers.

TABLE C *

Table of Chi-Square

df	P = .99	.98	.95	.90	.80	.70	.50	.30	.20	.10	.05	.02	.01
1	.000157	.000628	.00393	.0158	.0642	.148	.455	1.074	1.642	2.706	3.841	5.412	6.635
2	.0201	.0404	.103	.211	.446	.713	1.386	2.408	3.219	4.605	5.991	7.824	9.210
3	.115	.185	.352	.584	1.005	1.424	2.366	3.665	4.642	6.251	7.815	9.837	11.341
4	.297	.429	.711	1.064	1.649	2.195	3.357	4.878	5.989	7.779	9.488	11.668	13.277
5	.554	.752	1.145	1.610	2.343	3.000	4.351	6.064	7.289	9.236	11.070	13.388	15.086
6	.872	1.134	1.635	2.204	3.070	3.828	5.348	7.231	8.558	10.645	12.592	15.033	16.812
7	1.239	1.564	2.167	2.833	3.822	4.671	6.346	8.383	9.803	12.017	14.067	16.622	18.475
8	1.646	2.032	2.733	3.490	4.594	5.527	7.344	9.524	11.030	13.362	15.507	18.168	20.090
9	2.088	2.532	3.325	4.168	5.380	6.393	8.343	10.656	12.242	14.684	16.919	19.679	21.666
10	2.558	3.059	3.940	4.865	6.179	7.267	9.342	11.781	13.442	15.987	18.307	21.161	23.209
11	3.053	3.609	4.575	5.578	6.989	8.148	10.341	12.899	14.631	17.275	19.675	22.618	24.725
12	3.571	4.178	5.226	6.304	7.807	9.034	11.340	14.011	15.812	18.549	21.026	24.054	26.217
13	4.107	4.765	5.892	7.042	8.634	9.926	12.340	15.119	16.985	19.812	22.362	25.472	27.688
14	4.660	5.368	6.571	7.790	9.467	10.821	13.339	16.222	18.151	21.064	23.685	26.873	29.141
15	5.229	5.985	7.261	8.547	10.307	11.721	14.339	17.322	19.311	22.307	24.996	28.259	30.578
16	5.812	6.614	7.962	9.312	11.152	12.624	15.338	18.418	20.465	23.542	26.296	29.633	32.000
17	6.408	7.255	8.672	10.085	12.002	13.531	16.338	19.511	21.615	24.769	27.587	30.995	33.409
18	7.015	7.906	9.390	10.865	12.857	14.440	17.338	20.601	22.760	25.989	28.869	32.346	34.805
19	7.633	8.567	10.117	11.651	13.716	15.352	18.338	21.689	23.900	27.204	30.144	33.687	36.191
20	8.260	9.237	10.851	12.443	14.578	16.266	19.337	22.775	25.038	28.412	31.410	35.020	37.566
21	8.897	9.915	11.591	13.240	15.445	17.182	20.337	23.858	26.171	29.615	32.671	36.343	38.932
22	9.542	10.600	12.338	14.041	16.314	18.101	21.337	24.939	27.301	30.813	33.924	37.659	40.289
23	10.196	11.293	13.091	14.848	17.187	19.021	22.337	26.018	28.429	32.007	35.172	38.968	41.638
24	10.856	11.992	13.848	15.659	18.062	19.943	23.337	27.096	29.553	33.196	36.415	40.270	42.980
25	11.524	12.697	14.611	16.473	18.940	20.867	24.337	28.172	30.675	34.382	37.652	41.566	44.314
26	12.198	13.409	15.379	17.292	19.820	21.792	25.336	29.246	31.795	35.563	38.885	42.856	45.642
27	12.879	14.125	16.151	18.114	20.703	22.719	26.336	30.319	32.912	36.741	40.113	44.140	46.963
28	13.565	14.847	16.928	18.939	21.588	23.647	27.336	31.391	34.027	37.916	41.337	45.419	48.278
29	14.256	15.574	17.708	19.768	22.475	24.577	28.336	32.461	35.139	39.087	42.557	46.693	49.588
30	14.953	16.306	18.493	20.599	23.364	25.508	29.336	33.530	36.250	40.256	43.773	47.962	50.892

* Table C is abridged from Fisher's *Statistical Methods for Research Workers*. Edinburgh and London: Oliver and Boyd. Reprinted by permission of the author and publishers.

TABLE D

Square, Square Roots, and Reciprocals

n	n^2	$\sqrt{n}$	$\sqrt{10n}$	$1/n$	n	n^2	$\sqrt{n}$	$\sqrt{10n}$	$1/n$
1	1	1.000	3.162	1.00000	51	2601	7.141	22.583	.01961
2	4	1.414	4.472	.50000	52	2704	7.211	22.804	.01923
3	9	1.732	5.477	.33333	53	2809	7.280	23.022	.01887
4	16	2.000	6.325	.25000	54	2916	7.348	23.238	.01852
5	25	2.236	7.071	.20000	55	3025	7.416	23.452	.01818
6	36	2.449	7.746	.16667	56	3136	7.483	23.664	.01786
7	49	2.646	8.367	.14286	57	3249	7.550	23.875	.01754
8	64	2.828	8.944	.12500	58	3364	7.616	24.083	.01724
9	81	3.000	9.487	.11111	59	3481	7.681	24.290	.01695
10	100	3.162	10.000	.10000	60	3600	7.746	24.495	.01667
11	121	3.317	10.488	.09091	61	3721	7.810	24.698	.01639
12	144	3.464	10.954	.08333	62	3844	7.874	24.900	.01613
13	169	3.606	11.402	.07692	63	3969	7.937	25.100	.01587
14	196	3.742	11.832	.07143	64	4096	8.000	25.298	.01562
15	225	3.873	12.247	.06667	65	4225	8.062	25.495	.01538
16	256	4.000	12.649	.06250	66	4356	8.124	25.690	.01515
17	289	4.123	13.038	.05882	67	4489	8.185	25.884	.01493
18	324	4.243	13.416	.05556	68	4624	8.246	26.077	.01471
19	361	4.359	13.784	.05263	69	4761	8.307	26.268	.01449
20	400	4.472	14.142	.05000	70	4900	8.367	26.458	.01429
21	441	4.583	14.491	.04762	71	5041	8.426	26.646	.01408
22	484	4.690	14.832	.04545	72	5184	8.485	26.833	.01389
23	529	4.796	15.166	.04348	73	5329	8.544	27.019	.01370
24	576	4.899	15.492	.04167	74	5476	8.602	27.203	.01351
25	625	5.000	15.811	.04000	75	5625	8.660	27.386	.01333
26	676	5.099	16.125	.03846	76	5776	8.718	27.568	.01316
27	729	5.196	16.432	.03704	77	5929	8.775	27.749	.01299
28	784	5.292	16.733	.03571	78	6084	8.832	27.928	.01282
29	841	5.385	17.029	.03448	79	6241	8.888	28.107	.01266
30	900	5.477	17.321	.03333	80	6400	8.944	28.284	.01250
31	961	5.568	17.607	.03226	81	6561	9.000	28.460	.01235
32	1024	5.657	17.889	.03125	82	6724	9.055	28.636	.01220
33	1089	5.745	18.166	.03030	83	6889	9.110	28.810	.01205
34	1156	5.831	18.439	.02941	84	7056	9.165	28.983	.01190
35	1225	5.916	18.708	.02857	85	7225	9.220	29.155	.01176
36	1296	6.000	18.974	.02778	86	7396	9.274	29.326	.01163
37	1369	6.083	19.235	.02703	87	7569	9.327	29.496	.01149
38	1444	6.164	19.494	.02632	88	7744	9.381	29.665	.01136
39	1521	6.245	19.748	.02564	89	7921	9.434	29.833	.01124
40	1600	6.325	20.000	.02500	90	8100	9.487	30.000	.01111
41	1681	6.403	20.248	.02439	91	8281	9.539	30.166	.01099
42	1764	6.481	20.494	.02381	92	8464	9.592	30.332	.01087
43	1849	6.557	20.736	.02326	93	8649	9.644	30.496	.01075
44	1936	6.633	20.976	.02273	94	8836	9.695	30.659	.01064
45	2025	6.708	21.213	.02222	95	9025	9.747	30.822	.01053
46	2116	6.782	21.448	.02174	96	9216	9.798	30.984	.01042
47	2209	6.856	21.679	.02128	97	9409	9.849	31.145	.01031
48	2304	6.928	21.909	.02083	98	9604	9.899	31.305	.01020
49	2401	7.000	22.136	.02041	99	9801	9.950	31.464	.01010
50	2500	7.071	22.361	.02000	100	10000	10.000	31.623	.01000

AUTHOR INDEX

SUBJECT INDEX

1